Sex Education in the Schools

A Study of

Objectives, Content, Methods,

Materials, and Evaluation

Sex Education in the Schools

H. Frederick Kilander

Wagner College, Staten Island, New York

The Macmillan Company / Collier-Macmillan Limited, London

A portion of this material has been adapted from
School Health Education, by H. Frederick Kilander, ©
1962 by H. Frederick Kilander and © copyright 1968
by H. Frederick Kilander.

Library of Congress catalog card number: 69–13570

The Macmillan Company

Collier-Macmillan Canada, Ltd., Toronto, Ontario

Printed in the United States of America

Preface

The purpose of this book is to help prospective teachers at both elementary and secondary school levels to organize and conduct meaningful learning experiences in family life and sex education.

The book is divided into two parts. Part I is about the teaching of sex and sexuality in schools. Included are the usual chapters on the broad goals of sex education, objectives, curriculum planning, methods, evaluation, and unit and lesson planning. Tables are included to give the reader a better idea of the extensive scope of sex education. Many of the units, lesson plans, and objective tests found in the text have been prepared by graduate students for the grade they were teaching. These examples are not necessarily perfect, but they do indicate to the reader what others have done for their own use. This information may serve as an incentive to the reader to try his own hand at doing the same to meet his own teaching needs.

Part II contains basic sex education content presented simply and clearly in outline form, yet with sufficient detail to ensure adequate comprehension. This format should help the teacher in the following ways:

1. The outline form makes it possible to present concepts in a logical learning sequence.

2. It makes key concepts easily identifiable.

3. It makes it simpler for the teacher to select concepts for use in the construction of unit and lesson plans.

4. It will serve as a source of scientific information for the teacher who may not be well prepared in this area.

The appendixes include an up-to-date bibliography, a list of audiovisual aids, a glossary of over two hundred terms, a number of objective tests, and other useful supplementary material.

Viewpoints Presented. A major purpose of sex education should be to indicate to children and youth as well as to adults the immense possibilities for human fulfillment that human sexuality offers. Educators realize that education of the whole child necessarily implies a consideration of psychosexual aspects of his development along with the physical. Although the emphasis in this text may seem to be on subject matter, it is hoped that those using the curriculum suggestions will be aware that the creation of wholesome attitudes is far more important than the remembering of facts, and that wholesome attitudes and values are the foundation of a strong moral character.

Sex education is and should be a continuous process from birth until old age. It is meaningless to ask when sex education should begin, because it is going on all the time. In order for a youth to be isolated from sex, he would have to be isolated from newspapers, radio, television, magazines, his peer group, and most adults. We must not ignore this obvious fact. As teachers or parents we cannot control the time and place of sex education except to a limited extent. We can, however, help to determine the nature of that sex education to the extent that we personally are a part of it.

To ask who should teach sex education is to miss the point. All teachers, parents, and others who influence children and youth contribute to sex education of children. What is meant by such a question is presumably who should teach the more complicated and delicate aspects of human reproduction. It is granted that all teachers and others can learn to do a better job, which is a contribution that it is hoped this book can make.

For Whom Intended. This text is intended to serve both undergraduate and graduate students preparing to teach sex education at either the elementary or secondary school levels.

It should also be valuable for the in-service education of school administrators, supervisors, school nurses, school psychologists, and elementary and secondary school teachers in health education, biology, science, home economics, social studies, and English. In fact, all those concerned with sex education should find this book helpful—whether educators, parents or others.

The Purpose of the Book. The major purpose of the book is to show the broad and varied content and scope of sex education, to suggest ways in which this can be organized into curriculum by grade levels, and to suggest appropriate teaching methods and materials and evaluation procedures for such instruction.

So many educators and others are not aware of the many facets that comprise sex education and so have a too limited view of what is meant by the term. The author, hopes, therefore, that the plan of presentation will enable those concerned to prepare more effectively and more wisely for their own programs using the suggested guidelines here presented.

How This Book Meets a Need. This book presents suggestions *both* for content and for appropriate methods related to the teaching of that content. The text seeks to provide the needed perspective and to bring about a closer coordination between content and method.

There is special emphasis throughout the text on the three outcomes of learning as applied to sex education, namely, acquisition of knowledge, development of wholesome attitudes, and improvement in sex behavior. The book also considers the current needs as applied to the home, church, and youth-serving agencies.

Considerable attention is given to correlation and integration of sex education with other subject areas and programs at both the elementary and secondary school levels, since this is the principal way in which it should be incorporated into the school curriculum.

Why One Book for Both Elementary and Secondary School Levels? Sex education for the elementary and secondary school is included in this treatment because sound principles of curriculum planning are as valid for one level as for the other. Furthermore, what is or should be taught at one level influences the planning for the other level.

Guidelines for Text Content. This book has been developed over a period of years. Its various parts have been tested both through the author's classroom use and through students' use in their own schools. All pertinent sources have been drawn upon for the views and materials presented herein. Recommendations of various national groups have served as guides in its preparation.

How to Use the Book. Where sufficient time is available, it is recommended that the book be studied in its entirety. However, where there is a restriction on the amount of time that can be devoted to sex education, it is suggested that Part I be used, leaving Part II for reference purposes. The comprehensive appendixes and index will also be helpful for reference purposes when special phases of the subject are to be considered.

Acknowledgments. The author wishes to express his appreciation to the many students, undergraduate and graduate, who have made available suggestions in its preparation. Similarly appreciated has been the excellent help received from many elementary and secondary school teachers, health and biology teachers, specialists in sex education, and other co-workers.

I also wish to thank Sheroo Daruvala and Robert Nilsen for assistance with bibliographies and other aspects, and my wife, Juanita Kilander, and H. F. Kilander, Jr., Nell Lewis, and Evelyn Kassubski for help with the manuscript.

H. F. K.

Contents

Part I. Sex Education in the Elementary and Secondary Schools

Part II. Outlines of the Science Content of Sex Education

Appendixes

Part I

Sex Education in the Elementary and Secondary Schools

This book is divided into two parts. Part I, comprising the first thirteen chapters, deals with the teaching in K–12 of sex and sexuality—or education for family living, as it is often referred to. Included are the usual chapters on the objectives, methods, evaluation procedures, and lesson planning. There are also some special chapters on Venereal Disease Education, the Problems of Offensive and Obscene Material, and the Home and Family in Sex Education.

1

Introduction

Sex education as defined today includes all educational measures which in any way may help young people prepare to meet the problems of life that have their center in the sex instinct and inevitably come in some form into the experience of every normal human being. These problems extend over a vast range of life's experiences, from simple little matters of personal sex health to the exceedingly complicated physical, social, psychical, and moral problems that concern successful marriage and family relationships.

Further, sex education stands for the protection, preservation, extension, improvement, and development of the monogamic family, based on accepted ethical ideals.

That the term *sex education* is not a new one is indicated by the fact that the International Congress on Hygiene in 1912 adopted the term as the heading of a special report which recommended a broader outlook on this educational field. It replaced the term *sex hygiene* which had been used in a more restricted sense.

Other terms that have been used over the years and sometimes continue to be used as synonyms for sex education are family life education, social hygiene education, sex-character education, social-sex education, education about human sexuality, health and human relations, personal and family life, and family living. The term *sex education* is to many people limited to the study of the physiological facts of life dealing with human reproduction. *However, to many others family life education and sex education are considered to be synonymous, assuming that both terms imply the broader definition of this important area of education.*

Although family life education seeks to support every constructive effort for the preservation and improvement of the family, the home economists interpret the meaning even more broadly to include additional interests that pertain to the home and family. Included are such important topics as meal planning and preparation, furnishing the home, and baby care. However, their interpretation is *not* the one being used in this book.

An Overview

The functions and impulses of sex, mating, and reproduction are basic to animals and human beings alike. Related to these powers there have grown up keen passions, satisfactions, and devotions—ranging from the most physical to the most psychical, and from the wholly selfish to the self-denying and refining.

Probably more than any other of our functions, sex and reproduction have kindled emotions, molded thought and imagination, determined conduct, modified personal development, influenced relations, organized society, and colored all the philosophies and moralities which have cramped or inspired human behavior, personality, and character.

Specifically, sex and reproduction produce the individuals of which society is made and by which it is perpetually renewed; sex and reproduction directly originate all the differences and the consequent attractions that draw boys and girls and men and women together. But for this there could be no such realities as lovers and courtship, husband and wife, marriage, fatherhood and motherhood, sons and daughters, brothers and sisters, families and home life, nor any of the fine sentiments and devotions which are natural to these relations.[1]

Even though sex and reproduction is thus natural and fundamental, it by no means follows that its various expressions are of the same grade and value. Both ideally and practically, human sex phenomena are of extreme range. They include, at one extreme, the most immediate, selfish, and irrational use of the physical aspect without the accompaniment of the psychical, esthetic, and social, as is indicated in such results and consequences as masturbation,

[1] Thomas W. Galloway, *Sex and Social Health,* The American Social Hygiene Association, 1924, p. 4.

homosexuality, rape, promiscuity, prostitution, illegitimacy, venereal disease, unhappy marriages, and divorce.

At the other extreme of this continuum is the harmonious blending of the physical and the psychical, of the individual and the social as seen in the high friendships and affections between the sexes; in mutual consideration and faithfulness of lovers and mates; in love, marriage, and parenthood; and in the sacrificing spirit of the family.

There are a number of things about sex education or education for family living which may be considered settled: (1) sex and reproduction and the impulses connected with them introduce factors into conduct, personality, and character that are too complex and too full of importance to be ignored or to be left to instinct; (2) adults must therefore undertake to guide and educate youth in regard to these factors; (3) such education and training means much more than just information about the anatomical and physiological facts or than the forcible repression of the normal sex impulses; (4) personality development and character training in respect to sex should begin in the earliest years and should be continuous and closely related to life relations and progress; (5) *no single agency acting alone*—whether the home, the church, the school, or youth-serving organizations—*is comprehensive enough* in its contacts with the child and youth to present this group of problems so as to have them accepted and solved soundly by the young; and (6) all the social and educational agencies in the community that have to do with childhood and youth must take their appropriate part in this work.

A few additional statements are included briefly at this point:

1. Sex education is a hybrid field drawing upon several areas of life and education—namely, biology, medicine, sociology, psychology, morals, ethics and religion, education, and recreation.
2. We know more than formerly about the field of sex and sexuality as well as sex education from the information that research is contributing.
3. The emphasis needs to be on all the three major goals of education: namely, knowledge or information, attitudes or values, and behavior or conduct.
4. Most of the big problems that have made sex education desirable, if not necessary, are problems of sex apart from reproduction.

DEFINITIONS OF SEX EDUCATION

There has been a great divergence of opinion as to just what kind of education sex education or education for family living is. At one extreme is the urgent recommendation that the subject be restricted to an exposition of the facts of reproduction by biology teachers. At the other extreme is the enthusiastic identification of sex education with the effort to make boys and girls "good" by frightening them with the horrors of the venereal diseases and the stigma attached to unwanted pregnancies.

Sex education means vastly more than instruction concerning the facts of sex or reproduction as biological or physiological principles. It means rather a comprehensive and progressive process of care, guidance, and example, as well as information. It becomes necessary to conceive of education in relation to sex as a phase of character and personality development that extends from infancy to maturity and beyond.

Sex education is, at bottom, an education calculated to bring about adult attitudes and behavior that assure desirable homemaking—the establishing and building of families. It is important to remember that our youth of today become family units tomorrow.

Sex education is thus a social and a socializing process. Both in its progress and in its results, it reaches far beyond the boundaries of the physical person. Because of the far-reaching effects of the eventual attitudes and practices of the individual, sex education carries with it obligations of the widest social importance.

As a phase of character education, sex education must include instruction and training in all that may help to form normal and wholesome attitudes, values, and ideals in relation to sex, and to shape conduct in accord with these attitudes, values, and ideals. Such education must, therefore, be developed as an organic part of the entire educational program and not be considered a special and isolated bit of ritual to be performed at a given time and then dismissed as finished.

According to Rubin and Kirkendall,[2] sex education is *not* merely a unit in reproduction, teaching how babies are conceived and born. It has a far richer scope and goal: to help the youngster incorporate sex most meaningfully into his present and future life, to provide him with some basic understanding of virtually every aspect of sex by the time he reaches full maturity, to help him to recognize the existence of differential sex patterns so that he can interact harmoniously with those whose sex norms differ from his own, and to teach him critical judgment in dealing with ethical controversy. Thus the aim of sex education should be to indicate the immense possibilities for human fulfillment that sexuality offers, rather than primarily to control and to suppress sex expression. This approach indicates the broad scope of sex education. At the same time, we should be very realistic about the limits of sex education. No educator can undertake alone to change the moral climate of his community

[2] Isadore Rubin and Lester A. Kirkendall, *Sex in the Adolescent Years,* Association Press, New York, p. 18.

or to cut down the rate of illegitimacy or venereal disease. These social ills are the responsibility of society as a whole; no one agency can cure what society as a whole permits. Sex education based on this perspective is foredoomed to failure.

An examination of Table 1, "An Outline of Family Living," pages 8–9, and Table 2, "An Outline of Major Topics in Area of Family Life and Sex Education," pages 42–45, will give the reader a more detailed idea of what the field deals with.

NEW TIMES MAKE NEW NEEDS

In former years education was carried on casually and incidentally by the family, the church, and the community. Social and cultural developments, however, have brought changes into the pattern of adult living that confuse the goals and the ideals of young people and which, in turn, have changed the traditional modes of guidance and instruction in the intimate matters of sex and family life.

The task of adjusting wholesomely to adult life is today complicated by the fact that many adolescents have anxieties and fears about sex and sexuality in addition to a multitude of ideas—often unsound—regarding sex and reproduction.

Changed conditions have raised new problems in mental and social health. The population trend has been urban—away from the daily contact with plant and animal life which earlier generations took for granted. Industry and business have been removing adults, especially mothers, from the routine of the home, in which important educational influences formerly accompanied normal family life. Families have become smaller. And more and more, children and youth are segregated outside of the home into groups about the same age.

Along with the aforementioned changes, extensive immigration has brought together families from varied cultural backgrounds. Consequently, old customs have often weakened. Those folkways that previously had served each of the several groups of immigrants and native Americans as a means of social control have come into conflict with strange and different ways, practices, and beliefs. Young people are caught in these conflicting cultures and subcultures— often with the culture in the home being quite different from that found outside the home.

All individuals who are intelligent should be personally responsible for the voluntary control of their sexual desires with reference to the ethical, the social, and the eugenic interests and rights of other individuals now and in the future.

TABLE 1. AN OUTLINE OF FAMILY LIVING

Age Groups (approximate years, much overlapping)

	INFANCY (BIRTH TO 6 YEARS)	CHILDHOOD (FROM 6 TO 10–12)	ADOLESCENCE (GIRLS: 12 TO 17–18; BOYS: 13 TO 18–19)	YOUTH (GIRLS: 17 TO 21)	EARLY MATURITY (21 TO 30)	MATURITY (30 TO 50)	OLD AGE
1. PHYSICAL CHANGES	Rapid growth during first year. More even rate of growth until adolescence begins.	Continued growth. Secondary sexual characteristics developing.	Second spurt in physical growth. Secondary sexual characteristics maturing.	Completion of physical growth in height. Manliness—strength. Womanliness—charm, attractiveness.	Increase in weight and muscle.	Gradual decrease in physical activity.	Decline. Senescence.
2. SEXUAL CHANGES	No special differentiation from physical changes indicated above.	Reproductive organs developing toward end of this period.	Reproductive organs are maturing. Girls—menses. Boys—emissions.	Sexual maturity. Procreative mechanism matures.	Most desirable period for parenthood.	Women—menopause after 45. Psychic and physical disturbances.	Sterility. Impotency.
3. NORMAL INSTINCTS, DESIRES, URGES	Alike in both sexes except as influenced by training.	Curiosity about own body. Little interest in opposite sex. Gang spirit developing.	Self-consciousness in early part of period, shyness. Interest in opposite sex. New interests in work and play.	Stronger biological urges and drives. Creative work. Chivalry. Dating. Interest in opposite sex narrows down to one individual.	Courtship. Marriage. Parenthood.	Late marriage. Parenthood.	Contentment. Happiness. Retirement.

TABLE 1. AN OUTLINE OF FAMILY LIVING (continued)

	INFANCY (BIRTH TO 6 YEARS)	CHILDHOOD (FROM 6 TO 10–12)	ADOLESCENCE (GIRLS: 12 TO 17–18; BOYS: 13 TO 18–19)	YOUTH (GIRLS: 17 TO 21)	EARLY MATURITY (21 TO 30)	MATURITY (30 TO 50)	OLD AGE
			Age Groups (approximate years, much overlapping)				
4. NATURAL AND DESIRABLE EDUCATION IN KNOWLEDGE, ATTITUDES, HABITS, AND CONDUCT	Home training. Other children as playmates. Elementary facts about body and reproduction.	Association with other children. More knowledge through biology. Understanding in later period of menses or emissions.	Desirable contact. Desirable interests, friends, work. Idealism. Character training. More sex education.	Conduct of a gentleman or a lady. Education for courtship. Sublimation of sex drive by desirable work, interests, recreation. Substitution of other interests for sex.	Education for marriage, parenthood, heredity. More substitution and sublimation if marriage is postponed.	Education for care of children. Providing for family. Creating desirable home environment. Understanding physical changes at end of this age group.	Interest in own children, grandchildren. Hobbies.
5. PATHOLOGICAL AND OTHER UNDESIRABLE ASPECTS	Poor home environment. Bad mental training, spoiled. No playmates or wrong type. Masturbation.	Same as in previous age group. Bad environment outside of home.	Day-dreaming. Secretive, unsocial. Wrong attitude toward opposite sex. Vulgarity, obscenity, smut, lewdness. Petting. Promiscuity.	Same as in previous period. Idleness—delinquency. Morbid curiosity about sex. Intemperance. Double standard. Homosexuality. Promiscuity. Prostitution. Illegitimacy. Venereal disease.	Same as before. Broken engagements. Postponement of marriage. Unemployment. Uneugenic marriage. Incompatibility. Divorce. Desertion. Homosexuality.	Sterility—childlessness. Unhappy homes. Divorce. Unemployment. Desertion.	Inability to accept fact of old age. Upsets over change of life. Lonesomeness.

Adapted from H. F. Kilander, *School Health Education*, 2nd ed., The Macmillan Co., New York, 1968, pp. 31–44.

One of the ways of obtaining such controls of sexual actions is to be found in the knowledge, along with the development of desirable attitudes and behavior, that might accompany such education.

Abundant evidence exists that family life education is needed, that it finds strong support among young people and their parents, and that good results are and will be achieved through it. This evidence comes from sociologists, psychologists, physicians, psychiatrists, educators, clergymen, and public health workers. They have shown the dangers of misdirected sex impulses to physical and mental well-being.

The problem that is always present can be stated as follows. The raw materials out of which the personality and character of the human individual are shaped are his inborn impulses and desires. These inherited drives, of which the sex impulse is one of the most powerful and pervasive, naturally seek expression and satisfaction. Society, however, through ages of accumulated experiences, has built up certain limitations, restrictions, conventions, and taboos that conflict with the natural desires of the individual. Hence, there often arises a conflict between the individual and the society of which he is a part. The sex instinct offers little guidance except for the timing of sex education units by age and maturity levels.

It is the essential task of family life education to harmonize this conflict as far as possible by directing the individual's sex nature so that it may contribute most richly to his self-development and happiness and at the same time conserve and advance the welfare of society.[3]

That this conflict has *not* been reconciled satisfactorily is evident from the fact that a large percentage of marriages are unhappy; that many of them end in separation and divorce; that venereal disease is still a serious problem in our country, particularly with youth; that many young people are so poorly prepared for life that they do not know how to go safely about the important project of choosing a marriage mate; that illegitimacy is on the increase; and that we in general are worried about the welfare of our children and youth from the standpoint of their sex behavior.

Some things that have increased the problems are modern transportation (for example, anonymity may be less than an hour away by car); modern housing (we live intimately but as strangers with our neighbors); advertising (we are taught to be glamorous and popular and to demand luxury); we have alcohol easily accessible; today venereal disease can be controlled and therefore acts less as a deterrent; and the home seems more sterile than ever as a cultural center and as a center of family life.

[3] White House Conference on Child Health and Protection, *Social Hygiene in Schools,* The Century Co., New York, 1932, pp. 3–4.

It has ceased to be a question of whether our children are to be informed with regard to sex; it is now a question merely of whether the truth regarding sex and its social implications shall be allowed to compete with the false concepts being commercially exploited, and whether it shall begin its competition early enough to establish an initial impression of naturalness, cleanness, and the desirability of self-restraint and moderation.[4]

LACK OF INFORMATION ABOUT SEX

There exists a lack of information about sex, in its various aspects, on the part of youth as well as adults. Studies through objective tests by the author lead to the conclusion that the public—high school students, college students, and adults of various socio-economic groups—are not adequately informed about human reproduction and hold numerous misconceptions in this area. Gratifyingly, there has been a slight but continuous improvement in the level of information during the past forty years, during which time this testing has been conducted continuously.

Whether there has been a corresponding improvement in sex attitudes and sex behavior is difficult to establish. However, young parents with a high school and college education are better informed in regard to sex education, have a more wholesome attitude toward the subject, and are doing a better job of presenting it to their children than was true one or two generations ago.

There are a number of important sex problems of our times that today offer reasons for sex education, since ignorance plays a large part in each problem. The major ones are here listed.

1. Many people, especially youth, need hygienic or health knowledge concerning sexual processes as they affect their personal health.

2. There is a general prevailing unwholesome attitude of mind that needs to be gradually altered concerning all sexual processes.

3. There is need of more general development of more wholesome value systems regarding sexual relationships.

4. There is a general misunderstanding of sexual life as related to health and happy marriages.

5. There is need for eugenic responsibility for sexual actions that concern future generations.

6. There is an alarming amount of venereal disease which is distributed by the sexual promiscuity and immorality of many men and women.

7. The uncontrolled sexual passions of men have led to an enormous development of organized and commercialized prostitution.

[4] Willard W. Beatty, *Sex Instruction in Public Schools,* The American Social Hygiene Association, 1936.

8. There are living today thousands of unmarried mothers and their illegitimate children—the result of common sexual irresponsibility and ignorance of men and women.

9. There is the matter of a lack of sexual identity today concerning femininity and masculinity, with its many implications.

10. It is necessary to reduce and hopefully eliminate those conditions which result in temptation and opportunity, especially before children and youth and some adults have acquired the necessary maturity and understanding.

11. Even if the above problems did not exist or were not so pressing, there still would be great value in sex education for making life even better for children and youth who are growing up today. *The aim of sex education is not primarily to control and suppress, as in the past, but to indicate the immense possibilities for human fulfillment that human sexuality offers.*

PUBLIC OPINION CHANGES

There has been a radical and widespread favorable change of public opinion in recent years on the question of sex education. However, there probably will remain with us for many years a few frightened adults who will continue to foster the cult of ignorance though an increasingly large section of the population is allowing the myths, fallacies, and superstitions related to sex and sexuality to fade into oblivion. The few remaining reactionaries have for some time ceased to seriously count.

Since the sex impulses are so powerful and have been so abused and perverted, our thoughts about sex have for ages been peculiarly directed to these perversions. As a consequence, there has been a growing reticence about the whole matter of sex as our morality and social sense have increased. This undue reticence of decent people has left the field open to those who, for commercial reasons or for the love of the vulgar, would exploit sex—which they have done. Our very "delicacy" has assured that a coarse and degraded interpretation of sex shall first come to our young people. When they discover the fine and high meanings of sex—if they ever do—they are already full of the complexes and embarrassments on the subject that make them deal unnaturally and evasively with it to their own children or those with whom they deal, such as in the schools and in church.

This situation, of course, should not be. Sex should be emphasized neither more nor less than its tremendous place in life demands. Neither should parents, teachers, and children set it apart from the other great factors that determine personality, attitudes, conduct, and character.

Sensitiveness on sex education matters when carried to the extreme is called "prudishness." Prudery is being outmoded; however, an appropriate reticence is always in order. Judgment has to be made depending upon the readiness of a given individual or group to receive the education or information that is thought to be needed. Many people are extremely sensitive, but experience has shown that they can usually become involved and brought along whether it be in counseling situations or in classroom situations.

The more cynical disbelievers in sex education answer negatively concerning this method of coping with the problem by asking in Biblical phrase, "Can the leopard change his spots?" In other words, these doubting ones believe that the sexual instinct is so firmly fixed in the nature of men and women that there is no hope of radical change through education in their sex attitudes and sex behavior.

One of our most serious difficulties in coping with this situation in past years —and to some extent even today—has been the defeatist attitude taken by many of our ablest physicians, judges, and social workers, as well as educators. When these social cynics act on the assumption that the major portion of humanity will always be degenerate in morals, of low mentality, and utterly selfish in motives, what chance have we heretofore had for any real progress?

Probably nothing better shows the touchiness of the public in past years on matters related to sex and sex behavior than the way in which we have toned down into some convenient, and often evasive, euphemisms the sordid facts of sexually charged life situations. Today we are likely to speak of perversions as only "deviations"; the prostitute has become merely an "unfortunate girl"; venereal diseases are "social diseases"; and what St. Paul boldly labeled fornication we tend to mildly cite as "unconventional behavior."

Men and women of good will, over the years, have had doubts about sex education, and often those doubts were understandable. Eager sex educationists —stepping in at times where others feared to tread—were often contributing to this situation. In their very proper enthusiasm for an excellent cause, they tended to alienate more orthodox opinion.

But now the situation is changing. Parents are beginning to see that in this field, as in others, honesty is the best policy; and teachers and youth leaders are realizing that they also have a responsibility in the matter and are increasingly showing willingness to participate. One education authority after another is changing its attitude from opposition to benevolent neutrality, and others are moving from such benevolent neutrality to enthusiasm.

The fear that parents might object to their children receiving sex education in the schools or in these other agencies is a bogey that has been enormously magnified. In fact, most informed parents tend to be very grateful when the teachers offer to do something about the sex education of their children.

At the same time, there are those teachers who still remain on the other side as far as the schools are concerned. Having had thrust on them in recent years so many new tasks outside their main one of basic education, many teachers are profoundly, and quite understandably, suspicious of any attempt to lay another burden on their shoulders. Yet, even while recognizing and insisting on parental responsibility for some aspects of sex education, they are on the whole now willing to agree that much needs to be done in the schools as well.

Younger children just do not usually give the matter of sex education any special thought. Instead, they tend to accept such lessons as perfectly normal and natural. As one young pupil was heard to say so wisely, "When you come to think about it, there's nothing strange about it."

In emphasizing the responsibility of the school, consequently, the intention is to enlarge the opportunity of the child and youth, not to reduce the responsibility of the home and parents.

Sex education, as taught in past years, has largely been merely for the wayward part of the younger generation. Leaders of youth are today interested in learning what effect sex education will have on the finest youths who will be the leaders of the future, and how in turn they will continue to improve conditions.

Agencies for Family Life Education

Conferences on family living show complete agreement with the idea that such education should be the shared responsibility of the home, school, church, and community. Neither one can do the full job alone; consequently, they need to supplement and reinforce each other.

We may safely leave mathematics, writing, and reading almost exclusively to the schools. But sex education or education for family living will fail or fall short in its potential unless the schools can also get such cooperation from the homes, the churches, the boys' and girls' clubs, and all other organizations that reach young people socially, religiously, ethically, educationally, and recreationally.

THE HOME AND FAMILY

The home is the best place for most family life education—provided, of course, that circumstances within the given home are favorable for such sex teaching. Family life education starts for the infant when he enters this world, and the home, including all of its members, has the initial and contributing responsibility for developing sound attitudes and habits and conduct. The home is viewed as the primary molder of underlying emotional patterns so closely related to this subject. The home is the proper agency for giving children and youth, through example and precept, such information and guidance as they should receive regarding the meaning and place of sex in life. The environment of the home presents many opportunities for instruction that would have to be manufactured artificially in the school situation. The home is the proper place for family life teaching, if the home can and will accept such a responsibility. (See Chapter 13, "The Home and the Family in Sex Education.")

Unfortunately, many homes—probably a large majority of them—will not as yet accept this responsibility. Although more children are being trained in family life education in the home as each generation of parents becomes better educated about these matters, there still are too many children who come from homes where parents do not know how to discuss such matters or, if they do, their ideas of family life are warped, distorted, or discolored, or the home may be broken.

Many parents do not know what to teach or how to provide the experiences conducive to such learning. Worse yet, not a few are conveying, without realizing it, mistaken ideas and unwholesome attitudes, although they may be attempting to do the best job they can. Some parents, although competent in this field, do not take the time to know and talk with their children about problems that concern them and many children do not have living parents.

Society must find ways, through the school and otherwise, both to supplement and to support the home that is doing a good job, and to make up, if possible, for the shortcomings of the home where parents are falling down on their responsibilities.

THE CHURCH

The church affords an unusually fine opportunity for sex education. The most important contribution by the church in this area lies in the development of acceptable *attitudes* about sex morals, marriage, home, and related topics. Churches of many denominations are providing classes and discussion groups which deal with family life and adjustment for both adults and young people. Many ministers now refuse to officiate at weddings unless the prospective bride and bridegroom are willing to discuss with them facts and attitudes about marriage that may have an important bearing on its success or failure. Regretfully, often due to the attitudes of some of the parishioners, churches are not usually assuming their full role in family life education.

THE COMMUNITY

Within the community there are many youth-serving and other agencies that are giving considerable attention to family life in their programs. Youth groups, such as the YMCA, YWCA, YMHA, CYO, Boy Scouts, Girl Scouts, and Campfire Girls, are giving attention to activities which will aid more directly in family life experiences.

Groups such as the American Social Health Association, the American Institute on Family Relations, the Sex Information and Education Council, the Family Service Association of America, and the Child Study Association are active in this field. So also are workers in public health, especially in their work with adult groups. Even the armed services, through the Chaplains' Corps, are showing a steadily growing interest in family life education particularly as related to marriage and family counseling.

Mass media of education provide another channel for education for family life. The better women's magazines carry informed, well-written articles on the subject. Syndicated newspaper columns dealing with marriage and family relations are popular. Radio and television are producing promising programs. Popularly written pamphlets have an enormous circulation. Unfortunately, however, many people turn to less acceptable forms of mass media such as pulp magazines and pornographic literature (see Chapter 12, "The Problem of Offensive and Obscene Material").

THE SCHOOL

If family life education is to be taught in such a way as to really meet the needs of most young people, it seems that the schools must do it. This definitely does not mean that the school takes over the job, but that it supplements the home and other institutions in their endeavor to instruct in this area of education.

Adolescent boys and girls need and desire scientific answers to their questions about human reproduction and related technical areas, and the school should meet this need. At school, the information can be given objectively and without emotional block, for the teacher is interested in all boys and girls and not just in one specific child.

The school's responsibility for certain aspects of sex education has been recognized for a number of years by various professional organizations, some of which are here mentioned. The views expressed are equally appropriate today.

The Midcentury White House Conference on Children and Youth [5] had this to say on sex education: education for parenthood should be made avail-

---

[5] Midcentury White House Conference on Children and Youth, *Platform Recommendations and Pledge to Children,* Health Publications Institute, Raleigh, N.C., 1950, pp. 2–3.

able to all through education, health, recreation, religious, and welfare agencies maintaining professional standards and staffed by properly qualified individuals; and elementary, secondary, college, and community education should include such appropriate experiences and studies of childhood and family life as will help young people to achieve the maturity essential to the role of parenthood.

In 1944, the National Congress of Parents and Teachers adopted a resolution stating that a well-planned program of social hygiene instruction should be instituted in the public school system of the United States beginning with the preschool child, continuing throughout public school training, and carrying over into the education of adults. New resolutions have recently been adopted.

The Educational Policies Commission [6] has listed family life education as one of the "Ten Imperative Educational Needs of Youth."

The 1941 [7] Yearbook of the American Association of School Administrators was devoted to education for family life. Recognition of sex education as an integral part of education and of the school's responsibility in sex education was discussed.

A review of the history of the sex education movement shows that these early leaders already had a broad view of what is needed today, even though their ideas may have been phrased in slightly different terms.

Additional Supportive Statements

With the upsurge in interest in sex education in recent years, a number of organizations have gone on record in their support of sex education and family living in the schools. The following is a selection from a long list. Many of these organizations and agencies also publish excellent material on sex education.

The American School Health Association has registered its endorsement of sex education in the schools by issuing "Growth Patterns and Sex Education: A Suggested Program Kindergarten Through Grade Twelve," 1967. It defines sex education as follows:

Sex education is to be distinguished from sex information and can best be described as character education. It consists of instruction to develop understanding of the physical, mental, emotional, social, economic, and psychological phases of

[6] Educational Policies Commission, *Education for All American Youth,* The National Education Association, Washington, D.C., 1944.

[7] American Association of School Administrators, *Education for Family Life,* Nineteenth Yearbook, The National Education Association, Washington D.C., 1941, p. 96.

human relations as they are affected by male and female relationships. It includes more than anatomical and reproductive information and emphasizes attitude development and guidance related to associations between the sexes. It implies that a man's sexuality is integrated into his total life development as a health entity and a source of creative energy.[8]

The School Health Section of the American Public Health Association approved a resolution in 1966 which recommended for every school system the development of a comprehensive sex education program extending from elementary through senior high school.

In the interest of providing a wider scope of opinion about the appropriateness of sex education programs in the schools, several quotes are included. These are listed in chronological order.

The initiative of the school in the strengthening of family education can be effective only if the school understands its own role correctly. . . . The starting point is the children, with their individual and pre-school histories, their family relationships and the conscious and unconscious attitude of their parents. The school should be well informed about all this, for it then can cooperate with the parents in developing various methods to help the child attain balanced adjustment.

UNESCO Report, June 1960

. . . that the school curriculum include education for family life, including sex education. . . . The family life courses, including preparation for marriage and parenthood, be instituted as an integral and major part of public education from elementary school through high school and that this formal education emphasize the primary importance of family life.

Sixth White House Conference on Children and Youth, 1960

The responsibility of the school in education for family life is no longer a matter of debate. The tasks of the school in supplementing and complementing those of the home and of the social structure in which children and youth are growing and developing their attitudes, character, and capabilities for relating themselves to other people, are now recognized as inescapable in total balanced education.

Elizabeth S. Force, Director of Family Life
American Social Health Association, 1962

. . . that the schools accept appropriate responsibility for reinforcing the efforts of parents to transmit knowledge about the values inherent in our family system, and about the psychic, moral, and physical consequences of sexual behavior, and be it further resolved that this be done by including in the general and health education curriculum the physiology and biology of human reproduction beginning at the elementary level and continuing throughout the school years at increasing levels of sex education including human reproduction as one part of a complete

[8] *Journal of School Health,* May 1967, 136 pp.

health education program . . . urge colleges and universities to include family living instruction including sex education in the general education of all students . . . encourage churches, civic organizations, and other community groups to strongly support programs of sex education.

Resolution, Board of Directors, AAHPER, 1966

If our aim is adults who will use their sexuality in mature and responsible ways, we cannot begin sex education later than early childhood . . . inasmuch as parents are also entirely unprepared to do the in-depth kind of job that is required, the schools will have to assume the main burden and responsibility for planning and carrying out adequate sex education programs.

Mary S. Calderone, M.D., Executive Director, SIECUS, 1966

To assist communities and educational institutions which wish to initiate or improve programs in this area (family life education and sex education), the U.S. Office of Education will support family life education and sex education as an integral part of the curriculum from pre-school to college and adult levels; it will support training for teachers and health and guidance personnel at all levels of instruction; it will aid programs designed to help parents carry out their roles in family life education and sex education; and it will support research and development in all aspects of family life education and sex education.

Harold Howe II, U.S. Commissioner of Education, 1966

While parents have the primary responsibility for family life and sex education, the school cannot ignore its responsibility for education in this area. Family life and sex education should be included as a planned portion of the regular curriculum and should recognize the sociological and psychological aspects of sex education as well as the biological processes of maturation and reproduction. A sequential, coordinated program with clearly defined objectives is necessary for grades K-12 if we are to provide children with a sound basis for making rational judgments regarding human interaction.

Duane J. Mattheis, Minnesota Commissioner of Education, 1966

Summary

A large part of our difficulties with sex education is that we are most uncertain how to evaluate the changes which thrust themselves upon us. We recognize that certain evils exist but we hesitate to change customs or conventional moral standards lest we destroy all morality. Unless we put some restraining hand on the changing customs we shall find, as in many instances we already have, that by the time we get a generation of teachers and parents ready for effective leadership, cultural pressures of the day will have swept the younger generation out of our reach to sink or swim by their own wits in a sea of confusing ideas and philosophies. Even in Russia, it was found that the pendulum there could swing too far, and in recent years there has been a retreat toward a more conservative pattern of sex and family behavior.

On the other hand, we must beware of the grip of an outmoded conservatism which taboos all frankness and still believes that ignorance is bliss. Only the frank admission of today's problems in this area can help to set in motion those forces which will finally enable us better to control these problems.

The more recent enlightened rebellion against the ancient conspiracy of silence has been a very definite contribution towards the solution of many of the problems.

2

Educational Outcomes— Sex Knowledge, Attitudes, and Behavior

The health program of a school should produce two types of outcomes— *health* and *educational* outcomes. Illustrations of the former are an increase in height and weight, greater endurance, and, as related to sex education, a better personality, a reduction in the number of cases and severity of venereal disease, better prenatal and postnatal care resulting in healthier mothers and infants, and fewer instances of frigidity and impotence. These health results are the effect, in varying degree, of desirable health behavior.

This chapter, however, will not deal with health outcomes as such, but will give attention to the educational outcomes of the sex education program. The educational outcomes of sex education, as in other areas of education, can be grouped into three specific types—namely, *knowledge, attitudes,* and *behavior*.

Of these three educational outcomes of sex education, the most important one to achieve—the goal—is the development and practice of desirable behavior.

Attitudes are essential in conditioning an individual to desirable behavior; and knowledge gives rational insight into behavior, therefore influencing an individual's attitudes, strengthening them, and tending to make them last longer.

Individuals with greater knowledge and understanding about sex and sexuality are more likely to have more favorable attitudes and, therefore, are more likely to practice more desirable behavior. Therefore, the main purpose in the modern school sex education program should be to bring about changes in what pupils know or understand, in how they feel about sex and sexuality, and in what they do.

We shall follow with a discussion of each of these three educational outcomes and their relationship to teaching.

Knowledge About Sex and Sexuality

Knowledge means those items of fact and procedure by which an individual learns *what* to do or not to do in a given situation and enough about *why* it is done or should not be done to make the procedure meaningful insofar as he is able to understand it. It should be knowledge that can be understood and be used by pupils and adults in their respective levels of maturity, experience, and ability. Here it includes knowledge about the various topics listed in Table 2 entitled "An Outline of the Major Topics in the Area of Family Life and Sex Education," on pages 42–45.

For the purposes of this book, the term *knowledge* is used to cover such related terms as facts, information, concepts, understanding, know-how, awareness, insight, wisdom, comprehension, perception, reason, meaning and experience. In fact of these terms, that which probably best describes this educational outcome is *experience,* whether acquired informally over the years through the process of living, or whether acquired more formally and vicariously in the classroom through such procedures as class discussion or reading a book. Book-learning is, of course, a way of acquiring the experiences of others without actually directly experiencing what they went through. In acquiring scientific sex knowledge, we become heirs to what great men have found to be matters of fact about things and events. In using these facts, we make them a part of our own experience. Mankind would not have progressed very far if each generation had had to depend solely upon knowledge acquired directly through one's own personal experience instead of benefiting from a store of accumulated knowledge.

The attitudes and behavior we so assiduously try to cultivate are, or should be, based on discoveries that required probing and prying into nature's secrets. Wrong ideas and guesses about how or why things happen or exist often linger on as superstitions long after the true scientific explanation is given. Nevertheless, the store of true explanations (scientific knowledge) has been accumulating over the years of the human race. This statement applies particularly to

the biological and medical aspects of sex and, unfortunately, less to the sociological and psychological aspects. Once acquired, such knowledge is durable
and capable of being passed along from one generation to the next. Consequently, children are not obliged to learn by direct experience everything they
are capable of learning. Instead they need to apply the learning of previous
generations.

Knowledge does give meaning to emotional attitudes and fixed habits. It
strengthens them. If a person knows the right thing to do, he may do it, whereas
he may do the proper thing only by chance *unless* he knows the right course to
follow. The type of knowledge desired in sex education is that which stimulates
self-analysis and serves as a motivating force.

Also, it is not possible in school to form or to practice all the specific sex
behavior, habits, and conduct needed by an individual child, youth, or adult.
Knowledge, therefore, is essential in aiding the individual to make satisfactory
responses to new or altered situations outside of the classroom and later in
life. Through the informational aspect of education, we learn not only how to
improve our living in various ways, but we also first are made aware of the
improvements that should be made. It is important, therefore, that a person
develop a sense of responsibility for using scientific thinking and knowledge in
the conduct of his daily life.

Sex knowledge, of course, does not guarantee correct conduct, for it does not
always motivate the desired action. But *no action occurs without motivation,
and no motivation occurs unless it is based upon previous experience of some
type*.

We may know why we should eat certain foods without this knowledge
appreciably affecting our conduct, just as we may know certain rules of gram-
mar and yet speak incorrectly. But, in such instances, the information may not
have been put in a usable form, or may not have been taught inspiringly, or
for other reasons may be nonoperative. But to argue that the teaching of facts
or the imparting of knowledge and understanding is not important in sex education, as many do, cannot be defended. Many individuals who take that viewpoint confuse the level of information that can justifiably be presented in the
lower grades with that needed and understood by those in higher grades or in
college.

KNOWLEDGE VS. IGNORANCE

When the Kinsey report first came out, Mead [1] suggested that "the sudden
removal of a previously guaranteed reticence has left many people singularly

---

[1] Margaret Mead, *Male and Female,* William Morrow and Co., New York, 1949,
p. 450.

defenseless in just those areas where their desire to conform was protected by a lack of knowledge of the extent of non-conformity."

Others have noted that possible dangers of knowledge must be weighed against possible damaging effects upon youth of an adult "conspiracy of silence," which psychiatrists have noted.

According to one psychiatrist, "The silence of the adult means to the child a silent acquiescence in the child's confused and often unexpressed misinterpretations of experience"; and "what the adult world fails to talk about to the child becomes taboo."

There is often a mental health value in giving early information. The reason lies not in any practical need but in the emotional shock which may occur when information is belated, as a result of the discrepancy between the real and the imaginary picture built up when information is not given and there is a great deal of curiosity. Psychiatric thinking suggests that the best time for the youngster to receive factual information is the period when his emotions in respect to that information are dormant or less involved.[2]

Health Attitudes

The term *attitude* is applied in a technical way to an acquired predisposition to react in a characteristic way, usually favorably or unfavorably, toward a given type of person, object, or situation.

The term as used here is meant to include a long list of related terms such as values, motivation, interests, drives, incentives, emotions, purposes, morale, ideals, and preferences. Additional related terms are likes and dislikes, prejudices, the desire or will to do something, disposition, feelings, intentions, wants, wishes, concerns, expectations, convictions, urges, inclinations moods, fears, and even conscience, morals, ideals, and philosophy.

An attitude is a state of mental and emotional readiness to react to situations, persons, or things in a manner in harmony with a habitual pattern of response previously conditioned to or associated with these stimuli. *Attitudes may determine the conclusions we derive from facts and even influence the very facts we are willing to accept.*

The term is also defined as an established response to any or all of a class of situations that the individual identifies as fundamentally alike. The attitude is the mental reaction to the situation.

An emotionalized attitude is one that is accompanied by strong "feelings"

[2] O. S. English and C. J. Foster, "Sex Education for the School-Age Child," *Parents' Magazine,* May 1950, pp. 37, 127–129.

or emotional reactions. This is particularly true in the sex field because of the powerful sex drive.

Our emotions and feelings are expressions that may be directed toward, for example, ideas, a doctor, the eating of some food, the opposite sex, or one's spouse.

Attitudes furnish uniformity to one's behavior and human social relations. Knowing a person's attitude about something makes it possible to predict more readily his behavior or actions in relation to it. It is also well to understand that there isn't just one attitude about a thing. Particularly in the field of sex and sexuality there are powerful conflicts between the different attitudes toward various sex behaviors and sexuality which eventually determine our individual choices of sex behavior.

HOW SEX ATTITUDES ARE ACQUIRED

A person's attitudes are acquired, not inherited. Attitude development involves socialization and habituation. An attitude may be acquired in the following ways:

1. It may be the final result of a gradual accumulation of related experiences, including the acquisition of facts, over a period of time, giving us our likes and dislikes, interests, and prejudices toward food, people, exercise, and sexuality, as well as other things. Examples of attitudes acquired in this way are honesty, patriotism, affection, love, and fear. They develop in the daily atmosphere in which we live, work, and play.

2. It may be the result of one sudden, dramatic, intense experience. Under such circumstances, the attitude can frequently become permanent. Seeing a person killed through the carelessness of a driver may make a person unusually careful (an attitude) about driving; a child may continue to fear (an attitude) the doctor because he used a needle that resulted in pain when the child was very young; and suddenly learning that one has VD may make a person despondent (an attitude).

3. It may have been taken over from other people in the form that was already held or developed. Examples include one's attitudes toward other races or creeds, toward certain sex practices, and toward love and marriage. The pattern of acceptable behavior in a given social class is often called its subculture, such as of teenagers in a given age and place. Our cultural group or other groups determine our attitudes—what we think, what we expect.

Rosenstock [3] suggests that an individual's motivation in relation to a particular health issue is determined largely by three kinds of beliefs: (a) the extent to which he sees the health problem as having a high probability of occurrence

---

[3] M. Rosenstock, *Keys to People: Motivation Bases for Health Education,* Public Health Service, Washington, D.C., 1959.

in his personal case; (b) the extent to which he believes the problem would have serious consequences for him if it did involve him; and (c) the extent to which he believes some reasonable course of action open to him would be effective in reducing the threat. There appear to be many implications in this as applied to sex education.

Income, occupation, education, and other indicators of socio-economic status have a bearing on people's attitudes, including their attitudes toward and participation in wholesome or unwholesome sex activities. In the lower socio-economic levels, there is usually a lower level of compliance with the recommendations of health and other authorities. It may be that information has the greatest effect where there is initially a sufficiently high level of education.

There does not appear to be any set of standard attitudes toward sex that can be formulated that would be acceptable to persons of differing value systems. However, Kirkendall [4] has analyzed seven common attitudes held toward sex as follows:

1. The need to move from an attitude regarding sex as primarily physical to a concept of sex as an attribute of personality.

2. The need to move from irrational moralism and nonmoral attitudes to insightful morality.

3. The need to move from a hush-hush or garrulous attitude to an objective consideration of sex.

4. The need to move from grim, dour, or frivolous to poised acceptance.

5. The need to move from an attitude of fear and dread or shocking bluntness to straightforward frankness.

6. The need to move from an attitude of strictly individual concern to a recognition of social implications of sex.

7. The need to move from an attitude of rigid masculine dominance and female subordination, or of regarding the sexes as alike in all respects, to a flexible equalitarian regard for individual personality and an acceptance of the unique values of sex membership.

APPLICATION TO LEARNING

Getting the facts is only part of education; what is needed is an acceptance (an attitude) of the facts, and the integration of them into our lives.

Learning on the part of the learner (the pupil) requires a *will* (an attitude)

[4] L. A. Kirkendall, "Sound Attitudes Toward Sex," in J. T. Landis and M. C. Landis, Editors, *Readings in Marriage and the Family,* Prentice-Hall, Englewood Cliffs, N. J., 1952, pp. 419–426.

to learn. Also the *receptiveness* (an attitude), for example, of a patient to dental treatment, at the dentist's office, determines how effective any attempt at education might be; or the receptiveness of an expectant mother to the advice given by her physician; or the decision of a teenager to follow his own moral judgment rather than that of the peer group, if these differ.

Since attitudes are usually set in the early years of life, it is to be expected that parents and teachers will have the most influence in the development of the various attitudes of children.

However, the student needs to be challenged in order to create for himself a set of sex values—his own personal value system—for without this he slips into the value system of the group to which he belongs. The latter may or may not be desirable, depending upon whether the group has a higher or lower set of values than the individual.

SEX BEHAVIOR

The term *sex behavior* is here used to refer to habits, conduct, deportment, actions, responses, works, accomplishments, achievements, applications, decisions, follow-through, participation, reactions, acts, results, and deeds. It is the doing, the behavioral outcomes as related to sex. It is that which happens to the individual and in which he himself participates.

Many of our daily or regular practices are referred to as *habits*—such as going to bed at a regular time, drinking milk regularly, going for a walk each afternoon, and brushing teeth after meals and before retiring. A habit is defined as a fixed or established response to a commonplace situation. Habitual responses do not involve mental activity.

Sometimes the desirable conduct, deportment, or behavior is that of inaction, that of refraining from *doing* that which might be injurious—such as not smoking, not crossing the street against the red light, not drinking an alcoholic beverage, not being too daring, not having premarital sex relations, or not reading pornographic magazines.

Most people know, or know approximately, what is best for them to do. Then why don't they do it? It is because their attitudes are incorrect, or not strong enough, to sustain the doing of the right thing when they are pulled in other directions by other conflicting but, to them, more satisfying motives. However, the more knowledge people acquire about the reasons for practicing certain wholesome sex behavior, the more likely it is that their attitudes will be strengthened; then the desirable behavior is more likely to take precedence over other less desirable behavior.

Unfortunately, good and desirable sex practices do not always show results as short-term investments. The value of many of them may not become apparent in actual experience until many years later.

Relationship of Knowledge, Attitudes, and Behavior

Education goes on all the time regardless of circumstances. If the individual is not learning new facts, he at least is experiencing something, is developing some attitude rightly or wrongly, and is reacting to this attitude rightly or wrongly.

There is a gap between that which we know and that which we do, and there is a gap between what we believe and what we do. Without the needed information or understanding, our practices may lack direction, or be wrong, or be absent. Without favorable motivation through attitudes, the desirable actions do not occur. It has been said that "knowledge without action is sterile" and that "action without knowledge is blind." Sometimes when we say, "We don't like," the meaning is often, "We don't understand." One cannot make up his mind to support a program until he has the necessary information.

We have stressed that knowledge of sex facts does not always assure desirable sex behavior; yet a pupil cannot, in any case, practice what he does not know. Also it has been said that "motivation without understanding is propaganda, whereas motivation with understanding is education." Sex information is obviously necessary, but instruction must go a step further and help children to live better lives.

Information that is not put to immediate use does not become meaningful. Presumably, a person is motivated more strongly to do something while the knowledge about the given topic is fresh in his mind. If the opportunity to do something is delayed, the motivation lessens and so, often, nothing is done.

It is commonly agreed that information, to be readily accepted and acted upon, must be related to needs and desires that have been recognized by the people for whom it is intended. And so sex education will be more functional if it is organized around the children's needs and interests. Knowledge gained at one period is forgotten unless it is used in and has application to the personal or workday life of the individual pupil or adult.

In Table 2, pages 42–45, are listed the main topics within this area. Pupils in our schools need to acquire some knowledge about each of these topics, wholesome attitudes and values about each, and some acceptable behavior pattern concerning each.

CHANGING HEALTH ATTITUDES AND PRACTICES

Evidence indicates that attitudes and practices can be modified although it may be a difficult process. One significant study showed that children's attitudes were changed after viewing even one motion picture.[5]

Remmers [6] showed that teaching materials of only fifteen minutes' duration caused significant changes in children's attitudes toward various social problems, and that the changes resulting from these teachings were valid after a year's lapse. He suggested that such marked changes occurred because well-integrated attitudes do not as yet exist in young children.

Sutton [7] conducted a study to determine the health attitudes and practices held by college students as a basis for more effectively planning their educational experiences in the health instruction classes. One area of the study dealt with the "need for secrecy concerning occurrence of certain illnesses." It was found that a high percentage of the students felt a need for secrecy for three problems listed: mental illness as indicated by the need for treatment by a psychiatrist, hospitalization in a mental institution, and alcoholism. Marked as confidential by many of the students were three additional items: tuberculosis, cancer, and the use of public clinics for medical services.

At the end of the semester of instruction, the students were given a re-test. There was a definite improvement in respect to all illnesses, with fewer students holding to the view that there was a need for secrecy. Yet the number of students who still retained the feeling of secrecy about problems associated with mental illness pointed up the need for an intensified educational program for students and the general public regarding mental health.

Presumably the same applies, but for different reasons, to topics in sex education such as venereal disease or unwanted pregnancy or impotence.

Other studies have similarly demonstrated that sound teaching can contribute to changes in attitudes in the various areas of education. And with a change in attitude there goes a change in practice.

It is clear, however, that to change attitudes that have been rooted in childhood, that reflect centuries of social conditioning, and that are even today reinforced by sanctions of law and by a large section of public opinion requires a process of re-education.

[5] Ruth C. Peterson and L. L. Thurstone, *Motion Pictures and the Social Attitudes of Children,* The Macmillan Co., New York, 1933, pp. 38, 53–55.

[6] *Ibid.,* p. 75.

[7] Wilfred C. Sutton, "An Appraisal of Health Attitudes and Practices of College Students," *Journal of School Health,* April 1956, pp. 125–130.

In many cases, special counseling and therapy are required to effect any change in deeply-rooted inhibitions or deviations in sex-role or object. Tenacious attitudes "cannot be altered by a casual, superficial sex education," but only by a process of serious education conceived in "reconstructive terms." [8]

At a conference of the Academy of Psychosomatic Medicine in 1967, it was stated by gynecologists and obstetricians that about fifty per cent of all feminine disorders, from girlhood to old age, have psychosomatic causes. Dr. Leonard H. Biskind stated that "heredity, parental training, damaging experiences in childhood and adolescence all play vital roles in the individual women's attitude toward childbirth." Dr. Robert W. Rutherford denounced the highly romanticized "boy meets girl" version of love popularized by motion pictures and novels. He also cited four leading causes for pseudo-frigidity (real frigidity is rare): (1) Negative sex training—"a wedding ceremony cannot easily change a lifetime of thinking that sex is sinful"; (2) fear of pregnancy, even though a child is desired; (3) hostility toward her husband, because this is "a man's world"; and (4) unconscious conflicting loves, such as the girl who unfavorably compares her husband to her father or brother.

ILLUSTRATIONS OF KNOWLEDGE, ATTITUDES, AND PRACTICES

Each of these educational results can be graded on a scale that changes as follows:

Knowledge: From that of having considerable knowledge (plus), to having no knowledge (0), to having misinformation (minus).

Attitudes: From that of having a favorable, positive, and desirable attitude (plus), to having no attitude on the subject (0), to having a negative or wrong attitude (minus).

Behavior: From regularly carrying out the desirable or correct habit, practice, or conduct (plus), to not doing anything about it (0), to carrying out the wrong, undesirable, or injurious practice or habit (minus).

The ideal situation is, of course, where a plus value can be assigned to all of the educational results; but that is not ordinarily the case, unfortunately, as is illustrated by the following varied examples.

[8] M. A. Harper and F. R. Harper, "Education in Sex," in A. Ellis and R. Brancale, Editors, *The Psychology of Sex Offenders,* Charles C Thomas, Springfield, Illinois, 1956, pp. 344–349.

HEALTH EDUCATION ILLUSTRATIONS

1. A man knows (plus) that his cough is the result of excessive smoking of cigarettes; however, he does not wish (minus) to give up smoking, because he enjoys it; but he eventually stops (plus) smoking on his doctor's orders.

2. Frank who is in college knows (plus) the importance of visiting the dentist periodically; but he has a fear (minus) of the dentist based on previous experience; consequently, he regularly postpones (minus) going to the dentist or breaks his appointments (minus) until he really is in pain. (It no doubt is difficult to convince such an individual that there is less likelihood of it being painful if he would have his teeth checked regularly and taken care of before serious decay has set in.)

3. Jane, a high school girl, knows (plus) that a good breakfast is important but she doesn't particularly care (minus) whether she eats or misses this meal (minus); consequently, she often oversleeps and runs out of the house without having eaten any breakfast (0). (Probably she needs added information about the value of an adequate breakfast; and perhaps her mother should see that she gets up ten minutes earlier to provide enough time for her to eat her breakfast.)

4. Helen, who is eighteen, knows (plus) the scientific evidence against being overweight; however, she enjoys food *very* much (in her case, a minus); and so she indulges by eating at every inclination (minus). (Her problem may be an emotional one, and she does not have dates.)

5. George is a member of the local high-school football squad. His coach has admonished (plus) the boys not to smoke and they have learned (plus) from him about the effects of this practice on their athletic performance. George has been convinced of the value of following this regulation (plus), but now takes less stock (0) in what his coach says because he has seen his coach smoke; as a consequence, George, who did not smoke (plus), has taken to smoking occasionally (minus). (This illustrates the power of example in influencing conduct.)

6. John, in seventh grade, is not too well informed (0) on proper attire and the general rules of good grooming; furthermore, he does not like (minus) to dress up or comb his hair, feeling that it is somewhat "sissy" (minus); consequently, he regularly dresses in dirty dungarees (minus), and at social events wears sloppy clothes (minus). (Through class discussion on good grooming and through some social pressure of his peers, he will no doubt, in time, change his attitude.)

7. A middle-aged woman knows (plus) that she is in need of psychiatric attention; however, she is unwilling (minus) to accept this knowledge because she feels that "only crazy people need the help of a psychiatrist"; and so she does not secure (0) psychiatric help. (This is a difficult situation and may require tact in handling.)

8. Mr. Smith knows (plus) that he is in need of an operation, and he also knows (plus) that the physician who will operate is a successful surgeon; consequently, Mr. Smith is not afraid (plus), for he has full confidence (plus) in his doctor; he follows the doctor's advice (plus) and enters the hospital for the operation (plus).

9. An insurance salesman believes that alcohol has healthful qualities (minus); and he likes and even craves (minus) alcoholic beverages; the result is that he drinks excessively (minus). (This person has incorrect information and is less likely to change his attitude and practice without first acquiring correct information about alcohol. Even then it may be difficult to change his attitude and practice without some drastic action on the part of his family.)

SEX EDUCATION ILLUSTRATIONS

10. John, about to enter first grade, has been taught the correct terms for body elimination by his parents (plus). Consequently, he is not embarrassed (plus) about using (plus) these terms at appropriate times in school.

11. Mary's parents understand (plus) that curiosity about sex is normal on the part of children and youth, and so they are not disturbed (plus) over certain questions asked of them by Mary and her brother. The parents consequently react in a mature way (plus) to these questions.

12. Mrs. H. who is in her middle forties holds some misconceptions (minus) about the menopause which results in her fearing (minus) its approach. Her subsequent behavior is very emotional (minus).

13. One high school girl stated that she abhors (plus) obscenity but likes (plus) to read good books. She has consequently developed a fine personal library (plus).

14. Mr. Jones, a high school biology teacher, has adequate knowledge about the biology of sex for teaching purposes (plus), but his attitude toward the subject is immature (minus). As a result, he avoids (minus) dealing with the topic when and where it could be appropriately included in his biology teaching.

Application of Understanding About the Three Educational Outcomes

The previous discussions dealing with the distinctive characteristics of knowledge, attitudes, and behavior should be a basis for curriculum planning by grade levels, for determining what can be correlated with other courses and programs, and for deciding on teaching methods.

GRADE PLACEMENT OF SEX EDUCATION

It is, of course, desirable that all individuals, regardless of age, acquire the needed sex attitudes and apply the related sex practices and conduct. Consequently education from first grade through twelfth grade, and even later, must emphasize this.

As the child matures, the amount and type of information which he needs and can understand increases until he is an adult. While emphasis is given largely to facts in such an instructional program, there should also be provision, as far as possible, for the exercise or application of this information in the daily routine of living.

Interest, as one of the most powerful attitudes, needs to be considered in curriculum planning. Where interest exists or where it can be aroused in a given sex education topic, it is probably an area wherein the pupils are most in need of, and ready for, the learning experience. However, to base curriculum planning primarily upon interest is unwise for there are many topics about which young people show little interest but which are very important to their well-being in learning.

RELATION TO CORRELATION AND INTEGRATION

The extent to which correlation and integration are possible is dependent, similarly, upon whether a unit or topic deals primarily with knowledge, attitudes, or behavior. Ordinarily, an area of sex education that contains a considerable amount of factual biological content, such as reproductive processes, endocrine glands, heredity and eugenics, and venereal disease, should be mainly handled as one unit in one course. It should be taught in a part of the school curriculum where it is possible to teach the subtopics in sequence so that each succeeding lesson can build on the previous one, and thus some broader application can be made after the study of all the related topics has been completed. If such content were distributed among several subject fields, learning would not be as effective.

In contrast to the teaching of facts, as just indicated, the teaching of attitudes should be included wherever any course or situation offers the opportunity. Attitudes tend to weaken by disuse, and so it is desirable to strengthen them by having them brought into the teaching situation and presented by different teachers in different subjects. To illustrate, if the facts of menstruation have been covered in the health education class, the encouragement by the physical education teacher in applying this knowledge would reinforce any similar recommendations from the health teacher.

It would be unfortunate if, for example, only the health or biology teachers gave special consideration to the teaching of good grooming or sex attitudes. These teachers can present the bulk of the topic, but it is important that *all* teachers make application of various aspects of this learning in their own teaching situations.

Application to the Selection of Teaching Methods

The methods that should be selected for teaching in the field of sex education are in part related to whether the specific teaching is primarily directed toward the acquisition of knowledge or a change in attitude or the improvement in sex practice.

The end purpose of sex education is not the acquisition of knowledge *per se,* but the use of that knowledge. It is relatively easy to set up a program aimed at imparting facts to the individuals concerned, whereas it is a more difficult task to assure that the desirable attitudes are developed and that opportunities are then made available so that the individual or group can act on the facts when motivated to do so.

For years emphasis has been primarily on the teaching of content—that is, on facts and information. In sex education that is not enough. It is equally important to use the best techniques for strengthening attitudes and for developing desirable sex behavior. We need methods of education that will change or improve behavior.

A good program in sex education takes all aspects into consideration. The methods selected, and how well they are executed by the teacher, determine whether favorable attitudes, behavior patterns, and conduct are forthcoming.

The chapters on teaching methods, audiovisual aids, and evaluation are definitely related to a recognition of the fact that the techniques used must be geared to the educational outcomes desired—knowledge, attitudes, or behavior.

Activities

1. Make a list of ten to twenty-five attitudes for several of the areas of sex education listed in Table 2, pages 42–45.

2. Make a list of health practices to match the attitudes that you have prepared for Activity 1.

3. Prepare five statements of knowledge, attitudes, and practices using the plan illustrated on pages 30–31. Avoid duplicating those listed. Select them from various sex education areas.

References

Allport, Gordon W., "Attitudes," *Handbook of Social Psychology,* 1957, pp. 698–844.

American Association for Health, Physical Education and Recreation, *Health Concepts: Guides for Health Instruction,* National Education Association, Washington, D.C., 1967, 56 pp.

Beyrer, Mark K., et al., "A Bibliography on Misconceptions Related to Health," *J. School Health,* Vol. 32, 1962, p. 412.

Cauffman, J. G., "Appraisal of the Health Behavior of Junior High School Students," *Res. Quart.,* American Association for Health, Physical Education and Recreation, Vol. 34, September 1963, p. 431.

Denver Public Schools, *Health Interests of Children,* Denver, Colo., 1947, 121 pp.

Droba, D. D., "Methods for Measuring Attitudes," *Psychol. Bull.* Vol. 29, May 1932, pp. 309–23.

Flanagan, J. C., et al., "New Tool for Measuring Children's Behavior," *Elem. School J.,* Vol. 59, 1958, p. 163.

Galdston, Iago, et al., *Motivation in Health Education,* Columbia University Press, New York, 1948, 320 pp.

Hartley, E. L., R. Straus, and M. Mead, "Determinants of Health Beliefs and Behavior," *Amer. J. Pub. Health,* Vol. 51, March 1961, pp.1541–44.

Harrison, Price E., and Leslie W. Irwin, "Certain Harmful Health Misconceptions of Junior High School Students Attending Public Schools in Metropolitan Areas," *Res. Quart.,* American Association for Health, Physical Education and Recreation, Vol. 35, 1964, p. 4.

Hively, W. "Implications for the Classroom of B. F. Skinner's Analysis of Behavior," *Harvard Educ. Rev.,* Vol. 1, 1959, p. 37.

Johns, Edward B., and Warren L. Juhnke, *Health Practice Inventory,* Stanford University Press, Stanford, Calif., 1952, 8 pp.

Kilander, H. Frederick, "Health Knowledge," *J. Health, Phys. Educ., Rec.,* Vol. 32, December 1961, pp. 625–27.

Kilander, H. F., "Health Knowledge, Attitudes, Practice and Skills," in *School Health Education: a Study of Content, Methods and Materials,* Macmillan, New York, 1962, 500 pp.

Kirkendall, L. A., and D. Calderwood, "The Family, the School, and Peer Groups: Sources of Information About Sex," *J. School Health,* Vol. 35, 1965, p. 7.

Knutson, A. L., *The Individual, Society, and Health Behavior,* Russell Sage Foundation, New York, 1965.

Lantagne, J. E., "An Analysis of the Health Interests of 3,000 Secondary School Students," *Res. Quart.,* American Association for Health, Physical Education, and Recreation, Vol. 21, 1950, p. 34.

Lantagne, J. E., "Health Interests of 10,000 Secondary School Students," *Res. Quart.,* American Association for Health, Physical Education and Recreation, October 1952, pp. 330–46.

Mayshark, C., "Critical Analysis of Attitude Measurement in Health Education, 1927–57," *Res. Quart.,* American Association for Health, Physical Education, and Recreation, Vol. 29, 1958, p. 309.

Mead, M., "Cultural Determinants," *Amer. J. Public Health,* Vol. 51, 1961, p. 1552.

Rosenstock, I. M., *Keys to People: Motivational Bases for Health Education,* Public Health Service, Washington, D.C., 1959.

Sliepcevich, Elena M., *School Health Education Study,* American Association for Health, Physical Education and Recreation, Washington, D.C., 1964.

Solleder, Marian K., *Evaluation Instruments in Health Education,* American Association for Health, Physical Education, and Recreation, Washington, D. C., 1965.

Tyler, R. W., "Health Education Implications from the Behavioral Sciences," *J. Health, Phys. Educ., Rec.,* Vol. 31, 1960, p. 17.

Tyler, R. W., "Implications of Behavioral Studies for Health Education," *J. School Health,* Vol. 33, January 1963, pp. 1–5.

Veenker, C., Editor, *Synthesis of Research in Selected Areas of Health Instruction,* American Association for Health, Physical Education, and Recreation, Washington, D. C., 1963.

3

Curriculum Planning
for Family Life
and Sex Education

The curriculum in family life and sex education needs to be planned with great care since it is an area where the greater emphasis is on the development of attitudes, values, and conduct and, to a lesser extent, on factual material, although this is also important.

Objectives of Family Life Education

The following general objectives of family life education have already been implied in the definitions presented:

1. To develop normal and wholesome attitudes and ideals in relation to sex and the family.
2. To develop desirable habits, behavior patterns, and conduct in accord with such attitudes and ideals.
3. To acquire knowledge and understanding of matters related to the physiology of human reproduction and related aspects of family life.
4. To learn to use the proper terminology in reference to the body.
5. To understand some of the possible consequences and outcomes of various courses of conduct.

6. To correct and alleviate some of the common worries and misconceptions in the field of sex adjustment.
7. To contribute to the emotional and social growth of the individual so that he can function adequately as a member of a family and, eventually, as a parent.

PRINCIPLES OF FAMILY LIFE EDUCATION

Following is a set of principles or guides to curriculum planning for family life and sex education. These are based upon the experiences of many individuals who have taught in this area in the elementary and secondary schools.

1. Family life education should be recognized as a natural phase of life which can make valuable contributions to wholesome living.
2. Emphasis should be on the sociological, psychological, and moral aspects as well as on the biological.
3. Family life education should be a continuous process.
4. Family life education should progress toward the consideration of an increasingly wide range of sex topics in mixed groups.
5. Factual instruction in sex education should be well advanced by the end of puberty.
6. Family life education must be based on the recognition and utilization of individual differences and needs.
7. Family life education should meet and slightly anticipate the needs of each child.
8. Family life education should preferably not be departmentalized but should rather be integrated into the curriculum and the activities of the school.
9. Counseling should be provided to support and parallel classroom teaching.
10. An objective and unemotional, yet moral, approach to sex instruction is desirable.
11. Disease and immorality should not be over-emphasized but should be discussed.
12. Instruction should preferably be given by regular members of the school staff, and instruction should involve both men and women teachers.
13. Family life education in the schools is furthered by the establishment of cooperation with parents.

CONCEPTS IN FAMILY LIFE EDUCATION

Here are listed nine examples of family life concepts with some explanatory statements about each.[1]

1. *Good family life assists in meeting the needs of family members.*
The relationship among family members determines the quality of family living.
The individuality of each member of the family must be recognized and preserved.

[1] National Education Association, *Health Concepts, Guides for Health Instruction,* 1967, pp. 37–39.

The family guides individual members so that each demonstrates the ability to understand, respect, and accept himself and others.

2. *Early conditioning of individual values, religious beliefs, and respect for social mores and laws serve as a basis for conduct during courtship and marriage.*

The family, as the basic unit of our society, has primary responsibility for helping children to develop values, including self-discipline.

Moral and spiritual values prevailing in the family group help to shape present and future family relationships and serve as a basis for decision-making.

Parents need to help children and youth to learn why certain kinds of behavior are acceptable in developing attitudes and in building resources for inner strength and serenity.

3. *In our culture, dating, going steady, and engagement are significant phases in the selection of a life partner.*

Courtship, including dating, going steady, and engagement, is the period during which partners find out about each other.

Dating depends upon how one feels about himself, his attitude toward the opposite sex, how socially expert he is at making friends, and how well he functions in mixed groups and in intimate associations.

The engagement period is a natural outgrowth of dating and courtship experiences and provides an opportunity to predict future marital adjustments.

4. *Mature love is a major factor contributing to the choice of a life partner.*

Health factors often influence the choice of a life partner.

A good marriage partner has a healthy self-concept. He is one who has the ability to analyze critically and constructively.

Love is primarily giving, not receiving, and is based on the realities of everyday family living.

5. *Marriage presents challenging opportunities and responsibilities to each marriage partner.*

Successful marriage depends upon choosing the right partner and each partner making satisfactory adjustments.

Each spouse should have an opportunity for personal growth and development.

Achievement of satisfactory adjustments by both partners leads to the development of a stable and lasting marriage.

6. *Family members experience physiological, psychological, and sociological problems and make adjustments as they progress through part or all of a family cycle.*

Each family grows and lives out the family cycle in its own unique way.

Health influences individual and family living throughout the family cycle.

Family living is enhanced when individuals understand and accept individual differences in patterns of growth and development.

Communication is likely to be more effective when family members use socially acceptable vocabulary concerning sex and reproductive functions.

7. *Parenthood, which is a biological gift and a modifier of personality, perpetuates the life cycle.*

Parenthood begins a new era of responsibilities in the role of the family.

Parents should understand the characteristics of normal child growth and development.

Good prenatal and postnatal care should be secured for mother and child.

The nature and quality of family relationships affect a child's growth and development.

8. *People who do not marry make adjustments as single individuals in an adult society organized basically around family groups.*

Some unmarried persons adjust in a completely satisfactory manner, while others fail to make good adjustments. Persons who desire marriage but do not find a mate are most likely to have difficulty in adjusting.

The unmarried may achieve a normal satisfaction of their affectionate needs through relationships with their family group and with friends.

The unmarried can contribute effectively to society through attention to a successful career and through community service.

9. *Professionally competent individuals and recognized agencies and institutions within the community are important resources for helping individuals and families solve their problems.*

Community resources serve to prevent family disorganization and to reinforce the family as the basic unit of society.

Individuals and family members should consult appropriate resources in the community when they are unable to solve their own problems.

Note: See Part II, which comprises outlines on major content topics. These have been prepared in the form of listings of additional concepts and subconcepts.

A Sequential Program—Kindergarten Through Grade Twelve

The next two chapters will describe in detail suggested programs for the elementary and secondary schools. Therefore, at this point, only a brief overview is presented.

PRESCHOOL AGES

Sex education of some type in the home will have been going on from the time of birth until the child enters school for the first time. A minimum of factual information will have been acquired, but certain attitudes will already have been forming.

By the time the child enters school, he has definitely acquired attitudes which affect his sex identity—masculinity and femininity, and his social behavior, including attitudes toward home, parents, other children, and human relations in general.

The school now has the opportunity of assisting the home and parents in continuing the sex education of the child. When the development of wholesome attitudes about sex and sexuality is neglected in early childhood, the children so affected may later be seriously handicapped by conflicts occurring during adolescence and in following years. Therefore, it is very important that the school provide sound guidance in family life education beginning with the kindergarten and the primary grades.

KINDERGARTEN AND PRIMARY GRADES

All education for family life in the primary grades should be gradual and a continuous preparation for oncoming physical, emotional, and social changes. Such education should not be a separate subject but should be integrated with the school program. It should occur in natural situations as children's problems and interests arise. A few of these problems are so common and fundamental that they may be anticipated and planned for in advance. Information should not be volunteered that is beyond the child's interest, readiness, and experience.[2]

There are certain routines in school that are strongly connected with the preschool family living. The child needs to take care of himself in the toilets and develop habits of neatness, sanitation, and courtesy to others in the bathroom. He also becomes aware of the difference between the girls' and boys' toilets. In the homes of these young children, baby sisters and brothers often arrive, which furnishes a natural opportunity to supplement the home teaching with acceptable terminology instead of babyish terms. Raising animals in the classroom, visiting the farm, pictures of life of people in other countries, and children's questions will bring occasions for giving further information.[3]

Familiarizing children with the correct vocabulary and bodily functions will enable them to talk with their teachers and parents more freely and without embarrassment and will free them from a sense of false shame.

INTERMEDIATE GRADES

This period of the intermediate grades is of particular importance because of its influence upon the more difficult period of adolescence to follow. Also, this is the period when the child's personality is at a critical stage.

In addition to expanding on the sex education of the primary grades, attention should be given to developing an understanding of the physiological

[2] New Jersey State Department of Education, *Education for Family Life in the Primary Grades,* Trenton, N. J., 1948, p. 4.

[3] Helen Manley, "Personal and Family Life Education in University City Schools," *Journal of School Health,* March 1959, p. 121.

changes that are taking place and to an appreciation of their significance; to a respectful and courteous attitude toward children of the opposite sex, free from sex consciousness; to a definite appreciation of the value of wholesome comradeships and friends, and practice in securing them; to correct habits of bodily care including the sex organs; to a wholesome attitude toward the facts and relationships of sex in general; and to a sense of the significance and dignity of the child's own sex and sexuality.

Children at this age are interested in the physiology of their bodies. They continue to be interested in reproduction of plants and animals.

This period is also the age when children begin the use of "bad" words and of boy-girl interests and mixed parties with kissing games. It is time for the boys and girls to discuss certain aspects of their growing up and their problems. Films on reproduction and menstruation are appropriate to show at this time.

It is important to remember that, today, sophistication in youth has been pushed back into much earlier years than formerly. However, this situation may enable parents and teachers to more readily and better prepare youth for the urges of adolescence *before they arrive* at adolescence.

JUNIOR HIGH SCHOOL

With the beginning of adolescence, new and powerful factors enter in to complicate the problems of adjustment to life and of character training. A curiosity about sex is developing to which we should seek to give wholesome direction and control.

There is a strong undercurrent of idealism developing during adolescence which should be related to an early philosophy of life in which the sex factor is soundly adjusted. The pupil needs to know that these factors are the normal manifestations of developing manhood and womanhood related to sex. Considering the stages of physical and emotional maturity through which pupils develop during the secondary school period, it is desirable to have one type of emphasis on the junior high school level and another one, more advanced, on the senior high school level.

Topics for consideration in the junior high school include the importance of growth, the changes in the boys and girls due to functions of the endocrine glands, the physiology of sex glands, reproduction, boy-girl relations including understanding each other and dating, and ideals for living in a world of today.

Preparing the boy, by knowledge, for the experience of seminal emission and the girl for menstruation should have begun in the prepubertal period.

TABLE 2. OUTLINE OF MAJOR TOPICS IN AREA OF EDUCATION FOR FAMILY LIVING

Topics	Grade Levels							
	Presch.	1–3	4–6	7–9	10–12	College	X	Y
A. Boy and Girl Relationships								
1. Building friendships								
2. Reasons for popularity and unpopularity								
3. Qualities in girls admired by boys								
4. Qualities in boys admired by girls								
5. Good grooming								
6. Social behavior, conduct, manners, etiquette								
B. Dating								
1. Kinds of dates								
a. Glamour dates								
b. Blind dates								
c. Growing friendships								
2. On the date								
a. Planning for dates								
b. Responsibilities of boys in dating								
c. Responsibilities of girls in dating								
3. Dating problems								
4. Wholesome recreation								
5. Petting								
a. Meaning of petting and necking								
b. Effect on boy and girl								
6. Parents and their children's dating								
7. A code of conduct								
8. Going steady: advantages, disadvantages								
C. Growth and Development								
1. Emotional growth and maturity								
2. Puberty: physical changes in boys								
a. Height, weight, body proportions								
b. Secondary sex characteristics of boys								
(1) Physical changes								
(2) Seminal emissions								
c. Secondary sex characteristics of girls								

TABLE 2 (continued)

Topics	Grade Levels							
	PRESCH.	1–3	4–6	7–9	10–12	COLLEGE	X	Y
(1) Physical changes								
(2) Menstrual cycle								
3. The endocrine system								
a. Hormones and glands in general								
b. Sex hormones								
D. REPRODUCTION								
1. Reproduction of plants and animals								
a. Asexual reproduction (unicellular)								
b. Sexual reproduction (biparental)								
c. Care of plants and animals								
2. Male reproductive system: anatomy and physiology								
3. Female reproductive system: anatomy and physiology								
E. HEREDITY								
1. The mechanism and principles of heredity.								
2. The interaction of heredity and environment								
3. Some applications to people								
a. Sex determination								
b. Sex-linked traits								
c. Blood types								
d. Twins								
e. Cousin marriage								
f. Inheritable diseases								
g. Congenital inheritance								
F. SOCIAL AND EMOTIONAL PROBLEMS RELATED TO SEX								
1. Conflict between sex impulse and social and moral code								
2. Masturbation								
3. Homosexuality								
4. Perversion								
5. Promiscuity								
6. Illegitimate births								
7. Abortion								
8. Birth control								
9. Venereal disease								
10. Prostitution								

TABLE 2 (continued)

Topics	Grade Levels							
	PRESCH.	1–3	4–6	7–9	10–12	COLLEGE	X	Y
G. PREPARATION FOR MARRIAGE								
1. The role of the family								
a. The evolution of the family								
b. The functions of the family								
c. Characteristics of the family in our society								
d. The role of each member in a family								
e. Factors which strengthen family life								
f. Factors which weaken family life								
2. Selection of a mate								
a. Personal preparation for making a choice								
b. Making friends—as an approach to mate selection								
c. Major considerations in choosing a mate								
d. Desirable personal qualities of a mate								
e. Mixed marriages								
f. How to know that it is love								
3. Courtship								
a. Purposes of courtship								
b. Accepted practices in courtship								
c. Length of courtship								
4. The engagement								
a. Purposes								
b. How long it should be								
c. Customs of engagement								
d. Behavior during engagement								
e. What the couple should discuss in relation to their future marriage								
f. Education for marriage for the couple								
g. Marriage counseling for the couple								
5. Laws regulating marriage								
a. Legal requirements for marriage								
b. Variations of laws between states								

TABLE 2 (continued)

Topics	Grade Levels							
	PRESCH.	1–3	4–6	7–9	10–12	COLLEGE	X	Y
6. The premarital examination								
a. The state-required examination								
b. The general health examination								
c. Corrections before marriage of discovered defects								
H. ADJUSTMENTS IN MARRIAGE								
1. Basic human needs of marriage partners								
2. Adjustments within the marriage								
a. Personality adjustments								
b. Social and cultural adjustments								
c. Economic adjustments								
3. Sources of conflict within the marriage								
4. Crises in the family								
5. Social problems related to marriage								
a. Unhappy homes; desertion								
b. Annulments; divorce								
c. Effect on children								
6. Agencies that can help								
I. PREPARATION FOR PARENTHOOD								
1. The meaning and responsibilities of parenthood								
2. Family planning								
3. How life begins								
a. Fertilization								
b. Signs of pregnancy								
c. Duration of pregnancy								
d. Superstitions related to pregnancy								
4. Prenatal medical examinations: general, state-required								
5. The care of the mother during pregnancy								
6. The birth of the baby								
a. The birth process								
b. The care of the newborn								
c. Birth registration								
7. Good infant care; periodical medical checkups, diet, immunization, clothing								

A full understanding and a healthy appreciation of these functions as signs of developing sexuality must be assured.

In the *health instruction class,* a unit is needed on family life education that will include the topics that have been presented. It might logically follow the unit on mental and emotional health since there is a real relationship between these two health areas.

In the upper year of the junior high school, the boy or girl feels grown-up, but underneath is insecure and needs and wants information on such things as etiquette, dating, and the whole area of growing into maturity. Next year they will be entering senior high school.

SENIOR HIGH SCHOOL

Family life education at the adolescent level may be briefly defined as an introduction to the problems of life as they relate to friendship, courtship, marriage, and homemaking.

By the time that youths enter the senior high school, they have already assimilated adult ways, and they understand to a great degree their physical growth pattern and are accepting it or doing something about it. Kinsey and others have shown that the sex patterns of the American male are reasonably well established by the age of sixteen.[4] Their chief problems are concerned with their independence, including such topics as where to get money, the car, the date, and clothes, how to look, act, and be grown-up, and thinking of the future, including a job, a vocation, a home and marriage. An examination of Table 2 will suggest, in more detail, subtopics that need to be included under the aforementioned broader topics.

Dr. Judson T. Landis, University of California sociologist, recommends that there be more courses in family life education to prepare young people for the realities of marriage and family living. He states that preparation for marriage should improve the student's chances of success in marriage by helping him to become more realistic about the responsibilities and obligations of marriage and help meet the desired goal of preventing ill-advised marriages.

A major unit is recommended for the twelfth grade since young people are at that time really looking ahead to a vocation, to marriage, and to other adult problems of living. In schools where there is a high dropout rate, such a unit might come prior to the twelfth year. The topic of venereal diseases, when a part of the health instruction class, is best placed with

---

[4] Alfred C. Kinsey, Wardell Pomeroy, and Clyde E. Martin, *Sexual Behavior in the Male,* W. B. Saunders Co., Philadelphia, 1948.

other communicable diseases rather than with the unit on family life education.

In a few high schools, a separate course in family life education is offered under a variety of titles. Where health instruction is given on a one- to three-hour-a-week basis, one semester is often given to family life education. In some schools, this same unit may be a part of the psychology course, or combined with a large mental health unit.

Correlation and Integration

Since this topic is discussed in detail later, only a sketchy presentation is made at this point.

Family life education lends itself extensively to correlation and integration in the school program. Many authorities feel that this is the only way to teach it and that the offering of a separate course in the subject is justified primarily by a breakdown in the integrated plan and restricted to the high school level.

Real progress and final success require the participation of all teachers in the instruction. So that teachers in the self-contained classroom and the teachers of special subjects can make their contributions through integration, it is essential that they know what body of information, attitudes, and behavior each child should have in his various stages of development. All subjects and programs lend themselves in some degree to correlation since emphasis in this area is on attitudes and conduct as well as on facts.

Health Education. The courses in health education lend themselves well to the inclusion of most of the aspects of family life education.

Biology. In biology we have the logical place to consider anatomy and physiology of the human body including the reproductive system, the endrocine glands, and heredity and eugenics.

Physical Education. In physical education classes opportunities occur for encouraging wholesome sex attitudes. Since physical education classes are normally segregated by sex, those topics that an instructor finds difficult to present in a mixed health class, such as menstruation and emissions, might be discussed in physical education. Co-physical education, when appropriately taught, can be of help in developing wholesome recreational skills of interest to both sexes.

Home Economics. Excellent work can be done in home economics classes on such topics as home and family living, living successfully with parents, dress and etiquette, infant and baby care, and baby sitting.

Social Studies. In social studies, there can be included units on topics such as family living around the world, growing populations, marriage and divorce, family planning, law enforcement, and housing.

English. It is in the literature classes where the children sometimes first meet some of the facts of life in an educational setting under the guidance of a teacher.

Methods of Teaching

Since an entire chapter is devoted to teaching methods and materials of instruction, we shall only make a few major points here. First of all, most methods of teaching will apply to the teaching of sex education at some point concerning some unit and individual topic. However, because of the importance of stressing attitudes, values, behavior, habits, and conduct, as well as factual material, certain methods that lend themselves best for such emphasis need to be used extensively.

The most important methods include the asking of questions by the pupils, a climate of easy discussion, the development of a vocabulary, the use of audiovisual aids, and the use of selected readings.

Beginning in first grade, teachers are urged to create an atmosphere in which children will feel free to ask questions, and this method should be applied throughout the high school years as well. Question boxes are often used in the secondary schools.

Selected teaching devices are often needed to open the way for discussion in a course or unit and before the students have gotten over some of their initial reticence. Educational films are very helpful—especially if they deal with the human relation aspect of sex behavior or with physical development. Current news items and episodes in movies and plays often provoke worthwhile introductory discussions.

The use of one of the fine texts and pamphlets written for adolescents is recommended for the high school level. Extensive use of additional reading and reporting on books and articles which stimulate thinking in this area is strongly recommended.

It is important that there be a period during which the pupils and the teacher become acquainted before beginning a unit on family life. In a health course, for example, this unit might be delayed until the middle or end of the course rather than be taught at the beginning.

It is generally accepted today that the use of the special lecture or lecturer is not a desirable teaching procedure in this field. However, there are times when a professional person can supplement the regular teaching with a lecture on a specific topic such as etiquette or dating problems.

There is great need for opportunity for individual conferences to deal with unique circumstances, since individual student problems cannot all be presented or handled in a regular class situation.

Parents' Relationship to School Program

An increasing number of parents are recognizing that their children need education about family living both within their own homes and in the schools and from other agencies which deal with children and youth. However, there are some individual parents and parent groups who seemingly are not ready for their own role or are not willing to recognize that the school has a contribution to make.

Such difficulties may arise if the community has not been prepared for sex education in its schools even when disguised by a name such as family life education. Parents of children in such classes should be informed in advance in regard to the purpose of the course or unit and should be given some knowledge concerning content and methods. The children should be urged to discuss the work of the course at home. In the introduction of such instruction, a quiet, sensible approach, without fanfare, will do much to win approval and allay suspicion. A policy statement should be prepared and approved by the school administration so that it can be used as a buffer should any opposition develop later.

Activities

1. Using the Outline of Major Topics in the area of "Education for Family Living" (Table 2, pp. 42–45), check the topics that you consider appropriate for the respective grade levels. Use the scale of 0, 1, 2, 3 as explained in the table.

2. Examine the list of objectives on pp. 36–37. On the basis of your estimation, rate these in the order of importance for a specific grade level. Can you add any additional objectives?

3. Examine the list of principles in curriculum planning on p. 37. Rate these in the order of importance in the light of your personal judgment. Can you add any additional objectives?

4. Prepare a paper on "The Pros and Cons of a Program of Family Life Education in the Schools." Have in mind that this paper might be delivered before your own fellow teachers or before your school's PTA.

References

American Association for Health, Physical Education, and Recreation, *Health Concepts: Guides for Health Instruction,* Washington, D.C., 1967, 52 pp.

American Association for Health, Physical Education, and Recreation, *Sex Education Units for Grades 5, 6, and 7,* Washington, D.C., 1967.

American School Health Association, Committee on Health Guidance in Sex Education, *Growth Patterns and Sex Education,* Kindergarten through 12, Kent, Ohio, 1966.

Amstutz, H. Clair, M.D., *Growing up to Love: A Guide to Sex Education,* Herald Press, Scottsdale, Pa., 1956, 103 pp.

Baruch, Dorothy W., *New Ways in Sex Education,* McGraw-Hill Book Co., New York, 1959, 288 pp.

Bibby, G., *Sex Education,* Emerson Books, New York, 1946, 311 pp.

Child Study Association of America, *Sex Education of America,* Columbia University Press, New York, 1967, 117 pp.

Child Study Association of America, *Sex Education and the Morality: A Search for a Meaningful Social Ethic,* Columbia University Press, New York, 1966, 50 pp.

Daniels, Rose, *Getting Started: A Pioneer Program in Health Guidance and Sex Education,* Glen Cove Public Schools, New York, 1967, 30 pp.

Force, Elizabeth S., *Teaching Family Life Education, The Toms River Program,* Bureau of Publications, Teachers College, Columbia University, New York, 1962, 297 pp.

Glen Cove Public Schools, *Getting Started: A Pioneer Program in Health Guidance and Sex Education,* Glen Cove, N. Y., 1967, 31 pp.

Jackson, Julian A., *Modern Sex Education,* Holt, Rinehart & Winston, New York, 1967, 91 pp.

Johnson, Warren R., *Human Sex and Sex Education,* Lea & Febiger, Philadelphia, 1963, 205 pp.

Lerrigo, Marion O., and Helen Southard, *Sex Education Series,* Joint Committee on Health Problems in Education, National Education Association and the American Medical Association, Washington and Chicago, 1962, 71 pp.

Manley, Helen, *A Curriculum Guide in Sex Education,* State Publishing Co., St. Louis, 1964, 59 pp.

McHose, Elizabeth, *Family Life Education in School and Community,* Bureau of Publications, Teachers College, Columbia University, New York, 1952, 182 pp.

Schoel, Doris R., "The School Nurse—Her Role in Sex Education," *J. School Health,* Vol. 36, May 1966, pp. 200–206.

Strain, Frances B., *New Patterns in Sex Education,* Appleton-Century-Crofts, New York, 1951, 261 pp.

Strain, Frances B., *Sex Guidance in Family Life Education,* The Macmillan Co., New York, 1942, 340 pp.

4

Sex Education
in the Elementary School

There are a number of reasons why sex education should be included at all grade levels of the elementary school, as indicated in earlier chapters. The most important are the following:

1. Sex education is not as emotional a problem at this age level as it will gradually become at and following puberty.
2. The child is most likely already beginning to pick up inaccurate information and unwholesome attitudes from undesirable sources.
3. The child accepts sex education more readily and naturally at this age level.

The special role of the elementary school is to provide satisfactory means for children to learn about themselves and to answer their questions in a way that will strengthen their value structures. The small child reacts to information about his own origin and that of other children very matter-of-factly and objectively unless he has already been taught otherwise.

See Table 2, pp. 42–45, for a list of the topics that should be included in the elementary schools.

The elementary school can make an extremely important contribution to family life. Through its curriculum, methods of teaching and environment, the elementary school can help children grow in ways which will improve relationships in their present and future homes.

In order to escape the hazards and limitations of being merely sex-fact instruction, family life education must begin in the very first school years. It must be integrated into all possible subject matter in the curriculum.

Educators recognize the fact that the schools must deal with the child as a unified whole and that it is impossible to separate his mental development from other phases in his life and growth. If the schools are to be of maximum assistance to the child, their program of instruction must cover the needs of the total individual.

An individual's happiness as a person, his success as a family member and a social being, and his contribution as a citizen are either enhanced or destroyed by his success or failure in fitting into his sex role (sexuality) and in directing his sex impulses wisely.

Every child needs information and assistance in establishing attitudes, habits, and ideals about sex, just as he needs information and assistance for other phases of his growth.

Curriculum Planning

Certain suggestions follow concerning the planning of a sex education curriculum in the elementary school. Included are preschool sex education, major contributions of sex education in the elementary school, questions asked by children, and the aims of sex education at this level.

PRESCHOOL SEX EDUCATION

The first obviously direct sex education takes place during the preschool years when children ask questions to satisfy their curiosities. The questions usually revolve around two main puzzles: (1) What is the difference between boys and girls? (2) How do babies get born?

Children are likely to take matters into their own hands by direct sex play focused usually on seeing anatomical differences. From such observations, little children are likely to gather no more than the nature of the purely external differences between the sexes. Some may, therefore, decide that boys are more desirably equipped than girls. This may easily lead to a feeling of superiority on the part of the male child, or of resentment and envy in the female child.

If adults do not help children understand the real nature of the sex differences, such feelings may easily become the dominant note in their relationships. The ways in which grownups answer children's questions and react to their curiosities may establish other fundamental attitudes. For instance, the child may discover that sex can readily be used to upset adults. The first perception may provide a springboard for later conduct.

During the early school years, children begin to explore more fully the psychological and social meaning of sex rules. In the home, they begin to develop preferences for their mothers or their fathers. Mixed with the feelings of respect and admiration which many boys have for their fathers, we also find jarring undercurrents of hostility and jealousy. These may be derived from such commonplace household occurrences as the fact that the homecoming of the father acts to deprive his son of the undivided attention of the mother. The mixture of conflicting feelings may have very complicated outcomes which could be predicted only after taking into consideration a host of factors peculiar to each home situation. One of the many possibilities, for example, is that this may lead to irritability toward the father, and later toward masculine teachers. On the other hand, the very guilt about this irritability may lead to fearful overdocility. It also happens that boys may fear that their fathers will retaliate against them or that they may suffer loss of manhood.

Similar events take place in the development of girls. The jealousies which can grow up in the home may later be echoed in an overpossessive jealousy during dating days. Another common outcome is for the children to shun body contact with parents; in some cases this type of touchiness may persist.

In dramatic play among themselves, children practice using their concepts of what men and women do. The outside world is also teaching them important lessons. Boys, for example, may be permitted greater freedom in play and are allowed to get dirty with less interference than girls. On the other hand, a boy may learn he is expected to behave more bravely and not to cry out when hurt. Such incidents may strengthen or weaken feelings about having been born a boy or a girl. We find, for example, a significant number of grown women who resent womanhood and everything connected with it. Among young girls, tomboy behavior may be a temporary reaction to the same forces. Social pressures among boys may be brought to bear against those who behave like sissies; eagerness to reverse such deeply feared opinions may lead to overemphasis upon masculinity. Later, for some, this may lead to a penchant for making Don Juan conquests.

MAJOR CONTRIBUTIONS OF SEX EDUCATION AT THE ELEMENTARY SCHOOL LEVEL

Kirkendall [1] believes that the elementary school can make six major contributions to a well-rounded sex education program that has been planned on a continuous kindergarten-through-twelfth-grade basis. The elementary school can do the following:

1. Provide wholesome social experiences for the children. The school should build toward a happy, harmonious adjustment between the sexes in work and play, thus helping each child to make a satisfactory personal adjustment in his proper sex role.
2. Provide assistance to parents to enable them to do better teaching with their own children.
3. Provide skillful handling by the teacher of certain happenings that are common to most schools, i.e., risqué literature, undue curiosity, and suggestive speech. The teacher's understanding of human behavior and development should allow her to appraise accurately the significance of such pupil behavior.
4. Assist in the development of the child's abilities and capacities in various fields of accomplishment. Socially acceptable behavior commonly requires a postponement of heterosexual experience and a redirection of sex desires through the period of adolescence and early adulthood.
5. Assist in the development of socially responsible and emotionally stable individuals through the development of desirable patterns of conduct.
6. Provide curriculum experiences to familiarize the child with all of the various life processes. While the child should know that reproduction and birth are a part of the life cycle, he should also know that the cycle also includes growing up, coming to full maturation with active participation as an adult in our social environment, and reaching old age and decline. Children nearing puberty should know and understand the physical changes which occur at puberty. They are much better prepared to accept this information prior to puberty than after they enter the period of active physical change with its emotional involvement.

The writer suggests these additional contributions of the elementary school:

7. The development of an appreciation for and pride in one's family and a desire to contribute one's share to a satisfactory family life is an important emphasis.
8. The preschool children should be taught the proper words for parts of their own body. When children start to study science or health, they should be taught words such as ovum, sperm, fertilize, mature, birth, reproduction, embryo, vulva, penis, and scrotum.

Also, see Table 5, pp. 137–143, for a list of those words that children should be learning to understand and use.

[1] Lester A. Kirkendall, *Sex Education as Human Relations,* 1950, pp. 231–233.

The family life emphasis at school should include activities which help unite parents and children.

QUESTIONS ASKED BY SCHOOL-AGE CHILDREN

Here are a few examples of questions asked the teacher or parents by young school children of the ages indicated:

1. Why do girls and boys have to go to separate bathrooms at recess?
   (Asked by child about six years of age.)
2. Why do boys have to be polite to girls?
   (Second grade girl, about six and one-half years old.)
3. My mother never tells me anything. Why not?
   (Fourth grade boy, eight years old.)
4. Why are some girls excused from gym just for the day?
   (Fifth grade girl to physical education teacher, child about 10.)
5. What were those dogs doing outside of school this morning?
   (First grade child, six and one-half years of age.)
6. Why is Mrs. Smith so fat?
   (Second grade girl.)
7. Where do people get their babies?
   (First grade boy.)
8. How big is the place where babies grow?
   (First grade boy.)
9. How do the babies get out?
   (Second grade boy.)
10. How does the baby start to grow?
    (Second grade girl.)
11. Must there always be a father?
    (Second grade girl.)
12. What does a girl mean by her period?
    (Fourth grade girl.)
13. Why can't a boy dog have puppies?
    (Girl, age six, asked of child's mother.)
14. Why does Johnny kiss Mary?
    (Boy, age five, asked of his father about his sister and her boy friend.)
15. How can you tell that the dog was a boy dog?
    (Boy, age five.)
16. Why doesn't Maureen have teeth?
    (Girl, age six, asked mother about her newborn sister.)
17. I know babies are in the mother's tummy, but how do they get out?
    (Girl, age eleven, asked her mother.)
18. Can an old woman have a baby?
    (Girl, age eleven, asked her mother.)
19. Can a baby cry before it is born?
    (Girl, age five, to mother.)

ADDITIONAL QUESTIONS ASKED BY YOUNG CHILDREN

20. Where did I come from?
21. How are babies born?
22. Did the stork bring me?
23. Did the doctor bring me in his satchel?
24. Why did I have to be born in the hospital? Were you born there?
25. Why do mothers get sick when they have babies?
26. Can I have a baby when I grow up?
27. Did you know that you were going to have a baby?
28. Can we have babies?
29. How big is a baby before it is born?
30. Can the baby breathe before it is born?
31. Where does the baby get its food?
32. How did I get into your body before I was born, Mother?
33. Why am I a boy and not a girl?
34. Does it hurt when the baby is born?
35. Where does the milk come from that the baby has for food?
36. What makes babies start to grow?
37. A girl said she did not have a father. Can that be true?
38. Can Aunt Dorothy have a baby?
39. Can people have babies if they are not married?
40. Where was I kept before you married daddy?
41. Can Blackie (a female cat) have kittens without a daddy cat?
42. I am going to marry brother when I grow up. Is that all right?
43. I want to marry daddy when I am older.
44. Why is Mrs. Blank so big?
45. Why don't Mr. and Mrs. Smith have any children?
46. Why does sister look different from me?
47. Do the little guppies have both a mother and a father?

THE AIMS OF SEX EDUCATION IN THE ELEMENTARY SCHOOL [2]

The following list of aims for sex education in the elementary school have been prepared for one elementary school by the school principal and the nurse-teacher working with groups of parents, classroom teachers, and upper elementary grade pupils in developing a program in sex education.

KINDERGARTEN
1. Recognize sex differences between girls and boys.
2. Give direction toward male or female role in adult life.

[2] Glen Cove Public Schools, *Getting Started: A Pioneer Program in Health Guidance and Sex Education,* Glen Cove, N. Y., 1967, 31 pp.

3. Learn correct names for body parts and terms concerned with elimination.
4. Develop idea of continuity of living things (incubate hens' eggs).
5. Understand that human baby develops inside body of mother.
6. Appreciate that there are good body feelings.
7. Learn to recognize signs of love and devotion within family.

FIRST YEAR
1. Appreciate wonder of human body.
2. Develop sense of responsibility for own body.
3. Appreciate efforts of mother and father for family members.
4. Understand that composition of family does not determine happiness of family.
5. Understand that egg is basic to new life.
6. Recognize influence of emotions on body health.

SECOND YEAR
1. Know that growing up means more than just getting bigger.
2. Recognize that growing up brings responsibility.
3. Learn that different animals need different amounts of time to get ready to be born.
4. Learn that some animals are born live through a special opening in the mother's body.
5. Understand that the egg does not develop into a baby by itself (role of father).
6. Appreciate importance of mutual love and consideration in family.

THIRD YEAR
1. Develop increasing sense of responsibility to self and family.
2. Understand relationship between a healthy body and mind.
3. Observe influence of heredity in your family.
4. Study life cycles of various animals, including that of human beings.

FOURTH YEAR
1. Learn that certain glands control body growth and development.
2. Appreciate superiority of brain of man over instinct reaction of animals.
3. Recognize importance of protecting vital body parts from injury (e.g., during sports).
4. Appreciate the miracle of reproduction among various forms of animal life.
5. Learn how families can work and play together.
6. Discuss greater dependence on parents of a human baby in contrast to various animal babies.

FIFTH YEAR (some discussions in separate classes)
1. Learn role of sex glands at puberty and body changes they bring.
2. Recognize that each living thing has a unique heredity pattern.
3. Learn that a human being's individual pattern of heredity is determined at time of fertilization of egg by sperm.

4. Develop increased understanding of role of father in human reproduction.
5. Discuss importance of wholesome life attitudes and values.
6. Discuss acceptable and unacceptable ways of showing emotions.

Examples of Programs in Sex Education

Here follow three examples of programs recommended by the American School Health Association for kindergarten and grade one and the Board of Education of the City of New York for grades four and six. Note that the plans of organization of the curriculum differ. Space limitations do not permit the inclusion of similar examples for every grade. These sources and many others should be studied by those planning to prepare a complete kindergarten-through-sixth-grade program in sex education for their own school or for their own class.

KINDERGARTEN AND GRADE ONE [3]

First discussed are the following topics: Introductory Comments, Typical Student Questions, and Teachable Material and Profitable Activities. Then follows a discussion of several units which are here included in their entirety.

Unit 1. Learning Correct Terminology
A. TEACHABLE MATERIAL

The genital parts should be named accurately from the very beginning to increase respect for the body by talking about it with respect and to discourage pupils' use of baby terms, slang terms, and possible "dirty words" picked up from family and friends. (Questions should be answered with the proper anatomical and scientific terms so that children begin early to accept and to use these terms.) Parts of the body such as penis, labia, buttocks, and breast can be referred to correctly in as natural a manner as can mouth, lips, eyes, and ears. The teacher who at first may feel slightly ill at ease in using the correct terminology will find that such usage becomes natural and comfortable with a little practice.

B. PROFITABLE ACTIVITIES

1. Rather than planning separate activities through which children will learn the proper names, this learning better and more naturally can be accomplished if the teacher uses and explains the correct terminology in connection with other pupil activities, where appropriate, and when answering students' questions.

[3] American School Health Association, Committee on Health Guidance in Sex Education, *Growth Patterns and Sex Education, A Suggested Program for Kindergarten Through Grade Twelve,* Kent, Ohio, 1967, pp. 7–12.

2. Children should be encouraged to substitute correct terminology for "baby terms" or slang whenever such words are used in their ordinary conversation with each other or with the teacher.

Unit 2. Respecting the Privacy and Rights of Others
A. TEACHABLE MATERIAL
1. Boys and girls go to the bathroom separately in school, and children should be helped to understand the wish for privacy as a normal desire, not as an expression of shame. Too often in trying to develop the attitude of respect for privacy, the impression is given that this is due to shame for the parts of the body that will be exposed. There should be ample opportunity to foster the concept that the private parts of the body are private, but not shameful. Students will exhibit normal curiosity concerning sex differences.
2. Children will need to learn what actions constitute acceptable behavior in the washroom or bathroom. They need help in making the transition between going to the bathroom alone at home and going in groups when they are at school.
3. The habit of washing one's hands after going to the toilet and before eating should be developed or reinforced.

B. PROFITABLE ACTIVITIES
1. As part of their orientation to school, boys and girls usually tour the buildings and visit such places as the library, art room, auditorium, health office, main office, and gymnasium. A trip to both the girls' and boys' bathrooms should be included for all students. Most boys have not been inside a men's room and are not familiar with a urinal or its use. Most girls will not have the opportunity to visit a boys' bathroom at any other time or place, and this tour will serve to satisfy their curiosity. This visit also lends itself naturally to the discussion of anatomical differences and learning the correct names of body parts. While in the bathroom, children may demonstrate the best way to wash and dry their hands. They also may be encouraged to note reasons why it is dangerous to run or to "fool around" in the bathroom. Acceptable behavior in the washroom or bathroom then could be discussed either while they are there or after they return to the classroom, and the class may wish to develop a list of behavior standards.

Unit 3. The Arrival of a New Baby
A. TEACHABLE MATERIAL
Young children are fascinated by babies, and the anticipation and arrival of a new baby in his family, or even in a neighbor's family, is an important event in a child's life. The teacher can capitalize upon children's natural interest in babies to foster the attitudes of happy anticipation of an addition to the family and of acceptance of the new baby when it does arrive. Such attitudes may be fostered by emphasizing the miracle of a new life and by easing a child's fear that a new baby will afford him competition for the love and attention of his parents. A child who understands and feels secure in his own role as a

member of his family will be better able to accept and to appreciate a new brother or sister and to adapt himself to a changing family situation.

B. PROFITABLE ACTIVITIES
1. Male and female guinea pigs or hamsters may be kept in the classroom. The pregnancy of the female will offer ample opportunity to discuss the miracle of the creation of new life and those aspects of pregnancy and birth and the care of the young which are of interest to children in kindergarten and the first grade.
2. Discuss ways in which human parents both differ from and are similar to animal parents in planning for and taking care of their young.
3. The teacher can observe attitudes toward family life and family members as these are revealed through play situations in the "playhouse center." These then can be discussed with the children.
4. Desirable attitudes and practices related to family living can be fostered through role-playing and skits. Some of these might pertain to family roles of mothers and fathers, to simple courtesies or "manners" displayed by family members toward one another and by boys and girls toward each other in the classroom, cafeteria, etc., getting along with older or younger brothers and sisters, helping to care for a new baby, ways in which young children can help with family activities. Other possibilities will occur to the teacher as she observes the children in her own class.

Unit 4. Childhood Safety Going to and from School
A. TEACHABLE MATERIAL
Children should learn that it is dangerous to accept rides from strangers and should know what to do if a stranger should offer them a ride to or from school. They should be helped to recognize that while some people really are trying to be kind in offering rides, others are not. The teacher should be sure to instill an attitude of caution in students by taking a definite stand against accepting rides from strangers. However, it is possible that such instruction will lead to the development of a general distrust of all persons. This hazard should be recognized, and specific efforts should be made to help children make critical distinctions.

B. PROFITABLE ACTIVITIES
1. Role-playing situations or skits may be used to dramatize what a child should do if offered a ride by a stranger. Individual communities may well have developed specific child-safety programs for the children in their communities. If so, the appropriate procedures from these programs should be incorporated into the role-playing situations or skits.
2. This aspect of safety may well be incorporated into teaching other aspects of safety. Children may be helped to develop their own safety rules, among which "Do not ride with strangers," "Never accept candy or gum from strangers," etc., should be included.
3. As they learn to read and to write numbers, children may be encouraged to write down the license plate number of any stranger who offers them a ride.

Supplementary Opportunities

Many opportunities for "incidental" or supplementary teaching will arise in the course of any given study period or school day. The observant teacher will notice them and, depending upon their value, their relation to the subject at hand, and their feasibility, may wish to capitalize upon them for purposes of additional learning. For example, in kindergarten and first grade such opportunities might present themselves in connection with a field trip to a farm or zoo, or with incidents related by children during "share time."

CONCEPTS AND ATTITUDES

The importance of the development of concepts and attitudes has been discussed in the Introduction. As a part of the learning process which takes place at each level of instruction, teachers should assist students to form impressions, arrive at conclusions, develop attitudes, and form concepts or generalizations. Mere acquisition of knowledge or a fund of factual information is not enough. The ultimate aim is the initiation or reinforcement of intelligent actions or practices, and the student's development of basic concepts and favorable attitudes influences greatly the extent to which he adopts or continues the desired practices.

A student acquires his knowledge about sex and sexuality from his experiences in a variety of situations, including those experiences with his family, with friends, and in the community. These same experiences influence his developing attitudes, values, concepts and, therefore, his practices. However, the teacher who has accepted responsibility for organizing and directing a portion of a student's total learning experience toward the attainment of specified instructional objectives will wish to consider the development of those attitudes and concepts so vital to the intelligent practice. It is to be expected that the basic attitudes and concepts formed as a result of instruction in kindergarten and the first grade will be reinforced and developed further through learning experiences occurring at more advanced levels of instruction.

A. CONCEPTS. As a product of their experiences in the study of this unit, it would be hoped that some such concepts as these would be formulated by children in kindergarten and the first grade.

1. All living things reproduce. Life comes from life.
2. The creation of new life is one of nature's greatest miracles.
3. Every child has a mother and a father in the beginning.
4. Every person needs to have a feeling of belonging.
5. Each member of a family is an important member. Children and parents

working and playing together help to make a home a happy place to live. There are many ways in which children can help to make their homes happy ones.

6. Each member of a family is interested in the well-being of every other member.
7. Using good manners lets other people know that we like and respect them. Thoughtful boys and girls are courteous to each other, to their mothers and fathers, their brothers and sisters, and to everyone else.
8. Every person desires privacy at some times. Each person has a right to privacy, and each should respect the privacy of others.
9. Each part of the body is an important part of the whole person, and there is nothing shameful about any part of the body.
10. We should be cautious in dealing with strangers. Although some strangers who offer rides or candy to children are trying to be kind, others are not. We should always refuse such offers and should tell our parents and teachers about them.

B. ATTITUDES. As an outcome of this unit, it is to be hoped that the student will form some such favorable attitudes as these toward himself, others, family living, and reproduction:

1. An appreciation for the role of each family member.
2. An appreciation for his own importance as a member of his family and a desire to contribute to his family's well-being.
3. A respect for the rights of others.
4. A sense of wonder in regard to reproduction.
5. A wholesome respect for all parts of the body and a desire to learn and to use correct terminology in referring to them.

RESOURCES FOR STUDENTS AND TEACHERS

GRADES K AND ONE

FILMS

"Human and Animal Beginnings," C. Brown Trust—Distributors: Henk Newenhouse, 1017 Longaker Boulevard, Northbrook, Illinois. 22 minutes. Young children express their beliefs about origin of human life in drawings. Kindergarten, Grades 1 and 2. (Excellent)

"Mother Hen's Family (The Wonders of Birth)," Coronet Instructional Films, 65 E. Southwater, Chicago. 10 minutes. Shows how eggs are hatched by hens. Depicts a small boy with the help of his father following the process from the laying of the eggs to the hatching of chicks. Shows the boy recording on a calendar the time of setting the day of the hatching of the young chicks.

FILM SLIDES

"How Babies Are Made," Creative Scope, Inc., 509 Fifth Avenue, New York, N. Y. 10017.

RECORDS
"Sex Education of Children for Parents," Francis L. Filas, S.J., Faith Through
Education Corporation, Box 517, Skokie, Illinois, 60076.

BOOKS AND PAMPHLETS
Bauer, W. W., M.D., et al., *Just Like Me,* Scott Foresman & Company,   Pupil
Chicago.
Child Study Association of America, Inc., *What To Tell Your Children*   Teacher
About Sex, Permabooks, New York, 1958.
Filas, Francis L., S.J., *Sex Education in the Family,* Prentice-Hall, Inc.,   Teacher
Englewood Cliffs, N. J., 1966.
Gruenberg, Sidonie M., *Wonderful Story of How You Were Born,*   Pupil
Doubleday and Company, Inc., New York, 1952.
How Your Child Learns About Sex, Ross Laboratories, Columbus,   Teacher
Ohio.
Irwin, Leslie, et al., *All About You,* Lyons and Carnahan, Chicago,   Pupil
1965.
Schneider, Herman, and Nina Schneider, *Science for Work and Play,*   Teacher
D. C. Heath and Company, Boston, 1955.

CHARTS
Beginning the Human Story: A New Baby in the Family, Scott, Fores-   Pupil
man & Company, Glenview, Ill., 1967. A preschool-primary family
living and sex education program consisting of twelve charts with
teaching suggestions and discussion aids printed on the reverse side.

GRADE THREE

The New York City Curriculum Bulletin gives suggestions to teachers and
then considers the program for each grade level from prekindergarten through
grade twelve. Then follows an extensive list of audiovisual materials and
books and pamphlets.[4]

1. Concept: Recognizing that successful family living embraces love and the
sharing of effort and possessions for the common good.
CONTENT
Sharing of personal belongings, family property, and family experiences.
Understanding family finances: learning the use of money, shopping experi-
ences.

LEARNING ACTIVITIES
1. Develop situations for sharing in the classroom (paint materials, library
books, etc.), and compare the classroom family to the family at home.

[4] Board of Education of the City of New York, *Family Living Including Sex Education,*
110 Livingston Street, Brooklyn, N. Y. 11201, 1967, pp. 22–24.

2. Show how committees serve the common good (care of class pet, etc.). Everyone enjoys the pleasure of the class pet. Compare this with pets and other items at home.
3. Plan a class party. Show that by sharing, the party can be made possible. Relate this to family sharing.
4. Arrange for all children having a birthday in a certain week to celebrate the day in class in order to emphasize sharing an experience with others. Designate responsibilities to members of the class to reinforce doing for others.

2. Concept: Understanding the importance of maintaining cleanliness.
CONTENT
Cleanliness contributes to good looks and comfort.
Cleanliness keeps the skin healthy and protects against body odor.
Cleanliness enhances one's personality.

LEARNING ACTIVITIES
1. Show the children a large picture of an unkempt child. Have them tell the class why they would not want this child as a friend. Emphasize that the child's appearance is not caused by poverty.
2. Have the children prepare an assembly program on the value of good grooming.
3. Have the children develop a good grooming and cleanliness bulletin board for the school corridor bulletin board.
4. Invite the nurse to the class to discuss cleanliness and grooming.

3. Concept: Accepting the fact that parents have their own needs in the family; that parents are husband and wife to each other.
CONTENT
Parents' special needs: being with each other, having privacy, watching adult TV programs, having time away from children.

LEARNING ACTIVITIES
1. Discuss need for sharing use of the TV so that adults are able to watch their favorite programs.
2. List things second graders can do in caring for younger brothers and sisters.
3. Tell experiences in staying with grandmothers or other adults when parents had to leave their children.

4. Concept: Understanding and learning to use the correct terminology for body parts.
CONTENT
Appropriate words.

LEARNING ACTIVITIES
1. Use correct terms when bathing dolls.
2. Use correct terms when answering questions children may ask.

5. Concept: Appreciating the fact that girls and boys learn their future roles as mothers and fathers by helping in the home. (Social roles should be emphasized.)
CONTENT
Ways boys and girls can help their parents: going to the store, taking out garbage, emptying waste baskets, putting away their own things, and playing with the baby.

LEARNING ACTIVITIES
1. Practice housekeeping tasks in housekeeping corner.
2. List the ways third graders can help their parents.
3. Make gifts which children can give to family members on birthdays. Example: cover coffee can with contact paper for use as a storage box.

6. Concept: Understanding that fertilized eggs (ova) vary in the time needed to produce a new individual.
CONTENT
Some fertilized eggs develop for a short time before they are fully formed and ready for coming into the world.
Some fertilized eggs (including those of humans) develop for a long time before they are fully formed and ready for coming into the world.

LEARNING ACTIVITIES
1. Discuss the length of time necessary for the egg of a chicken to develop.
2. Compare the time needed to produce a baby white mouse, hamster, elephant, and human baby.
3. Discuss the length of time necessary for the human baby to be born in terms of seasons (spring, summer, fall, winter).

7. Concept: Appreciating that animals vary in the number of offspring produced at a given time and in a lifetime.
CONTENT
Some animal mothers have many babies at one time.
Some animal mothers have only a few babies at a time.
Human mothers usually have only one baby at a time.

LEARNING ACTIVITIES
1. Have children tell about pet litters (dogs and cats).
2. Visit the local zoo in springtime.
3. Have children tell about babies born in their own families.
4. Ask children to tell about birds' eggs and chicken eggs.
5. Read books dealing with animal litters.
6. View films, "Birds in Your Backyard" and "Live Colorful Birds," on the approved list of the Bureau of Audio-Visual Aids.

8. Concept: Understanding and learning to use the correct terminology for body parts.

LEARNING ACTIVITIES
1. In discussing new work, use and teach correct terminology.
2. When children ask questions using unacceptable terms, answer these questions using the correct terminology.
3. Encourage students to use correct terminology at all times.

9. Concept: Understanding at an elementary level the meaning of friendship.
CONTENT
Qualities of true friendship.
Values of true friendship.
Extent to which friendships should govern activities.

LEARNING ACTIVITIES
1. Have students discuss "Why I Chose (Name) as My Best Friend."
2. Discuss the boundaries of friendship and why lying and stealing even to benefit a friend are not acceptable.

GRADE FIVE [5]

1. Concept: Understanding the body changes at the preadolescent period.
CONTENT
Individuals vary in the rate of growth. This is no reflection on one's femininity or masculinity. Changes are occurring in the male and female reproductive systems, though at this age there are no outward signs.

Girls are at the onset of menstruation. Boys are at the onset of nocturnal emissions.

Note: Materials of this type are good for parent workshops.

The following behavioral manifestations are sometimes evident among individual children:
General misbehavior.
Rebellion against adults; quarreling.
Sloppy appearance and work habits.
Tendency to tease.
Dallying and lateness.
Lack of attention.
Inability to remain still for long.
Lack of attention to grooming.

LEARNING ACTIVITIES
1. Review body changes in the animal world: the cocoon and the insect; the tadpole and the frog.
2. Have children make personal graphs on growth. Provide the height and weight information from health cards.

[5] *Ibid.*, pp. 27–30.

3. View the film, "Growing Girls," on the approved list of the Bureau of Audio-Visual Aids. (For girls.)
4. Invite the school doctor to discuss the physical changes in approaching puberty.

2. Concept: Becoming aware that puberty initiates the physical changes leading to manhood and womanhood. (Separate classes for boys and girls, where desirable. Information in this area is taught in a framework of instruction associated with organ systems as a whole.)

CONTENT

The onset of puberty varies with individuals.

The major change which takes place at puberty is in the gonads themselves.

The testes begin to produce the male germ cells, or sperm.

The ovaries begin to produce the female germ cells, or eggs.

Voice becomes deeper in boys; body fills out; shoulders and chest broaden; beard begins to grow.

The girl's body rounds out; hips become broader; breasts develop; menstruation begins; hair appears under the arms and in pubic region.

Girls reach puberty sooner than boys.

The endocrine glands play an important role in pubertal changes.

Changes occur in the sweat and oil glands.

LEARNING ACTIVITIES

1. Have children describe to the class changes noted in older brothers and sisters. Boys' voices become deeper and they shave. Although a girl may be the same height as last year, last year's dress does not fit.
2. View the films, "Boy to Man," "Girl to Woman," "Molly Grows Up," on the approved list of the Bureau of Audio-Visual Aids.
3. Read the chapter, "Becoming an Adult," in *The Wonderful Story of You* (Benjamin C. Gruenberg and Sidonie M. Gruenberg, Garden City Books, Garden City, N. Y., 1960) and hold a class discussion.

3. Concept: Understanding the influence of environment as a factor which affects growth.

CONTENT

Environmental factors that play a part in determining the lines along which one grows and develops include the following:

Living conditions.

Health habits.

Effects of illness.

Nutrition.

Outdoor exercise.

Sleep.

LEARNING ACTIVITIES

1. Integrate with other curriculum areas, such as social studies, by referring to lack of nourishment in children of other countries and the effect on growth and longevity.

2. Have boys and girls do research on the training habits of athletes and report (older brothers, friends, etc., who may be college athletes or professional athletes).
3. Have an alumnus or a junior or senior high school athlete known to most of the children speak to them on the value of outdoor exercise.
4. Have boys and girls select activities such as push-ups (for boys) or sit-ups (for girls) and record their scores. Guided by the health coordinator, set up a physical fitness training program. Retest after two months and show the effect of exercise, training, etc., on growth.

4. Concept: Learning to expect and handle intelligently emotional changes which accompany physical changes.

CONTENT

Anticipating growth spurts.

Recognizing that body changes are a normal and natural part of growing up.

Realizing that occasional awkwardness is a normal, temporary stage of growth.

Recognizing that one has to make adjustments based upon one's physical endowment.

LEARNING ACTIVITIES

1. Show how famous people were exceptional in one area but may not have been in another. (For example, Heifitz is a violinist, not an athlete; Pearl Buck is a writer, not a singer.)
2. Show how adults recognize their limits (the teacher who knows she cannot be a surgeon). Relate to recognition of limits by children. Have pupils interview adults and report.
3. Have a panel discussion on how to handle emotional outbursts.
4. Have children write an open-end composition on the topic, "How I Can Control My Temper."

5. Concept: Appreciating the importance of hygienic habits during preadolescence.

CONTENT

For some boys and girls preadolescence is a period of disorganization.

A preadolescent may rebel at bedtime, at keeping clean, at wearing the kind of clothes a parent regards as suitable.

Scolding or nagging an adolescent may make matters worse.

Warmth, affection, and understanding by parents and teachers will give stability to the preadolescent.

Support from adults will help him pass through the difficult years of preadolescence without too much strain or difficulty.

LEARNING ACTIVITIES

1. View the film, "Cleanliness and Health," on the approved list of the Bureau of Audio-Visual Aids.
2. Invite the nurse to discuss acne and skin care with the class.
3. Have panel discussions on topics such as "Is a Good Night's Sleep Neces-

sary?", "Why Is Cleanliness Important?" (include body odor in the questions asked of the panel).

6. Concept: Recognizing that each member of the family is entitled to privacy and respect.

CONTENT

Why acceptance and respect are important to every person.

Functions which are considered private: bathing, dressing, etc.

How children respect their parents' privacy: knocking at closed doors, not interrupting telephone conversations, etc.

How parents respect their children's privacy: not opening mail, allowing them to speak to friends without interference, etc.

LEARNING ACTIVITIES

1. Discuss ways in which children respect the privacy of other family members.
2. Have students role-play situations in which the love shared in a family becomes apparent (e.g., how a family celebrates a birthday together).
3. Have a panel discussion on the topic, "Can a 10-Year-Old Both Rebel Against and Respect the Older Generation?"

Suggested Audiovisual Aids: [6]

KINDERGARTEN

Film: "Tabby's Kittens" (Arthur Barr).

Books: Appell, Clara, and Morey and Suzanne Szasz, *We Are Six,* Golden Press, New York, 1959.

Darby, Gene, *What is a Chicken?* Benefic Press, Chicago, 1957, pp. 1–15.

FIRST YEAR

Film: "What Do Fathers Do?" (Churchill).

Books: Haynes, Olive, *The True Book of Health,* Children's Press, Chicago, 1954.

Hogan, Inez, *We Are a Family,* E. P. Dutton and Co., New York, 1952, pp. 1–24.

Selsam, Millicent, *All About Eggs,* Wm. R. Scott, New York, 1962.

Wood, Esther, and Theresa Kalab, *The House in the Hoo,* Longmans Green and Co., New York, 1941.

Bulletin: "Children's Health," *Children's Health,* Vol. 35, No. 1, Lansing, Mich.: Oct. 1965, Part I.

SECOND YEAR

Films: "Growing Up Day By Day" (EBF).

Kittens: "Birth and Growth" (Lawbetts Productions).

Books: Buck, Pearl, *Johnny Jack and His Beginnings,* The John Day Co., New York, 1954.

[6] Glen Cove Public Schools, *Getting Started,* Glen Cove, N. Y., p. 10.

Selsam, Millicent, *Egg to Chick,* International Publishers Co., New York, 1946.

Selsam, Millicent, *You and the World Around You,* Doubleday, New York, 1963.

THIRD YEAR

Film: "A Happy Family" (Class. Film Distributors).

Books: Darby, Gene, *What is a Chicken?* Benefic Press, Chicago, 1957, pp. 15 ff.

Hinshaw, Alice, *The True Book of Your Body and You,* Children's Press, Chicago, 1959.

McClung, Robert, *Possum,* William Morrow, New York, 1963.

Bulletin: "Children's Health," *Children's Health,* Vol. 35, No. 1, October, 1965, Part II.

FOURTH YEAR

Films: "Growing Up: Pre-Adolescence" (Coronet).

"You and Your Five Senses" (Walt Disney).

"The Day Life Begins" (Discovery TV Films).

Book: Ruchlis, Hyman, *What Makes Me Tick?* Harvey House Publishers, Irving-on-Hudson, N. Y., undated.

FIFTH YEAR

Films: "The Story of Menstruation" (Walt Disney).

"Growing Girls" (EBF).

"Your Body During Adolescence" (McGraw-Hill).

"Human Heredity" (E. C. Brown Trust).

"The Miracle of Reproduction" (Sid Davis).

Filmstrip and Record: "About Your Life" (Denver Public Schools).

Additional Suggestions for Curriculum Planning

Ideas for an elementary school sex education program can be obtained from the following chapters:

Chapter 7, "Methods and Materials for Teaching Sex Education."

Chapter 8, "The Vocabulary for Sex Education."

Chapter 9, "Evaluation of the Sex Education Program."

Chapter 10, "Teaching Units and Lesson Plans in Sex Education."

Chapters 14–21 in Part II, which supply content and concepts that are applicable at the elementary school level.

The Appendix, which contains an extensive bibliography, glossary, and additional lesson plans and units.

Activities

1. Prepare a program in sex education for the grade level which you are planning to teach or which you are presently teaching.

2. Prepare an additional set of children's questions similar to those listed on pp. 55–56. Also indicate the age of the child, its sex, to whom the question was directed, and the circumstances under which the question was made.

3. For one of the questions on pp. 55–56 or one of those which you have submitted for Activity 2, prepare the answer that you would give if you were the person to whom the question were directed.

References

American School Health Association, *Growth Patterns and Sex Education: A Suggested Program for Kindergarten Through Grade Twelve,* 1967, pp. 83–89.

Kirkendall, Lester A., *Sex Education as Human Relations,* 1950, pp. 231–233.

Manley, Helen, "Personal and Family Life Education in University City Schools," *J. School Health,* March, 1959, p. 121.

New Jersey State Department of Education, *Education for Family Life in the Primary Grades,* Trenton, N. J., 1948, p. 4.

Glen Cove Public Schools, New York, *Getting Started: A Pioneer Program in Health Guidance and Sex Education,* Glen Cove, N. Y., 1967, 31 pp.

New York City Board of Education, *Family Living Including Sex Education,* New York, 1967, pp. 43–48.

Swedish Royal Board of Education, *Handbook on Sex Instruction in Swedish Schools,* Stockholm, 1957, 93 pp.

5

Family Life Education
at the Secondary
School Level

In this chapter, consideration will be given to the program in family life and sex education at the junior and senior high school levels.

General Objectives of Family Life and Sex Education

Examples of *general* objectives are listed below, in accordance with the intent of the Illinois Sex Education Act: to promote the development of *comprehensive* and *wholesome* programs of family life and sex education in Illinois schools.[1]

Examples of general objectives to help students:

1. To understand the meaning and significance of marriage, parenthood, and family life, so they can help strengthen the family as the basic social unit of democratic life in Illinois.

2. To make affection, sex, and love constructive rather than destructive forces in modern life.

3. To develop feelings of self-identity and self-worth, respect for others, and

---

[1] Illinois Department of Public Instruction, *Policy Statements on Family Life and Sex Education,* 1967, pp. 19–22.

moral responsibility as an integral part of their personality and character develop-ment, so they can perceive their roles as marriage partners, as parents, and as ma-ture adults in our society. (This is important for all students but it is especially needed by fatherless and motherless boys and girls.)

4. To understand and appreciate the sexual side of human nature, so that their own psychosexual development may occur as normally and healthfully as possible, without feelings of indecency, embarrassment, or undue guilt.

5. To learn that human sexual behavior is not merely a personal and private matter but has important social, moral, and religious implications.

6. To realize that the Golden Rule also applies in sexual matters, based upon the ethical principle that no one has a right to harm another by using him or her exploitatively as a sexual object.

7. To learn about the dangers of illicit sexual behavior, and that boys and girls do not have to engage in heavy petting or premarital sexual intercourse to make friends, be popular, get dates, or to prove their love and affection to each other.

8. To emphasize the case for premarital chastity as the sexual standard approved by our society because chastity provides a positive goal for teenagers, linking human sexual behavior with love, marriage, parenthood, and family life and be-cause of the individual, family, and community problems associated with premarital or extramarital sexual relations.

9. To open channels of communication between children and their parents, teachers and counselors, and religious leaders concerning the meaning, significance, and potential values of sex and mating in human life, so that students will find it easier to seek information from reliable sources rather than rely on "hearsay," "gutter talk," or misconceptions; and so they will be able to discuss with openness and without embarrassment the problems of growing up sexually, while realizing that this is only one aspect of becoming a mature man or woman.

10. To understand that boy-girl and man-woman relationships of the right kind can add to their enjoyment and give meaning to their lives and that those of the wrong kind can result in a distorted attitude toward sex, love, and affection that may lead to undesirable consequences for the individuals involved and for society.

11. To understand the basic anatomy and physiology of the male and female reproductive systems and human reproduction; and the relationship of human mating to mutual love and affection expressed in marriage, parenthood, and family life.

12. To develop a healthy, wholesome attitude toward sex in human beings, in-cluding respect for their own bodies as an integral part of their personality, with knowledge of and respect for all body parts and their normal functions in human mating, reproduction, and family life.

13. To appreciate the significance of the sexual differences in boys and girls and the male and female sexual roles in our society, as related to wholesome boy-girl relationships and marriage, parenthood, and family life.

14. To develop a functional graded vocabulary, acquire a knowledge of key facts and basic concepts, develop wholesome attitudes and practices, and acquire skill in the critical analysis of basic problems and issues in sex education; and for students to bring information to their parents which the adults themselves may need and want.

15. To understand how to deal with personal sexual problems such as menstruation, nocturnal emissions, masturbation, petting, and personal hygiene. (See Item 9.)

16. To learn about the legal and ethical aspects of abortion, venereal disease control, marriage, divorce, broken homes and family disintegration, illegitimate children, pornography and obscenity, and sexual behavior.

17. To understand the key facts and basic concepts of human genetics as related to parenthood and family life; and where and how to secure "genetic counseling" if and when needed.

18. To learn the key facts and basic concepts about venereal disease, and the role of teen-agers and young adults in the prevention and control of these important communicable diseases.

19. To understand human pregnancy and the birth process; the need for good medical and public health care of mother and child before, during, and after birth; the care and rearing of small children; and the personal and social significance of the family in modern times.

20. To learn about the potential dangers of the world population explosion, and the need for an intelligent consideration of the basic issues of population growth as related to human health and welfare.

21. To consider critically the pros and cons of teenagers going steady versus going "steadily" as related to sexual behavior and as a preparation for mate selection and marriage.

22. To understand more fully and deeply the significance, in our society and other societies, of boy-girl relationships, dating, courtship, and engagement as related to marriage, parenthood, and family life.

23. To realize that there are important major differences, as well as some similarities, between sex and sexual behavior in animals as compared with man.

24. To understand the differences between love and infatuation and immature versus mature romantic love; to identify and appreciate the traits of a prospective husband or wife, which are most apt to make for a wholesome, healthy, and happy marriage.

25. To learn how to develop and maintain as *their own* positive standards of behavior based upon the progressive acceptance of moral responsibility for their own sexual behavior as it affects others as well as themselves.

26. To see clearly that progressive acceptance of responsibility for making wise decisions and moral choices in sexual matters requires an understanding of relevant facts, standards and values, alternatives and their consequences, as related to long-range as well as to immediate desires and goals.

BASIC PRINCIPLES

There are certain basic principles that need be given consideration if a functioning family life education program is to be achieved.

1. A program of education for marriage and family life should be planned in harmony with the needs and development of pupils. Knowledge of growth and

development clearly indicates a differentiation in the needs and development of early and late adolescents, and these differences are to be taken into account in planning educational programs at the secondary level.

2. Family life education implies a broader, more comprehensive educational program. In the early years of high school, the emphasis centers strongly about the need for helping the pupil to understand his own personal development and his changing relations to other persons. It is in these years particularly that personal guidance courses with a strong positive mental health point of view should be given. In the last two years of high school, the program centers much more about direct preparation for marriage. Pupils at this level are concerned with problems of courtship, mate selection, premarital standards, desirable attitudes in men-women relationships, and similar questions involving successful marriage and family relations.

3. Instruction in this field makes provision for helping each pupil meet his own personal problems more adequately.

4. The adjustment of the adolescent to his own parental home has a pronounced bearing upon his concepts and attitudes toward marriage and family life. Consequently, the school is concerned with helping in the family situation. The boy or girl may need help in gaining emancipation from home or an emotional acceptance of his family situation and otherwise in making the family relationship satisfying to all members.

5. Since parenthood is so important a part of the marriage relationship, considerable attention should be given to the place of youth and their contribution to the home. The significance of the parent-child relationship and preparation for parenthood should be stressed. An increasing number of schools are providing opportunity for actual experience with children through observation and care.

6. Sex education of children and youth is an essential part of their education for successful marriage and family life. The approach should be a positive one, however, in which sex is seen as an integral part of a total personality adjustment. The emotional, social, and ethical aspects of sexual conduct in dating and courtship relations and the contribution of sex to the success of the marriage relationship are of keen interest to youth in the latter years of high school.

7. The total school environment, not simply the curriculum, may be studied for its possible contribution to the objective of assuring better marriages. The social program of the school should provide opportunity for boys and girls to share experiences of many kinds. Likewise, the type of teachers chosen, the general organization of the school, and the extracurricular program can contribute to good marriages and improved family relations. Realistically, the influence of community forces outside, and sometimes beyond the control of the school, home, or church, have to be recognized. They sometimes operate to establish attitudes and concepts which have an important bearing upon the educational process, as well as on later marital adjustments.

8. While classes composed of both boys and girls would generally seem to provide the most desirable instructional arrangements, the educational principle of due regard for the pupil's developmental level, as well as his present state of insight, needs to be respected. This means that, on certain of the more personal matters

of sex adjustment, instruction of adolescents may need to be in separate and normally segregated groups, or provided in individual situations. However, as behavior is approached from the developmental point of view, and as the skill of the teacher increases, the number of topics suitable for discussion in mixed groups likewise increases.

9. Schools may incorporate units on Education for Marriage and Family Life into various subjects of the curriculum. As an exclusive method of handling the matter, this plan seems inadequate for two reasons. First, the content is extensive enough to make more intensive treatment desirable. Second, the subjects into which it is incorporated are too often academically oriented to subject matter rather than the improvement of personal adjustment. It, therefore, seems desirable to move in the direction of courses designed specifically to promote better marriages and family life.

10. Courses in preparation for Marriage and Family Life should be accredited and accorded a place in the school program with other subjects designed to improve pupil adjustments and to increase their capacity for satisfactory living. In the beginning, these courses should probably be elective. After they have established their value, and enough qualified teachers are available to teach all pupils, the elective-prescribed issue can be decided.

11. Careful planning to assure coordination (of instruction for marriage and family life) with other subjects and general acceptance by the school personnel itself should accompany the introduction of such a program. All teachers should be thoroughly acquainted with the program and be helped to see how, through their particular subjects, they can contribute to its objective.

12. Although these principles are directly applicable to secondary education, it is recognized that much education pertinent to satisfying family life may be begun at the elementary level. This suggests that a sound program cannot have its beginning and end in secondary education alone.

13. A program of community education designed to build an understanding of the contributions which the school can make to better marriages and more adequate families is a minimum essential. This effort can be supported by Parent-Teachers Associations, or by other appropriate groups in the community. Whenever feasible, the community program should be developed so as to include parent education designed to help parents guide their own children more effectively, and to achieve a satisfactory marital adjustment. While some may not regard the schools as the proper institution to assume this responsibility, they can stimulate action. Indeed, they are in a particularly strategic situation to demonstrate the need and value of such education.

14. The provision of adequate educational opportunities in marriage and family life must be recognized as a joint responsibility of various community institutions. It is particularly the responsibility of the home, school, and church. These three institutions should join forces to eliminate conditions inimical to satisfactory marriage and family life, and to provide a well-balanced, constructive educational program.[2]

[2] Adopted from *Report of National Conference on Family Life,* Washington, D.C.

VALUES AND ATTITUDES

1. An *appreciation* for family living as the primary force influencing the total development of the individual.
2. An *appreciation* of the need to guide sex impulses by reason, consideration, and social welfare rather than by impulses and gratification.
3. A *desire* to follow and improve sex-social conventions.
4. A *preference* for scientific rather than for vulgar sex information and terminology.
5. A *regard* for the sex functions with modesty.
6. An *appreciation* of the importance of selecting one's marriage partner.
7. A *regard* for the maturity of both partners as a critical influence on the success of their marriage.
8. An *appreciation* of the importance of the premarital examination.
9. A *respect* for one's own family's mode of living and for the contribution each member makes to the lives of all other family members.
10. A *regard* for the need to make mutual adjustments in marriage.
11. A *desire* to prevent the development of avoidable conflicts in marriage.
12. An *appreciation* of a two-way communication between husband and wife and between parents and children.
13. A *willingness* to postpone parenthood until one is willing and able to accept the responsibilities of parenthood.
14. An *appreciation* of the vital role played by individual couples to control the population explosion.
15. A *desire* to be a parent whose influence on his children will foster their optimal development.

The Junior High School Program

The junior high school has been a successful and favored starting point for sex education, when it has been impossible to start at the beginning. Because of the sexual maturation of boys and girls and the new social demands, the work receives ready justification and support in the minds of everyone. Parents welcome the assistance of the schools. Teachers and the principals recognize the acuteness of transitional adolescent needs of the students and are eager to find new avenues of approach to them.

THE NATURE OF JUNIOR HIGH SCHOOL STUDENTS

Here follows a summary of some of the major characteristics of youth of the junior high school age:

1. *Junior high school students show a wide variation in physical maturation.* This point is quite obvious to adults who deal with groups of this age. Psychologists

point out that a great premium is placed on physical development in this age group. These psychologists also indicate that ordinarily none of the physical changes are as important as the attitudes of the teenagers toward these physical changes. During prepuberty and early puberty, girls and boys need repeated assurance that their growth and development patterns are normal.

2. *Junior high school students show a wide variation in social maturation.* Social maturation depends partly on physical readiness, with girls maturing at an earlier age than boys. Much of that which happens to teenagers socially depends upon the expectations of the community and the culture in which they live. While the parents may exert a strong influence over these youth, they are often competing very strongly with the standards set by the teenagers themselves.

3. *As the junior high school students grow as individuals, they choose from the various pressures of the cultural environments.* They are pressured from the home, the school, their own social groups, the church, club groups, relatives, and older teenagers whom they may admire. However, eventually they must learn to weigh the values of these groups and choose which pressures they will yield to. The difficulty for these youths is that these pressures are often conflicting and this is especially true in the area of sex and sexuality. As a consequence, the real question becomes that of how to choose values and standards which will last for the rest of their lives.

4. *The junior high school student is alone in the crowd.* The teenager is sure that nobody understands him in the way that he needs to be understood. He thinks deeply but usually finds it difficult to express his thoughts to his closest friends. His own maturity will depend on his ability to handle and come to terms with his loneliness.

5. *Junior high school students have a rich interior life.* Fantasy and daydreams are a common form of expression during these years. The junior high school student has a varied interior world which, when expressed through drawing scenes, for example, reveals some of these interior feelings by scenes of violence, destruction, bloodshed, aggression, and sex. These fantasies may seriously affect his values, attitudes, and standards, and consequently his choices in the real world where the teenager lives.

6. *Junior high school students are active.* At this age, they are usually filled with energy. Consequently, learning for them must be connected with *doing*. They need to be involved in physical activity in school work and outside.

7. *They have their own opinions about themselves.* Here are a few examples of their answers to the question "How do you see yourself in the role of a teenager?"

    a. A person growing very fast physically and mentally.

    b. A teenager is a kid with good ideas and a questioning mind.

    c. A teenager is a young person learning to grow up. He or she must be prepared for the future.

    d. A teenager is going through a chemical change which causes emotional problems that are difficult for a teenager to understand.

    e. Someone who is looking for the meaning of life; someone getting ready for the future.

    f. I see myself taking responsibilities and learning to care for things I like.

A PROGRAM FOR GRADE EIGHT

The following program [3] for grade eight has been developed by the New York City Board of Education. It is one of the grade levels considered in their curriculum.

1. Concept: Understanding at a more advanced level the influence of the endocrine system on the appearance, body functions, and mental and emotional behavior of individuals. (The endocrine system is taught in a framework of instruction associated with systems as a whole.)

CONTENT
(A resource person—doctor, nurse—may be helpful in the treatment of this area.)
Endocrine glands and their hormones.
Sex glands and sex hormones.
The estrus cycle.

LEARNING ACTIVITIES
1. Review material learned in grade seven on endocrine glands and hormones.
2. Show transparencies of male and female bodies showing location of endocrine glands.
3. Use mannequin to show three-dimensional interrelationships of all body organs to endocrine glands.
4. Show film, "Endocrine Glands," on the approved list of the Bureau of Audio-Visual Aids.
5. Have students make reports on endocrine glands.
6. Discuss importance of:
Follicle-stimulating hormone.
Luteinizing hormone.
Luteotrophin.
Oxytocin.
Estrogen.
Progesterone.
Function of the placenta as an endocrine gland.
Relaxin from ovaries, uterus, and placenta.
Testosterone.
7. Show chart of complete estrus cycle.
8. Invite the school doctor to discuss the estrus cycle.

2. Concept: Learning to get along in a harmonious fashion with members of one's own and the opposite sex.

[3] New York City Board of Education, *Family Living Including Sex Education,* 1967, pp. 43–48.

CONTENT

Develop wholesome interests and hobbies.

Recognize that it is important to act in line with one's age.

Plan wholesome activities together.

Keep physically and emotionally fit.

Consider interests for the common good.

Be a responsible person.

Develop a social consciousness.

Practice health and safety habits.

Learn to respect varying points of view.

Use leisure time constructively.

Live in accordance with sound, basic standards.

LEARNING ACTIVITIES

1. Plan activities where boys and girls work together. Committees, athletics, school plays, and school government are some suggestions.
2. Plan a square dance program for purposes of learning to get along and for purposes of submerging interests for the common good.
3. Through panel discussions and debates, teach pupils to respect varying points of view.
4. Plan excursions such as a trip to a concert or theatre. These provide opportunities for social conversations.

3. Concept: Appreciating the depth and significance of "crushes."

CONTENT

Recognize that young people are capable of developing strong attachments for each other or for an older person.

Understand that these attachments, if properly guided, strengthen respect and admiration for one another.

Understand that appreciation and regard for another person reinforce a code for personal living.

LEARNING ACTIVITIES

1. Have students discuss the best way for a pupil to act who has a crush on an older person in authority.
2. Discuss with students the values for the future in sensibly experiencing and controlling crushes and puppy love.

4. Concept: Appreciating the need for making personal decisions consistent with appropriate values and a philosophy of life.

CONTENT

Making appropriate decisions:

Conflicts between peer group codes or activities and family or school regulations.

Conflicts between peer group codes or activities and personal values and beliefs of right and wrong.

Effect of making decisions:
    Achieving long-term goals.
    Achieving immediate goals.
    Maintaining self-respect.
Reasons for maintaining personal standards:
    Advantages and disadvantages of going steady.
    Responsibility for setting standards.
    Learning how to say "no."
    Learning to vary the tempo when on a date.
    Breaking off.

LEARNING ACTIVITIES
1. Discuss ways to handle situation of being offered a cigarette and refusing to accept it; role-play.
2. View film on going steady and discuss advantages and disadvantages.
3. Discuss question of setting and maintaining standards of behavior on a date.

5. Concept: Understanding the possible personal and social outcomes as well as the health hazards of indiscriminate relationships in any type of action with those of one's own or opposite sex. Appreciating that relationships in any type of action require social maturity and involve total responsibility for conditions that, result.

CONTENT
Indiscriminate relationships:
    Invoke feelings of guilt and shame.
    Create a conflict oftentimes between what one does and what one thinks.
    Create a reputation of which one cannot feel proud.
    May lead to health hazards such as venereal disease.
    May result in social dislocations. Recognize the consequences, personally and socially, of premarital pregnancies to the mother, family, and unborn child.
    May require assistance of family clergyman, or a community agency such as the Department of Health, Community Service Society, or others.
    May lead to homosexuality. (Introduce this topic with great sensitivity if pertinent to the children in the group. Be careful to avoid giving pupils guilt feelings because they prefer a best boy friend or best girl friend to being one of a group or with someone of the opposite sex. Distinguish between the life-long need of having best friends of the same sex and homosexuality.)
Responsible social relationships:
    Require social maturity.
    Provide opportunity for emotional security.

LEARNING ACTIVITIES
1. Have boys and girls—without using their names—tape their reactions to indiscriminate behavior. Play the tapes for other classes as a basis for discussion.

2. Have a clergyman, guidance counselor, and student panel discuss the psychological, moral, and physical aspects of such behavior.
3. Have the pupils write a brief composition, "What My Reputation Means to Me."
4. Invite the school nurse to discuss the hazards of indiscriminate behavior.

6. Concept: Understanding the fact that an individual's characteristics are the product of his heredity and environment.

CONTENT
  Heredity:
    Cells.
    Cell types.
    Chromosomes (including number).
    Mitosis.
    Maturation of sex cells.
    DNA and RNA (elementary discussion).
    Dominant and recessive traits.
    Blended inheritance.
    Defective traits.
  Influence of environment.

LEARNING ACTIVITIES
  1. Have pupils report on roles of DNA and RNA in inheritance.
  2. Use charts to illustrate color blindness, hemophilia, and other defects.
  3. Discuss methods of plant and animal breeding, including selection and hybridization.
  4. Discuss values of environment in terms of realization of inheritance.
  5. In discussing new work, use and teach correct terminology.
  6. When students ask questions using unacceptable terms, answer these questions using the correct terminology.
  7. Encourage pupils to use correct terminology at all times.

A PROGRAM FOR GRADE NINE

This program [4] for grade nine has been developed by the American School Health Association which includes a suggested program for each grade K–12.

Typical Student Questions

Questions asked by pupils are signs of curiosities or problems which can become material for classroom discussion, projects, or reading. The teacher should encourage students to ask questions; in fact, they should seek them out

---

[4] American School Health Association, *Growth Patterns and Sex Education, A Suggested Program Kindergarten Through Grade Twelve,* 1967, pp. 83–89.

and should be prepared to help the pupils find clear, simple, honest answers. The following are some typical questions, chosen from hundreds asked by students in the ninth grade:

1. How far should you go with the opposite sex?
2. Is it common for a boy to kiss a girl goodnight?
3. Should people of our age go steady?
4. How can girls attract boys and, if you succeed, what do you do after you have the boy?
5. How should one act on a date?
6. How should girls act with older boys?
7. How do you know if you're going with the right person?
8. When should you start dating?
9. Should parking be allowed?
10. Is petting beyond reason?
11. Why do some people hate people of the opposite sex while others seem crazy about them?
12. How long should you go with a boy before you let him kiss you?
13. Should you date boys more than two grades ahead of you?
14. If your parents want to meet the boy you're going out with, what is the best way to introduce them?
15. Why do boys or girls, when they are going with you, think they own you?
16. Is it normal to think about sex relationships at this age?
17. How can I overcome shyness with girls?
18. Why do people who disagree go together?

Unit 1. Mental and Emotional Health

A. TEACHABLE MATERIAL

1. Characteristics of mental and emotional health:
   a. The basic emotions are love, fear, and anger.
   b. Other emotions are a result of combinations of these three.
   c. Response to emotion needs direction and modification.
   d. Everyone needs to develop self-acceptance and a recognition of self-worth.
   e. Friendliness is important.
   f. Acceptance of responsibilities is necessary to the development of emotional maturity.
2. Influences upon mental and emotional health:
   a. Heredity.
   b. Intellect.
   c. Family.
   d. Peer group.
   e. Community.
3. Normal variations in mental and emotional health:
   a. Anxieties and tensions.
      (1) Worries.

        (2) Regrets.
        (3) Dislikes.
     b. Frustrations and unhappiness.
     c. Jealousy, envy, and resentment.
  4. Variations in mental and emotional health which indicate illness:
     a. Excessive anxiety (anxiety neurosis).
     b. Guilt.
     c. Phobias.
     d. Hysteria.
     e. Compulsions.
     f. Obsessions.
     g. Delusions.
     h. Hallucinations.
     i. Hypochondria.

B. PROFITABLE ACTIVITIES

1. Discuss what can be considered normal variations in mental and emotional health.

2. Have members of the class choose or develop an example of a hypothetical emotional crisis that might occur in their lives. Then ask various students to give monologues on how they would meet and deal with this situation.

3. Have students list ways in which they deceive (or "kid") themselves in order to meet some uncomfortable situation.

4. Give an attitude test. This may be developed by the teacher, or commercial ones may be purchased.

5. Have students list and analyze their own fears. Collect them and make a composite of the kinds of fears found within the class. These should be disguised in such a way that no student could be identified by the class. The list can then be used as the basis for class discussions about coping with fears.

6. Write essays on the ways in which emotions can be either beneficial or detrimental to effective living.

7. Discuss ways adolescents have of showing their need to be accepted by or belong to their peer group.

8. Discuss how the mental attitudes such as a feeling of self-worth, a sense of responsibility, and friendliness can be helpful to one's total adjustment.

9. Have students write an essay about the meaning of the phrase "mind over matter."

10. Role-play emotional situations that arise between students and their parents, students, and their friends.

11. Develop an unfinished story or "critical incident" that is centered around a student who has failed a required course for the semester. Have students write endings to the story, indicating how they would handle the situation. Then have students read the story endings aloud and discuss them.

Unit 2. Family Relationships

A. TEACHABLE MATERIAL
1. Problems in family relationships:
    a. Kinds of problems commonly experienced by adolescents.
    b. The need for making appropriate adjustments to problems in family relationships.
    c. Finding acceptable solutions to such problems.
2. Understanding the nature and purpose of discipline.
3. Growing in respect toward authority.
4. The development of independence and sound judgment.
5. Developing standards of belief and behavior:
    a. Understanding early influences upon one's beliefs and standards of behavior.
    b. Beliefs and standards of behavior are sometimes modified by maturity.
    c. Considering alternatives and different points of view.
    d. Making decisions.
6. Developing meaningful friendships:
    a. The extent to which friendships substitute for or complement family relationships.
    b. Resolving conflicts between one's family and one's friends.

B. PROFITABLE ACTIVITIES
1. Collect newspaper and magazine articles that might have influence upon behavior. Bring them to class for review and discussion.
2. Encourage students to analyze selected family television programs for their emotional appeal and ways in which they might influence one's attitudes.
3. Likewise, students might analyze television and magazine advertisements for their "sex pitch" and discuss their mode.
4. Create a role-playing situation in which a mother and father refuse their teenager permission to have a date or go out with the gang. Compare the different reactions of a boy in the part of the teenager to those of a girl playing the same part.
5. Have students list those behavior problems which they feel would be legitimate cause for being "grounded" by parents. Discuss feelings about being "grounded."
6. Discuss reasons why some adolescents would rather seek advice from friends and members of their peer groups than from their parents.
7. List those pressures which are placed upon students by adults and which they resent. Collect the lists and use them as the basis for an open forum.
8. Show the films, "Farewell to Childhood" and "Human Heredity."
9. Have each student list the things he likes and dislikes about himself. Then have the student use his list as the basis for developing a plan of action for eliminating or compensating for his undesirable characteristics and enhancing or making the most of his desirable characteristics.
10. Have students list those characteristics they like best and least about their parents. Collect and use as the basis for class discussion.

Unit 3. Boy-Girl Relationships

A. TEACHABLE MATERIAL

1. Dating:
   a. The purposes of dating.
   b. Kinds of dating experiences appropriate at various stages in one's development.
      (1) Double dating.
      (2) Single dating.
   c. How to choose a date.
   d. How to arrange a date (emphasize the point that dates should be planned).
   e. What to do on a date.
   f. Dating courtesies.
2. Going steady:
   a. Purposes of going steady.
   b. Advantages and disadvantages of going steady.
3. Parental reactions and attitudes towards dating and going steady.
4. Setting limits in boy-girl relationships:
   a. Necking.
      (1) Its purposes.
         (a) A means of expressing affection physically.
         (b) A means of knowing and being known (communication).
      (2) Its effect on the boy.
      (3) Its effect on the girl.
   b. Petting.
      (1) Its purposes.
         (a) A more intimate way of expressing affection physically.
         (b) A means of knowing and being known, of communicating physically on a deeper level.
         (c) A natural prelude to sexual intercourse.
      (2) Its effect on the boy.
      (3) Its effect on the girl.
5. Developing and adhering to valid standards of conduct:
   a. Resolving value conflicts.
   b. Finding acceptable means of sexual expression.
   c. Reasons why premarital sexual relations are not regarded as acceptable behavior by the majority of persons in our society.
6. Ninth-grade students should understand the meanings of the following terms:
   a. Sexual intercourse.
   b. Sexual relations.
   c. Premarital relations.
   d. Premarital intercourse.

B. PROFITABLE ACTIVITIES

1. View and discuss any or all of the following films:
   a. "Date Etiquette."
   b. "Going Steady."

    c. "How to Say No."

    d. "What to Do on a Date."

2. Develop and present a skit in which a group of girls at a slumber party discuss their reactions to various boys and their conduct on a date. Follow this with another skit about a group of boys, perhaps in a locker room setting, discussing their dates with various girls. Follow this with a general class discussion about the expectations that both boys and girls have of their dates' behaviors.

3. Write answers to the questions: "Why do the parents of teenagers object to necking and petting?" and "What are parents' attitudes toward going steady?"

4. Have students list and discuss the advantages and disadvantages of going steady.

5. Interview parents and adult friends concerning the behavior of teenagers in their generation and what they did on dates and parties to learn if attitudes and activities were vastly different a generation ago.

6. Develop a panel discussion about dating. The following are a few of the topics that might be discussed:

    What do girls like to do on a date?

    What do boys like to do on a date?

    Who should decide what is to be done on a date?

    What kind of behavior is expected of a date?

    What should be the limits established for behavior on dates and how does one set and stick to these limits?

7. Discuss the topic of "setting limits" including such questions as:

    Where would you like parents to set the limits?

    How much should you be able to influence the establishment of these limits?

    Whose responsibility is it to keep you within those limits?

Concepts. As a product of their experiences in the study of this unit, it would be hoped that some such concepts as these would be formulated by students in the ninth grade:

1. There is a reciprocal relationship between the quality of one's emotional health and the quality of his total function.

2. The normal range of emotional health encompasses a wide variety of qualitative emotional responses.

3. The behavior of the mentally ill person differs from that of the mentally healthy person more in degree than in kind.

4. Family living results in interactions among individuals with unique personalities, unique goals, unique needs. Therefore problems naturally may be expected to develop within family units as a normal consequence of this interaction among unique individuals.

5. One's own standards of belief and behavior as he grows toward maturity are influenced by what he is as a unique individual, what he wishes to become, and his interactions with the myriad factors and forces in his environment.

6. Dating customs vary from one community to another, and from one culture to another.
7. There are both advantages and disadvantages to the practice of going steady.
8. The quality of the dating experience will be influenced by the dating readiness, expectations, and behaviors of both dating partners.
9. Parents' attitudes toward dating customs and behaviors arise from their natural concern for and interest in the total welfare of their offspring.

Attitudes. As an outcome of instruction it is to be hoped that some such attitudes as these may be developed by students in the ninth grade:

1. An acceptance of self as a person worthy of respect.
2. An acceptance of other persons as individuals worthy of respect and a desire to treat others with the respect they are due.
3. A respect for authority appropriately exercised.
4. A desire to develop or to improve one's ability to solve personal problems.
5. An appreciation for the meaning of friendship and for the important roles friends play in the lives of one another.
6. A respect for one's parents' attitudes toward dating customs and behavior, and a willingness to consider parental points of view when deciding upon dating practices.
7. An appreciation of and respect for the purposes of necking and petting and for the effects of each on members of both sexes.
8. An appreciation for the importance of having appropriate limits set for one's behavior and a desire to assume greater responsibility for establishing and adhering to one's own limits.

The Senior High School Program

The program in family life and sex education needs to be adapted to meet current needs while the young continue to be teenagers and in school, and are looking forward to the time that they finish or leave high school to take a job, prepare further for a vocation, look forward to marriage and parenthood, and participate as responsible members of the community.

Family life programs can be included as major units in already existing courses such as health education, psychology, and home economics. A number of senior high schools offer a separate course in this area. Both plans have merit at this level of education.

A PROGRAM FOR GRADES TEN AND ELEVEN

The following program [5] is from the report of the American School Health Association. That report includes a suggested program for each grade from K–12.

[5] American School Health Association, *Growth Patterns and Sex Education, A Suggested Program Kindergarten Through Grade Twelve*, 1967, pp. 95–110.

Introductory Comment

Most tenth and eleventh graders characteristically are more concerned about their psychosocial development than about either the mechanics of body function, choosing a life partner, or the responsibilities of marriage. Therefore it is necessary to teach the following units from the standpoint of their major concerns, being ever-mindful of the basic characteristics of the adolescent and his subculture.

Teenagers appreciate and respond to the teacher who has the ability to accept them as they are and to treat them with respect as individuals. They equally appreciate and respond to the teacher who is a constructive example to them and who never underestimates the influence he has upon them. A chance remark or unwarranted ridicule on the part of the teacher could destroy students' budding positive attitudes.

It is reasonable to expect that in many situations the team teaching approach could be used. The school health educator might act as team leader, using the school nurse, guidance counselor, or school physician for those units or subunits of study in which these persons are capable of contributing most to the learning experience. However, all participating personnel should reach mutual accord concerning instructional goals and the kinds of desirable attitudes they are trying to help students develop.

It is important to remember that, although there will be little variation in the chronological ages of tenth and eleventh graders, the variations in their levels of physical and emotional maturity usually will be great, spanning a range of as much as six or seven years in some instances. Therefore, it is necessary to continue in-depth discussions concerning sexuality and personality development and the adolescent's roles as a contributing member of his family and of his peer group, and to correct any misconceptions that students may have about genital growth and development and reproductive functioning.

Boys this age need to understand that most adolescent girls have a relatively limited or moderate genital response to necking and petting, that they rarely build up pressures which demand coital relief, and that these indulgences produce, primarily, only a physically generalized, pleasurable sensation. Girls on the other hand, need to know that sexual stimulation produces in the boy a localized, genital excitation and that pressures *do* build up which frequently are overpowering in their demand for relief through sexual intercourse and ejaculation. The psychological commitment found in girls following sexual intercourse is rarely, if ever, found in adolescent boys. Hopefully, this knowledge will help them to make wiser judgments regarding their conduct with each other.

Although this material may seem highly sophisticated to some adults it is wholesomely accepted by teenagers. It should also be borne in mind that in many schools this may be the last chance the students will have to discuss these important topics in controlled group settings with the guidance of a mature individual.

It is desirable that tenth and eleventh graders understand before they assume adult responsibilities that sexuality is inextricably interwoven into one's personality and that it contributes to creative drives and abilities and thus helps to distinguish the person as an individual.

Topics About Which Girls Ask Many Questions
Dating behavior.
Dating customs.
Sexual attraction and stimulation.
Masturbation.
Homosexuality.
Boys.
Sexual intercourse.
The role of sex in marriage.
Birth control.
Conception, pregnancy, and childbirth.

Topics About Which Boys Ask Many Questions
Dating customs.
Dating behavior.
Understanding girls.
Sex and moral standards.
Adults' attitudes toward sex and dating.
Understanding and controlling the sex drive.
Homosexuality.
Masturbation.
Sexual stimulation and sexual intercourse.
Birth control.
Reproduction and the reproductive organs.
Conception, pregnancy, and childbirth.

Unit 1. Psychosocial Development
A. TEACHABLE MATERIAL
    1. The developing personality:
        a. Behavior acceptable to self and society.
            (1) Personal factors and forces influencing behavior.
                (a) The endocrine glands: chemical regulators of behavior (see units for upper elementary school).
                (b) Emotions.
                (c) Values.
                (d) Rational controls.
        b. Controlling emotions and getting along with others.

    c. The relationship of personal appearance to personality.

        (1) Appearance is one of the ways in which one's personality is revealed to others.

        (2) A pleasant appearance helps to make one more attractive to others.

        (3) First impressions of personality often are formed on the basis of appearance.

2. The personality in trouble:

    a. The influence of stimulants and depressants on personality development and expression.

    b. The use of stimulants and depressants as an attempt to solve personality problems.

    c. Ways in which the use or abuse of stimulants and depressants may affect the quality of dating experiences and marriage relationships.

3. Developing a philosophy of life:

    a. Understanding self; developing a realistic self-concept.

    b. Identifying loyalties.

    c. Developing standards of belief and values.

    d. The need for developing a moral code of ethics consistent with one's philosophy of life.

B. PROFITABLE ACTIVITIES

1. Develop a personality chart which includes both desirable and undesirable characteristics found in people. Point out how perceptions gained via the various senses (sight, hearing, smell, and touch) contribute to one's impression of the total personality of others.

2. Encourage students to analyze their own shortcomings and list ways in which they might improve the personal impressions they make on others.

3. Have student baby sitters report on common emotional responses they have found in babies and children. Compare these to the common emotional responses of adolescents when they are frustrated. Have the class look for signs of maturity or immaturity in these episodes.

4. Discuss ways in which adolescents compensate for their frustrations and determine which ones are constructive and which are destructive ways of compensating.

5. Discuss the difference between worry and health concern.

6. Have students describe or list on paper their own current problems and then formulate plans to solving them in a constructive manner.

7. Have students list their worries and categorize them according to whether they concern past events, possible future occurrences, or the immediate present situation. Discuss the fallacy of worrying about what *has* happened because it cannot be changed, the waste of effort involved in worrying about future situations that may never arise, and the opportunity one has for controlling the immediate present by taking constructive action instead of worrying.

8. Discuss the annoying habits people have and what actions might be taken to remedy these habits.

9. Ask several students to prepare and present to the class reports about various

kinds of psychosomatic illnesses and the causes and cures of these illnesses.

10. Interview the school nurse to determine the kinds of complaints reported by students when they come to the health office or clinic for care. Have students try to determine the frequency of complaints which might reflect psychosomatic illnesses. Then discuss some of the possible causes of psychosomatic illnesses in students and ways in which such illnesses might be prevented.

11. Write essays on the criteria that should be used in making decisions involving moral judgments, and in determining right from wrong.

12. Develop several hypothetical situations based on problems adolescents commonly experience in their relationships with siblings and have each of several students present a monologue on how he or she would deal with one of these situations.

13. Develop a panel discussion on topics pertaining to family activities. Some of the topics included for discussion might be the following:

    a. Whether or not teenagers want to participate in family activities, and why they either do or do not want to do so.

    b. Whether or not teenagers should be expected to participate in family activities, and why they either should or should not be expected to do so.

    c. Whether or not teenagers expect members of their family to show interest in their personally chosen activities regardless of whether or not they are willing to show interest in and to participate in family activities.

    d. Kinds of activities that members of families with teenagers and preadolescents might enjoy doing together. The panel might consist of students either appointed by the teacher or selected by members of the class, or it might be composed of both teenagers and parents.

14. Provided that the specific students involved are willing to do so, have students from divorced or one-parent homes write anonymous reports on ways in which they think their particular home situations have affected them, and ways in which they could compensate for the absence of one parent in the home. Without revealing the identity of the author (in some instances it may be necessary for the teacher actually to disguise portions of what the student has written in order to maintain anonymity), guide students in forming some conclusions about the effects of the one-parent home on the development and total welfare of children.

15. Discuss the problem of conflict between the adolescent's desire to make his own decisions and his parents' belief that he frequently needs their guidance in making decisions. Help students to identify those areas of living in which they might reasonably expect to be permitted to make decisions without parental guidance, and those in which parental guidance still may be desirable and helpful.

16. View and discuss any or all of the following films:

    "Understanding Your Emotions."

    "Family Life."

    "Farewell to Childhood."

    "Human Heredity."

    "Endocrine Glands—How They Affect You."

    "Emotional Health."

Unit 2. Boy-Girl Relationships in Light of Both Immediate and Long-Range Goals

A. TEACHABLE MATERIAL

  1. Dating:

    a. Types of dates.

    b. Deciding where to go on a date.

    c. Determining how much to spend on a date.

    d. Dating etiquette.

  2. The pros and cons of going steady.

  3. Developing personal standards for controlling emotional behavior:

    a. The importance of knowing one's limitations.

    b. Reasons for avoiding intense necking and petting.

    c. Responsibility for controlling behavior is shared by both partners; a girl "holds the reins on a spirited horse," but a boy has no right to make demands of his date which she will find difficult to refuse.

    d. The concept of mutual respect.

    e. Considering the total situation and the future instead of only the temporary pleasure of the immediate episode.

      (1) Marriage and monogamy contrasted with promiscuity, illegitimacy, forced marriage, or disease.

      (2) The potential consequences of premarital sexual intercourse.

      (3) Ways in which being married enhances the sex act and the total relationship between man and woman.

  4. Courtship:

    a. Ways in which it differs from dating.

    b. Purposes.

    c. Appropriate behavior.

    d. Opportunities and responsibilities.

  5. Engagement:

    a. Its meaning.

    b. Ways in which it differs from courtship.

    c. Purposes.

    d. Appropriate behavior.

    e. Opportunities and responsibilities.

  6. Marriage:

    a. Choosing a life partner.

      (1) The role of heredity in influencing choice.

      (2) The role of environment in influencing choice.

      (3) Distinguishing between love and infatuation.

      (4) Developing realistic expectations of marriage (e.g., marriage will not result in personality changes).

    b. Responsibilities in marriage.

      (1) Financial.

      (2) Social.

      (3) Sexual.

      (4) Psychological.

      (5) Religious.

      (6) Physical.

B. PROFITABLE ACTIVITIES

1. Develop and administer a pretest over material found in this unit and use the results to determine students' present levels of understanding and the nature of their attitudes. Results then can be used to plan learning experiences and content emphasis. Best results are obtained if the student is permitted to designate his or her paper as "boy" or "girl" without using names.

2. Discuss what kinds of behavior students expect of their dating partners and why they have these particular expectations.

3. Have a debate on the advantages and disadvantages of going steady. Compare the reasons girls go steady with the reasons boys go steady.

4. Discuss the subject of parental objection to having teenagers engage in the practices of necking and petting. Assist students in determining why their parents object to these practices and whether or not their objections are based on valid reasons related to concern for the adolescent's welfare.

5. Ask students to list the reasons why boys either do or don't "make out" and and the reasons why girls either do or don't "make out." Use the reasons offered as a basis for class discussions on topics such as:

   a. Handling conflicts between one's own wishes and the expectations of his date concerning this practice.

   b. The principle of mutual respect as a guide to dating behavior and the expression of affection.

   c. The effect on one's emotions of behaving in a manner contrary to his personal standards of behavior.

   d. The purposes of "making out" and whether or not the reasons consciously expressed actually are related to the attainment of these purposes.

6. Ask students to think as adults would think and from an adult point of view to identify the characteristics of mature love. List these characteristics on the board and then list beside them students' verbalized characteristics of teenage love.

7. Discuss whether the sex drive is as strong in adolescent girls as it is in adolescent boys.

8. Direct a student discussion toward the reasons why people marry—helping them to view sex and sexual expression in proper perspective.

9. Develop a panel discussion about the advantages of a comparatively long courtship and a short engagement.

10. Arrange a debate about the desirability of a long engagement versus the desirability of a short engagement.

11. Have student committees investigate the following problems and report their findings to the class:

    a. Illegitimacy in the United States.

    b. Illegal abortions.

    c. Marriages entered into because of premarital pregnancy. Some of the information to look for might include the immediate and long range effects these problems might have on the persons involved, the impact of these problems upon the community and upon society at large, etc. Discuss the pros and cons of the changing code of sexual behavior among teenagers and young adults in the context of information presented in the reports.

12. View and discuss any or all of the following films:
    "What to Do on a Date."
    "Dating, Do's and Don'ts."
    "Going Steady."
    "How Do you Know It's Love?"
    "Marriage Is a Partnership."
    "Choosing a Marriage Partner."
    "The Meaning of Engagement."
    "Are You Ready for Marriage?"
    "When Should I Marry?"
13. Play and discuss the audiotapes entitled:
    "Worth Waiting For."
    "About Men."
    "About Girls."
14. View and discuss the following film strips:
    "It's a Date."
    "Seeing Double."
    "With This Ring."

Unit 3. Family Planning
A. TEACHABLE MATERIAL
  1. Family planning means the development of a family according to a purposeful design, hopefully having children when they are wanted.
  2. Factors to consider in planning a family:
     a. Finances.
     b. Educational goals for children.
     c. The number of children wanted.
     d. The need of husband and wife to adjust to each other in a marital relationship before a third party enters the relationship.
     e. The acceptance of personal responsibility for controlling the population explosion.
     f. The effects of planning on parents' attitudes toward the arrival of each child and upon his being accepted.
  3. Spacing children:
     a. Child-spacing is an aspect of family planning that involves having children at appropriate intervals.
     b. Reasons for spacing children.
        (1) Mother's health; spacing allows mother to recuperate physiologically and psychologically from each pregnancy before having another child.
        (2) The long-range health and welfare of the children.
            (a) The importance of an affectional maternal-infant relationship to all aspects of the baby's growth and development.
            (b) Spacing allows each child ample time to develop a feeling of security within the family unit before he is displaced from his role as "the baby" by a younger child.
  4. Procedures involved in family planning:
     Discuss the fact that there are family planning procedures available to and

considered acceptable by persons of any social, religious, and ethnic group. No description of family planning devices or methods need be given; this information is available from physicians, religious advisors and, perhaps, parents at the time a person is ready for marriage. Many young people will accept from members of their peer group advice and information about contraceptive measures that are either ineffective or dangerous to their health. Let them know that there are appropriate methods, that families do use them, and that the subject may be one they will wish to discuss in greater detail with their families or religious or medical advisors or to explore further as a research project that can help to counteract the problems of unwise experimentation, misunderstandings, and unanswered questions. Depending upon local circumstances, the teacher may wish to mention specific sources of reliable family planning information.

B. PROFITABLE ACTIVITIES
   1. Prepare reports on several different aspects of the "population explosion." Discuss the following topics:
      a. The effects that value systems of persons in various cultures have upon the relative success of efforts to control the population explosion.
      b. The ways in which the population explosion is in turn affecting people's values.
      c. The role of the individual in controlling the population explosion.
      d. The right of an individual couple to determine the size of their family versus the right of a government to control family size in the interest of the total populace.
      e. The impact of the population explosion on such matters as the nation's economic development, family living, the individual's opportunity to realize his potential.
   2. Develop a debate on the pros and cons of family planning.
   3. Have each student in the class find out what it costs to rear one child in his particular family setting. Multiply this amount by the various numbers found in different families to determine the estimated minimum financial responsibility involved in rearing children.
   4. List the problems that might develop as a result of attempting to maintain too large a family on too small an income.
   5. Discuss whether children like to be members of a large family or of a small family. Point out the advantages and disadvantages of each situation.
   6. Discuss the changing patterns (as pointed out in the unit on Family Living) and the influence of family living in our culture upon family size.
   7. Debate the advantages and the disadvantages of having a working mother.
   8. A committee might be appointed to visit a Planned Parenthood clinic to talk to its director about the work done by the agency.

Unit 4. Growth and Reproduction (Separating girls from boys for discussion of these topics will permit in-depth discussion of the problem areas. This might be helpful to some students.)

A. TEACHABLE MATERIAL (Material marked * may better be taught in sections segregated as to sex.)

*1. Review of male reproductive organs:
  a. Penis.
  b. Testes.
  c. Scrotum.
  d. Spermatic duct and vas deferens.
  e. Urethra.
  f. Prostate gland.
  g. Seminal vesicles.
  h. Cowper's gland.
*2. The mechanism of erection:
  a. Purpose.
  b. Control.
*3. Orgasm and masturbation in the male.
*4. Sperm and seminal emissions.
 5. Sex and sexuality problems of the male:
  a. Homosexuality.
  b. Promiscuity.
  c. The "double standard."
*6. The female breast and breast feeding.
*7. Review of female reproductive organs:
  a. Clitoris.
  b. Labia majora and minora.
  c. Hymen.
  d. Perineum.
  e. Vagina.
  f. Cervix.
  g. Uterus.
  h. Fallopian tubes (oviducts).
  i. Ovaries.
*8. Erection in the female.
*9. Orgasm and masturbation in the female.
10. Ovulation.
11. Menstruation.
12. Fertilization.
13. Conception and implantation.
14. Pregnancy:
  a. Cell division and differentiation.
  b. The embryonic stage of development.
  c. Fetal development.
  d. Function of the placenta.
  e. The absence of nerve connection between mother and fetus.
  f. The expectant mother's structural, physiological, and emotional adjustments to pregnancy.
  g. The role of the expectant father.

    h. The need for mutual support and understanding between the prospective parents.

    i. The need for adequate medical care and supervision during pregnancy.

    j. Misconceptions and superstitions related to pregnancy.

15. Childbirth (refer to units for grades six, seven, and eight):
    a. Passage of the baby through the cervix and vagina.
    b. The episiotomy.

16. Sexual perversion. Questions concerning sexual perversion are asked sometimes. These should be answered as simply and as clearly as possible. Lengthy or descriptive discussions are to be discouraged. It is unfair and unwise to disillusion children and young people needlessly. Instead, the development of wholesome attitudes, self-respect, and belief in the dignity of sex as a positive, creative force in one's personality development should be stressed.

B. PROFITABLE ACTIVITIES

1. View and discuss such films as:
    "Biography of the Unborn."
    "Human Body: Reproductive System."
    "From Generation to Generation."
    "Human Reproduction."
    "Heredity and Pre-Natal Development."

2. Read appropriate selections in such references as:
    A Child Is Born: The Drama of Life Before Birth.
    Approaching Adulthood.
    Sex and the Teenager.
    Provide opportunity based on these readings for question-and-answer periods and class discussion.

3. Have students submit anonymous questions or descriptions of problems that they would like to have discussed.

4. Discuss frankly with students the differences between the male's and female's psychological, physical, and emotional responses to sexual stimulation. This may be done in such a way that it contributes positively toward their decisions concerning premarital sexual experimentation.

5. Take a field trip to a science center or health museum if there is one in the community. Follow the visit by discussion appropriate to the particular nature of the visitation experience.

6. Ask the school nurse or the school physician to serve as a resource person in the study of various aspects of this unit.

7. Have a student report on the nature of "natural childbirth" as compared to childbirth with anesthesia.

8. As questions from the students arise, discuss freely (or call upon a specialist to help in discussing) such topics as miscarriage, therapeutic abortion, illegal abortion, congenital and hereditary malformations, and variations in the birth process (e.g., breech birth, forceps delivery, caesarean delivery).

A PROGRAM FOR GIRLS IN GRADE TWELVE

The following program is used in a high school in New Jersey for a one-hour-a-week plan for teaching health alternating with physical education. An entire year of at least thirty-two class periods is devoted to the program.

I. INTRODUCTION
   A. Definitions.

II. ANATOMY AND PHYSIOLOGY
   A. Signs of maturity.
     1. Endocrine glands and their effects upon the maturation process:
       a. Thyroid.
       b. Parathyroid.
       c. Pituitary.
       d. Pineal.
       e. Adrenal.
       f. Thymus.
       g. Gonads.
     2. Physical and mental changes in puberty and adolescence related to maturation process:
       a. Male—primary and secondary sex characteristics.
         (1) Enlargement of penis.
         (2) Nocturnal emissions.
         (3) Development of hair.
         (4) Interest in opposite sex.
         (5) Increase in size—growth and muscular development.
         (6) Shape—broad shoulders, narrow hips.
         (7) Changes in voice, glands.
         (8) New interests and attitudes.
       b. Female—primary and secondary sex characteristics.
         (1) Thickening of the labia and lining of the vagina.
         (2) Menstruation.
         (3) Development of breasts.
         (4) Shape—narrow shoulders, broad hips.
         (5) Development of hair.
         (6) Changes in glands.
         (7) Interest in opposite sex.
         (8) New interests and attitudes.
   B. Organs of reproduction.
     1. Male—Structure and function of:
       a. Penis.
       b. Testicles.
       c. Scrotum
       d. Prostate.

        e. Cowper's glands.

        f. Seminal vesicle.

    2. Female—Structure and function of:

        a. Vagina.

        b. Labia.

        c. Cervix.

        d. Uterus.

        e. Fallopian tubes.

        f. Ovaries.

III. SEX RELATIONSHIPS

    A. Importance of proper relationships for the health and happiness of the individuals.

    B. As a healthy foundation for marriage and family life.

    C. Correct attitudes.

IV. TOWARD MARRIAGE

    A. Dating.

      1. Personality factors.

      2. Problems of dating:

        a. Going steady.

        b. Where to go; what to do.

        c. Petting.

          (1) Definition.

          (2) Effects on individual.

    B. Engagement period.

    C. State laws—marriage customs.

      1. Why we have them.

      2. Explanation:

        a. Premarital examination.

        b. License.

        c. Wassermann test.

        d. Age.

        e. Waiting period.

V. TOWARD PARENTHOOD

    A. Hereditary factors.

      1. Laws of heredity.

      2. Chromosomes.

      3. Genes.

      4. Multiple births.

    B. Birth.

      1. Process of:

        a. Natural childbirth.

        b. Caesarean.

        c. Instrument birth.

        d. Miscarriages.

        e. Abortions.

    2. Prenatal care.

    3. Postnatal care.

  C. Parental problems concerning children.

    1. Growth and development of children.

    2. Understanding adolescents.

    3. Parental guidance.

    4. Problems of teenagers.

    5. Parental attitudes.

VI. DIVORCE

  A. Causes.

  B. State laws.

  C. Results.

    1. Individual unhappiness.

    2. Effect on children.

    3. Effect on society.

VII. VENEREAL DISEASE

  A. Types—symptoms and treatment.

    1. Gonorrhea.

    2. Syphilis.

    3. Chancroid.

  B. Effects on individual and society.

VIII. PUBLIC AND PERSONAL HEALTH PROBLEMS

  A. Promiscuity.

  B. Sexual perversion.

  C. Homosexuality.

  D. Lesbianism.

IX. EVALUATION OF COURSE

  A. Strong points.

  B. Weak points.

  C. Recommendations.

Activities

1. Prepare an outline of topics for a twelve-class period unit on family life for the junior high school. Refer to Table 2.

2. Prepare an outline of topics for a fifteen-class period unit on family life for the senior high school.

3. Examine several books on family life intended for the secondary school level and summarize their relative merits. Which one would you prefer for the junior high school? For the senior high school?

OTHER PROGRAMS AND UNITS

For additional information and examples, see Chapter 6, "Correlation and Integration of Sex Education"; Chapter 7, "Methods and Materials for Teaching Sex Education"; Chapter 9, "Evaluation of the Sex Education Program"; and the Appendix.

References

American School Health Association, *Growth Patterns and Sex Education, A Suggested Program for Kindergarten Through Grade Twelve,* Kent, Ohio, 1967, 136 pp.

American Social Hygiene Association, *Social Hygiene in Health Education for Junior High Schools,* New York, 1938, 31 pp.

Community Service Society of New York, Committee on Family Life, *Education, Concerns of Adolescent Girls,* 105 East 22 Street, New York, 10010.

District of Columbia Public Schools, *Health and Family Life Education,* The Board of Education, Washington, D. C., 1965, 169 pp.

Illinois Sex Education Advisory Board, *Policy on Family Life and Sex Education,* State Department of Public Instruction, Springfield, Ill., 1967, 24 pp.

Methodist Church, Board of Education, *Workbook for Junior High Youth on the Role of Sex in Christian Living,* Box 871, Nashville, Tenn., 37202, 1967, 104 pp.

Michigan State Department of Instruction, *Education for Home and Family,* Bulletin No. 2141, Lansing, 1963, 57 pp.

New York City Board of Education, *Family Living Including Sex Education,* Curriculum Bulletin 1967–68 Series No. 11, Brooklyn, N. Y., 80 pp.

Pittsfield Board of Education, *Family Life and Sex Education,* Pittsfield, Mass., 1968, 11 pp. (mimeographed).

WNBC-TV Dorothy Gordon Youth Forum, "Sex and Youth—Are New Standards Acceptable?" June 19, 1966, 8 pp.

6

Correlation and Integration of Sex Education

The terms *correlation* and *integration* are concepts which, when applied to sex education, are in contrast to the idea of separate courses in that area.

Introduction

Correlation refers to the plan of including in another course or program certain aspects of sex education. Such correlation into a given subject or program enriches the content and the applications of that subject. It provides for the repetition of important topics in new and varied settings. It offers new and different approaches to the teaching of the same topics. It hopefully should interest the school staff in the total sex education program. And, as indicated in Chapter 2, the development of values and attitudes is best accomplished when these are presented by different teachers in different settings.

Integration, on the other hand, implies an organization of learning experiences around a central theme, in this case sex education, and drawing on the content of various school subjects and programs which are able to contribute. Integration means that there is a total plan for the curriculum for K–12 to be included in a number of subjects where and when appropriate. Integration of sex education takes place at the elementary school level since the same teacher usually teaches each of the subjects at a given grade level. Correlation, without necessarily integration, is more likely to be the situation at the secondary school level.

Where there is an integrated plan for sex education, there is, of course, a correlated program in each of the participating subject areas involved in the integration. Unfortunately, there may be correlation of sex education into one or more subjects without such sex education being integrated into an overall plan. It is possible and often very likely that, for example, the teacher of health education may not be informed about what is being taught in the biology class or in some other class. Coordination, through a committee, is obviously highly desirable.

In the correlation of units of education for family life, with various subjects, it is to be remembered that the topics are only a small part of the other courses and are so placed that they are a natural outgrowth of the work of those courses and not just an isolated and emphasized unit for which "time-out" is taken. For instance, the causes, prevention, and treatment for syphilis and gonorrhea should be an integral part of the study of communicable disease.

In a well-planned correlation, the units of education for family life would come to each pupil in definite sequence and would be incorporated into required courses so that every pupil received all of the essential education.

A careful examination of the Table 4 checklist will show the reader the extent to which the topics that were included in Table 2 can be distributed among the various subject matter areas and programs.

At the secondary school level, required courses are the ones which should be expected to carry the greatest weight in contributing to sex education, since this will assure that all students will receive such instruction. Elective courses can contribute above and beyond that in the required programs.

Many experts in sex education feel that it is only through correlation and integration that it should be taught, and that the offering of a separate course in this subject or area is justified primarily by a breakdown in the integrated plan. However, a number of high schools offer a separate course in the eleventh or twelfth grades usually on an elective basis.

Real progress and final success require the participation of all teachers in the instruction. So that teachers in the self-contained classroom and the teachers of special subjects can make their contributions through integration, it is essential that they know what body of information, attitudes, and behavior each child should have in his various stages of development. All

TABLE 4. CHECKLIST FOR INTEGRATION OF SEX EDUCATION IN THE SCHOOL PROGRAM

Topics	Subject or Program												
	General Science	Biology	Home Economics	Social Studies	Health Education	Physical Education	Literature	Psychology	Vocational Agriculture	Guidance	Extracurricular Activities	School Health Services	Healthful School Environment
A. Boy and Girl Relationships													
1. Building friendships													
2. Reasons for popularity and unpopularity													
3. Qualities in girls admired by boys													
4. Qualities in boys admired by girls													
5. Good grooming													
6. Social behavior, manners, etiquette													
B. Dating													
1. Kinds of dates													
a. Glamour dates													
b. Blind dates													
c. Growing friendships													
2. On the date													
a. Planning for dates													
b. Responsibilities of boys in dating													
c. Responsibilities of girls in dating													
3. Dating problems													
4. Wholesome recreation													
5. Petting													
a. Meaning of petting and necking													
b. Effect on boy and girl													
6. Parents and their children's dating													

Indicate the relative emphasis that you recommend for each topic in sex education for each subject or program. Use the following four-point scale for this purpose:

0—The topic does not apply to the subject or program.

1—Some or slight attention can be given to the topic as regards attitudes and behavior or to a few very elementary facts.

2—Moderate attention can be given to the topic; more facts can be included.

3—The major emphasis should be given from the point of view of the facts presented and the amount of time devoted to the topic.

TABLE 4 (continued)

Topics	General Science	Biology	Home Economics	Social Studies	Health Education	Physical Education	Literature	Psychology	Vocational Agriculture	Guidance	Extracurricular Activities	School Health Services	Healthful School Environment
7. A code of conduct													
8. Going steady: advantages, disadvantages													
C. Growth and Development													
1. Emotional growth and maturity													
2. Puberty: physical changes													
a. Height, weight, body proportions													
b. Secondary sex characteristics of boys													
(1) Physical changes													
(2) Seminal emissions													
c. Secondary sex characteristics of girls													
(1) Physical changes													
(2) Menstrual cycle													
3. The endocrine system													
a. Hormones and glands in general													
b. Sex hormones													
D. Reproduction													
1. Reproduction of plants and animals													
a. Asexual reproduction (unicellular)													
b. Sexual reproduction (biparental)													
c. Care of plants and animals													
2. Male reproductive system: anatomy and physiology													
3. Female reproductive system: anatomy and physiology													
E. Heredity													
1. The mechanism and principles of heredity													

TABLE 4 (continued)

Topics	Subject or Program												
	General Science	Biology	Home Economics	Social Studies	Health Education	Physical Education	Literature	Psychology	Vocational Agriculture	Guidance	Extracurricular Activities	School Health Services	Healthful School Environment
2. The interaction of heredity and environment													
3. Some applications to people													
a. Sex determination													
b. Sex-linked traits													
c. Blood types													
d. Twins													
e. Cousin marriages													
f. Inheritable diseases													
g. Congenital inheritance													
F. SOCIAL AND EMOTIONAL PROBLEMS RELATED TO SEX													
1. Conflict between sex impulse and social and moral code													
2. Masturbation													
3. Homosexuality													
4. Perversion													
5. Promiscuity													
6. Illegitimate births													
7. Abortion													
8. Birth control													
9. Venereal disease													
10. Prostitution													
G. PREPARATION FOR MARRIAGE													
1. The role of the family													
a. The evolution of the family													
b. The functions of the family													
c. Characteristics of the family in our society													
d. The role of each member in a family													
e. Factors which strengthen family life													
f. Factors which weaken family life													

TABLE 4 (continued)

Topics	General Science	Biology	Home Economics	Social Studies	Health Education	Physical Education	Literature	Psychology	Vocational Agriculture	Guidance	Extracurricular Activities	School Health Services	Healthful School Environment
2. Selection of a mate													
a. Personal preparation for making a choice													
b. Making friends—as an approach to mate selection													
c. Major considerations in choosing a mate													
d. Desirable personal qualities of a mate													
e. Mixed marriages													
f. How to know that it is love													
3. Courtship													
a. Purposes of courtship													
b. Accepted practices in courtship													
c. Length of courtship													
4. The engagement													
a. Purposes													
b. How long it should be													
c. Customs of engagement													
d. Behavior during engagement													
e. What the couple should discuss in relation to their future marriage													
f. Education for marriage for the couple													
g. Marriage counseling for the couple													
5. Laws regulating marriage													
a. Legal requirements for marriage													
b. Variations of laws among states													
6. The premarital examination													
a. The state-required examination													

TABLE 4 (continued)

Topics	General Science	Biology	Home Economics	Social Studies	Health Education	Physical Education	Literature	Psychology	Vocational Agriculture	Guidance	Extracurricular Activities	School Health Services	Healthful School Environment
b. The general health examination													
c. Corrections before marriage of discovered defects													
H. Adjustments in Marriage													
1. Basic human needs of marriage partners													
2. Adjustments within the marriage													
a. Personality adjustments													
b. Social and cultural adjustments													
c. Economic adjustments													
3. Sources of conflict within the marriage													
4. Crises in the family													
5. Social problems related to marriage													
a. Unhappy homes; desertion					—								
b. Annulments; divorce													
c. Effect of children													
6. Agencies that can help													
I. Preparation for Parenthood													
1. The meaning and responsibilities of parenthood													
2. Family planning													
3. How life begins													
a. Fertilization													
b. Signs of pregnancy													
c. Duration of pregnancy													
d. Superstitions related to pregnancy													
4. Prenatal medical examinations: general, state required													

TABLE 4 (continued)

Topics	Subject or Program												
	General Science	Biology	Home Economics	Social Studies	Health Education	Physical Education	Literature	Psychology	Vocational Agriculture	Guidance	Extracurricular Activities	School Health Services	Healthful School Environment
5. The care of the mother during pregnancy													
6. The birth of the baby													
a. The birth process													
b. The care of the newborn													
c. Birth registration													
7. Good infant care: periodical medical checkups, diet, immunization, clothing													

subjects and programs lend themselves in some degree to correlation since emphasis in this area is on attitudes and conduct as well as on facts.

The Contribution of Various Subject Areas

A brief summary is here given about the contribution that potentially exists in various subject and program areas of the elementary and secondary schools.

ART

The art program can contribute in its own special way through encouraging children to show, through drawings or paintings, their ideas of bird and animal family life, rearing of young, building nests, and many other facets of family living.

The E. C. Brown Trust Foundation has carried out an interesting study [1] through children's art in relation to their views of certain aspects of sex education.

[1] E. C. Brown Trust Foundation, "Children's Art and Human Beginnings," *The Family Life Coordinator,* July–October, 1967. Reprint 8 pp. Primary school teachers are encouraged to obtain a copy of the interesting report. It is available from Professor Curtis E. Avery, E. C. Brown Trust Foundation, University of Oregon, Eugene, Oregon.

In their early film, "Human Beginning," a little girl announced that she was "going to have a baby sister—or maybe a brother." The teacher and class jointly decided that they would make pictures of Susan's "sister" *before she was born*. They went to work with a will, resulting in a collection of art work that displayed a fascinating variety of misconceptions about human reproduction, and reflected an equally fascinating variety of feelings and attitudes associated with the subject. Lee, a disturbed child, came through with a picture of a mother with no arms or legs because "she didn't love her baby."

To expand on the above plan, for a new film more pictures were needed and so a number of teachers were asked to have children in grades one through three draw or paint their answers to either the question, "Where was I before I was born?" or "What did I look like before I was born?"

This experiment was a sort of projective technique based on the theory that children might, in this way, unconsciously reveal ideas, feelings, and attitudes they would not be willing or able to reveal consciously or verbally.

The Brown Trust Foundation suggests that an art project along these lines may be of inestimable value in at least two ways. The first is in stimulating interest and in opening the way for open discussion and the answers to questions perhaps long buried in the subconscious. The second value is the insight this approach provides the teacher concerning individual needs of her pupils.

BIOLOGY AND GENERAL SCIENCE

In biology and general science we have the logical places for the study of the biological aspects of sex education. Included would be the anatomy and physiology of animal, plant, and human reproduction, the endocrine glands, and heredity. School museums and local community museums can be very helpful to children in understanding certain aspects of reproduction. Also, a large number of simple experiments can be performed to help the pupils understand some of the processes involved in growth and development. Here follows a brief description of a few such experiments:

1. The germination of seeds and the transfer of pollen to the pistil of the flower and plant which bears the seeds can be performed.
2. Reproduction in animal life may be studied with a glass bowl of fish in the classroom.
3. In the spring, frogs' eggs may be kept in water, and the children can watch the development of the eggs into tadpoles, and then from tadpoles into frogs.
4. Turtle eggs can be hatched in warm sand in a box on the window ledge.

5. A pair of canaries in a cage in the schoolroom for younger children furnishes a valuable demonstration of the laying of the eggs, sitting on the eggs until they hatch, and the feeding and care of the little birds.

6. A chick embryology experiment is very enlightening, interesting, and easy to perform. It requires the incubation of a sufficient number of fertilized chicken eggs so that one can be opened and examined each day. The children can observe the day-by-day growth and development. Generally, the experiment should be concluded after the twelfth day, for at this point the chick's features are fully developed with the exception of the majority of its feathers.

7. Through the dissection of chickens, children can be shown that the actual organs of an animal are not too different from those of themselves. This can be done in almost any grade from third on up. All the basic facts are studied in the chicken and then a comparison is made with the human. The chicken is used because it is fairly easy to obtain, and it has few emotional connotations for children. In addition, it is important for children to understand that, despite great superficial differences, all living things share similar needs, functions, and structure, and it is very helpful to be able to refer to the chicken as something the children know a great deal about when discussing human biology.

ENGLISH

It is in the literature classes where children and youth sometimes first meet some of the facts of life in an educational setting under the guidance of a teacher. Children are seldom shocked by what they find in literature about sex and family life, for they have read newspapers and other materials as well.

Some English teachers have prepared lists of suggested readings for their classes. Especially at the secondary school level has this procedure been found of value. Class discussions can often be centered around, or at least included in, discussions about aspects of family life portrayed in a book— whether it deals with an earlier generation or the present one.

HEALTH EDUCATION

The health education curriculum from grades one through twelve lends itself best to the inclusion of most aspects of family life education. This point is amply indicated by the grade outlines in health education and in the content of textbooks, as well as the type of teaching material available.

A detailed examination of several health education series for the elementary grades one through eight show the following: In the early grades the emphasis is on attitudes and experiences within the family unit that develop the child into a would-be responsible parent and family member.

Some of the series include the biological aspects of sex education as well. In others, this aspect is limited, though the teacher's edition includes it. Junior and senior high school health texts contain a considerable amount on the biological and health aspects and often on other aspects of family life education.

In the secondary school program of health education, it is recommended that there be a health course in each of the junior and senior high school levels. Such courses ordinarily should include ten major units, as follows: personal health, nutrition, community and environmental health, consumer health, mental and emotional health, drugs and drug abuse, family living and sex education, safety, first aid, and home nursing. In a semester course of ninety class periods, the unit on family living could justifiably include about fifteen class periods at each of the two levels.

HOME ECONOMICS AND HOMEMAKING

Homemaking courses are taught in the upper years of high school. Topics comprising family living included in such courses are boy-girl relations, clothing and personal grooming, everyday food problems of the teenager, housing problems of concern to high school students, learning to understand children, living together in the family, looking toward marriage, personal and family finances, and personality development.

PHYSICAL EDUCATION

Ordinarily, content is not taught in physical education classes. However, since physical education classes are normally segregated by sex, those topics that an instructor finds difficult to present in a mixed class, such as menstruation and emissions, might be discussed in physical education.

Opportunities occur in this area for encouraging the development of wholesome attitudes and, to a certain extent, practices. Also, co-physical education, when appropriately taught, can be of help in developing wholesome recreational skills of interest to both sexes.

See the Appendix, pp. 402–409, for a consideration of physical activities appropriate for the girls with problems of menstruation.

The physical education teacher has a greater opportunity to learn to know his students than is possible in most other subject areas. Consequently, he tends to have more opportunities for individual and group counseling in the area of sex education as well in other areas of personal needs.

PSYCHOLOGY AND GUIDANCE

Psychology as a separate subject is offered in a number of high schools. Some of the topics that can be included here are personality development, attitudes and motivation in general, adolescent conflicts, social behavior, family relations, and preparation for marriage. An examination of texts in psychology for this age level shows that a high percentage of the content is in the area of family living.

In a few high schools, courses are offered in the guidance department which include a large number of the topics found in Table 4.

The school psychologist, in his special role, will meet with many of the emotional and behavioral problems of sex.

SOCIAL STUDIES

In the social studies there are units on such topics as family living around the world, growing populations, marriage and divorce, family planning, adoption, law enforcement, and housing. In many of the units, questions may also arise about prostitution, venereal disease, and illegitimate children. Many additional topics are indicated in Table 3.

THE SCHOOL HEALTH SERVICE

It is the school nurse and the school physician who become aware of many of the problems arising out of misdirected sex behavior. They often see this before other members of the school staff. In their counseling, they have many opportunities to talk with youth about their personal problems. The nurse and the physician can be helpful in the class work in sex education if invited to participate at special times.

It is important that the school have a policy concerning the procedure for dealing with situations of pregnancies among girls in the school which answers the following questions:

1. Should a pupil be required to withdraw when she becomes noticeably pregnant—in or out of wedlock?
2. Should pregnant students be dropped from school?
3. Should such girls be placed in special classes?
4. Should a teacher or married student be required to withdraw when she becomes noticeably pregnant?
5. Whatever your school's policy, what is the reaction of parents to that policy?

Activities

1. Examine the Table 4 checklist and note the number of subjects which are indicated as potentially being able to contribute to sex education.

2. Carefully examine a textbook in some teaching field such as biology, general science, home economics, psychology, or social studies and indicate which topics listed in Table 4 are included. What additional topics in sex education are included? Submit a report concerning your findings.

3. Make a study for a particular grade in some school to determine the extent that sex education is integrated into its school program.

References

Barnard, J. Darrell, Celia Stendler, and Benjamin Spock, *The Macmillan Science Series,* The Macmillan Co., New York, 1966.

Brandwein, P., E. K. Cooper, P. E. Blackwood, and E. B. Hane, *Concepts in Science,* Harcourt, Brace & World, New York, 1966, 103 pp.

Burton, Maurice, *Animal Courtship,* Frederick A. Praeger, New York, 1953, 267 pp.

Douglass, Harl R., *The High School Curriculum,* The Ronald Press, New York, 1964, 696 pp.

E. C. Brown Trust Foundation, "Children's Art and Human Beginnings," University of Oregon, Eugene, Ore., 1967. A reprint from the *Family Life Coordinator,* July–October 1967, 8 pp.

Martin, W. Edgar, *The Teaching of General Biology in the Public Schools of the United States,* U.S. Government Printing Office, Washington, D.C., 1952, 46 pp.

Nelson, B. Henry, Editor, *The Integration of Educational Experience,* Fifty-Seventh Yearbook, National Society for the Study of Education, Part II, University of Chicago Press, Chicago, 1958, 479 pp.

Richardson, John S., *Science Teaching in Secondary Schools,* Prentice-Hall, Englewood Cliffs, N. J., 1957, 385 pp.

Schoel, Doris R., "Role of the School Nurse in Sex Education," *J. School Health,* May 1966, pp. 200–206.

Schoel, Doris R., "Sex Education, Family Living and Human Relations—An Integrative Program That Grows with Youth," *J. School Health,* March 1968, pp. 129–139.

Sorensen, Herbert, and Marguerite Malm, *Psychology of Living,* McGraw-Hill Book Co., New York, 1957, 672 pp.

Also see texts in health, home economics, social studies, and other subject areas.

7

Methods and Materials
for
Teaching Family Living

In sex education the methods of teaching that can be used are the same as those used in teaching of other subjects. However, because we, as teachers, need to develop in our pupils desirable *attitudes* and *behavior* as well as knowledge, the methods and materials in sex teaching must be given more careful consideration than in many other teaching areas. A corollary to this is that sex education requires a specially capable teacher who can and will use the appropriate method.

THE ACTIVITY PRINCIPLE

The teacher can never assume that certain experiences designed as learning experiences will actually result in learning. He can only set up and encourage those student activities which are best calculated to facilitate learning. *Teaching is done by the teacher, but learning is done by the student.*

Learning comes through experiences. Experiencing is the only way that we know in which learning can occur at all. Therefore, our problem as teachers in encouraging learning is to find out what students need to be experiencing day by day and class by class in order to give them the kind and quality of experiences that will result in maximal learning.

All learning comes through some sort of active response on the part of the learner. There are many degrees of activity and many types of response, *but there is no kind of learning without some sort of active response.*

Also *there is no learning without involvement.* The learner must be able to see *himself* in the situation or the lesson being presented. He must think: "Why, that's happened to me!" "I've wondered about that," "I have that problem too."

Pupils become involved emotionally when the problems that we present in our teaching and in our textbooks have counterparts in their own experience. And when we help children to see that what they are learning functions in their own lives by meeting their needs and interests, facts are more likely to be acted upon.

Any good elementary school classroom illustrates these activity principles in operation. The boys and girls are constantly doing something. The doing may consist of listening to a story read by the teacher, working arithmetic problems, making a map for a social studies class, viewing a film, drilling in word recognition, memorizing a segment of the multiplication tables, taking a field trip, reading silently or orally, or writing.

Because the activity principle in learning is so commonly associated with the elementary school, it is sometimes thought to be more appropriate there than in high school. But the activity concept can be applied with equal facility there also. It is true that the activities of the high school will often be somewhat more formalized and even intellectualized—partly because of tradition and partly because the greater maturity of the students makes it possible to use more abstract and more formalized teaching methods.

The help given by the teacher is dependent at every point upon the need of the pupil for assistance. If the pupil has the ability to choose objectives and activities wisely, and if he realizes their value the teacher has no function. But it should be reaffirmed with emphasis that all pupils some of the time, and some pupils all the time, will need the help of the teacher. The methods of assistance should, of course, be such as to increase the ability of the learner to stand alone continually.

THE DETERMINANTS OF HEALTH TEACHING METHOD

There is a definite relationship, on the one hand, between (1) the purpose of the teaching unit, that is, the educational outcomes desired, the type of pupil who is the potential learner, and certain classroom factors, and (2) the methods that should be used. Therefore, the following specific factors need to be considered in the choice of teaching methods:

Whether *the educational outcomes desired* are:
a. Primarily the acquisition of sex knowledge—the topic containing much factual, scientific information; or
b. Primarily the development of sex attitudes; or
c. Primarily the development of desirable sex behavior; or
d. A combination of one or more of the above—which is the more usual situation.

The type of pupils:
a. The age of the pupils.
b. The sex of the pupils.
c. The maturity of the pupils.
d. The preparation or background of the pupils on the given topic.
e. The interests of the pupils.
f. The rate of progress of the pupils.

Classroom factors:
a. The size of the class.
b. The amount of time available for the specific teaching topic.
c. The availability of source material for teaching.
d. The teaching environment.
e. The training and experience of the teacher.
f. Other factors.

THE CONDITIONS CONTRIBUTING TO THE THREE EDUCATIONAL OUTCOMES

The conditions that give significance and retention value to *knowledge* have been relatively well identified through studies and validated in good teaching procedures. Knowledge has high retention value when it is discovered and utilized by the learner as an essential means to the attainment of some desired purpose. The vast difference in moving power between facts merely stated and facts acquired by direct experience is what makes the things that actually happen in everyday living so valuable as learning situations in education.

The question of *attitude* is crucial—since the ultimate test of teaching success lies in the extent to which pupils become *willing* to practice voluntarily desirable sex behavior. Within the learner, a feeling of satisfaction and approval must be associated with the essential sex ideas and activities. To be effective in directing later voluntary individual or group behavior, the emotional vigor of the learning experience must be strong enough to outweigh the sacrifices and inconveniences which the desired sex behavior may involve.

This apparently simple requirement is far from easy to fulfill in the classroom for several reasons:

1. First of all, the prevailing school atmosphere is not conducive to exciting emotional experiences in sex education.
2. The effort in sex instruction in our secondary schools is not too carefully planned and skillfully executed.
3. Too many teachers in too many classes are teaching too many things about which pupils care little or nothing, or of which they are less in need.
4. The task of the teacher in attempting to promote desirable attitudes is often complicated by the number and character of the attitudes that children already have.

Students' attitudes toward sex education instruction in the secondary schools must be changed if their health needs are to be met. A favorable climate must be provided in the classroom to nourish the growth of effective sex attitudes among these students. Good teaching methods can help to change student attitudes and thereby contribute to meeting their needs.

The establishment of good habits, practices, and conduct demands something more than sitting in a classroom and reciting about such behavior. It is important that the learner understand clearly the nature of the activity to be practiced, as well as the time, place, and conditions that are associated with it. Classroom discussions and demonstrations are often very useful in setting the correct pattern to be practiced, but the necessary repetitions must for the most part be performed elsewhere.

TRADITIONAL TEACHING METHODS

The common, conventional methods in teaching are here listed first.

Methods Adapted to Educational Outcomes Desired

It has been stressed that teaching methods should be selected on the basis of whether the primary objective of the day's lesson or unit is the learning of facts, the development of attitudes, the growth of desirable sexual behavior, or the acquisition of skills. Usually a combination of two or more of these is the goal.

In the teaching of *knowledge,* facts, scientific information, etc., the methods found to be most valuable include the use of written materials, such as textbooks, which the student can read at his own pace and in his own privacy where concentration on the topic is needed. Often such text learning needs to be supplemented by information given by the teacher, either verbally or by using the blackboard, or by diagrams, models, and other means.

In the teaching of *attitudes,* more subtle means are involved. Ordinarily they cannot be taught directly. Knowledge does contribute but, in addition, there is the need for the example of the teacher, parent, and classmates to strengthen the attitude or to develop a favorable one. Also, since most attitudes involve "feeling," that is, emotions, these are often best portrayed through the use of films. In a good twenty-minute film on a sex behavior topic such as dating, more attitude learning can no doubt be effected than might be possible by the teacher lecturing or talking about it. Teaching methods that involve group discussion, group opinions, and group decisions are also valuable in attitude formation.

The teacher, in attempting to develop desirable sex behavior, habits, conduct, and practices in his pupils will need to rely on the example of himself and others in whom the class has faith.

The use of evaluation procedures, such as objective testing, is most helpful in those areas with considerable content. (See Chapter 9, "Evaluation of the Sex Education Program.")

Charts, exhibits, and posters are useful in getting across single ideas. They may serve either in imparting some fact or in affecting one's attitude.

This brief statement on teaching methods for knowledge, attitudes, and behavior has been presented to give the reader an awareness that such distinctions are necessary for effective planning of the overall school program in sex education.

Methods of Teaching Sex Education

Of the various methods of teaching previously listed, the following need special consideration in sex education.

QUESTIONS AND ANSWERS

If a child asks a question, it should usually be answered. Beginning in first grade, teachers are urged to create an atmosphere in which children will *feel free to ask questions,* and this method should be applied throughout the high school years as well. Question boxes are often used in the secondary schools; whether signed or unsigned, the teacher can answer the question frankly without reference to the person who submitted them.

The Child Study Association of America has listed five ways to help the parent and the child speak together more freely:

1. Be patient.
2. Be a good listener.
3. Keep your terms simple—gear your level to the child level of experience and understanding.
4. Be honest and consistent.
5. Above all, be yourself.

HOW TO ANSWER A YOUNG CHILD'S QUESTIONS

Knowing just how much to relate to the child is difficult. Kirkendall's statement could serve as a guide, however. He says: "In education of children and youth, full and complete information suitable to the development level is desirable."

Gradually, the ideas will sink in although the child may ask the same questions at different stages of his development. He may want confirmation of his hazy notions; or he may at a later time be ready for more details; or he may have forgotten what he was told earlier because at that time the facts were only of passing interest to him.

Sudden and complete knowledge during adolescence for those who knew little beforehand will come as an emotional shock. This is therefore an important reason for the little-by-little method from babyhood up in sex education.

It also is harder on parents to wait until adolescence and then do all the instructing at once—for at that age the child is more emotional, more secretive, and more unapproachable.

The big problem in answering children's questions has not been the attitude of the child but the inhibitions of the adult—parent or teacher.

There also are many parents and teachers faced with the problem of not knowing how to answer a child's questions in the area of sex.

Never be shocked by the questions of children whether you are a parent or a teacher. Neither should one laugh when the child's concepts are comically askew.

For the child who does not ask questions about sex but who shows normal curiosity about other things, it is highly doubtful that he lacks curiosity about this subject. It is more likely that he has tapped another source of information, in which case it might be well for us, as parents, to broach the subject to him.

GROUP METHODS

Group method is the basic method of democratic socialization, and it is the framework in which the individual can improve himself as a contributing member of a class, group, or society. The use of group discussion—leading to decision making—enables individuals within the group to accept new ideas, since these ideas may have group sanction behind them. Also, as one writer has put it, "that which one has helped to plan is not easily put aside." Here are listed the more common techniques in which there is participation in small or large groups by an audience or class.

Group Discussion. Group discussion provides for student oral participation toward the resolution of a problem or question. Discussion may proceed with or without active teacher direction, but ordinarily some degree of moderating is employed to guide the thinking of the group. The method allows clarification of certain aspects of a presentation and stimulates thinking and expression.

Lecture-Discussion. This method utilizes both the lecture and discussion techniques during the same class period. It incorporates desirable qualities of both lecture and discussion when functionally utilized.

Committee Work. This technique consists of dividing the class members into designated groups to accomplish concentrated group study or research on a particular topic or unit of work. It stimulates group action and improves relations among students.

Role Playing or Sociodrama. This is a spontaneous, unrehearsed, and on-the-spot acting out of a problem or situation by selected students presented before the group. Role playing provides the student with means of gaining insight into his roles in relation to others. It offers on-the-spot opportunity to try out new ways of behaving in the light of such insight in an atmosphere where mistakes can be made without suffering the penalties of real-life situations.

The Lecture. The lecture was one of the first methods used in teaching. Through lecturing an attempt is made to teach by the use of verbal language with little student participation. It can be used to impart knowledge, create interest, influence opinion, stimulate activity, or promote critical thinking, and is one of the best methods for the comprehensive presentation of material. The method may or may not be followed by a question period or be supplemented by the use of a film or other technique.

There has been criticism of the lecture method in the teaching of sex education because it is considered to be an authoritative way of setting forth principles. The teacher or lecturer is likely to be the only active participant when this method is used exclusively. However, there are times when a professional person can supplement the regular teaching with a lecture on a specific topic such as on etiquette or dating problems.

The Use of Outside Speakers. The utilization of a well-informed specialist from the community to talk to the students about, or discuss with them, some relevant issue or subject on which he is an expert is common. It is an excellent method of obtaining information and assuring understanding from a practical viewpoint. It has limitations, however.

The experts on sex education brought into the school system often represent medicine, science, the clergy, and people representing certain specific manufacturers of needs of individuals at the age level of the group.

Bringing in outside speakers can often do more harm than good in serving to arouse concern of the elementary children in the incorrect manner of the educational process.

In the secondary school, however, it is an accepted practice to ask an authority on certain issues to speak on his knowledge of issue involved. Many times a woman will come into the school to speak on the different aspects of menstruation and to show a movie to illustrate the natural happenings of the phenomenon.

The use of outside lecturers—formerly the most frequently used of all approaches—is now generally disapproved by authorities in sex education and, as commonly used, properly so. In too many instances, a lecturer is brought in as an extraneous feature rather than as an integral part of a planned educational program. This method appears under conditions which make the whole arrangement seem surreptitious and furtive to the pupils.

A speaker can do little to build desirable attitudes under the circumstances under which he usually must speak. Lectures are necessarily short— fifty minutes possibly. He may impart some new and needed information, but the general attitude which results is that sex is something one cannot discuss like other topics, and something with which the school authorities cannot, and will not, concern themselves directly. This leaves little time for questions, discussion, or interchange of opinions, and none for individual work with pupils. The information is given in one concentrated dose to excited and self-conscious pupils. One lecture by an outside authority is almost valueless in correcting or expanding interest beyond the more obvious aspects.

The use of an outside speaker or discussion leader tends to shift all responsibility for sex education from the shoulders of school authorities. The result is that such education is given only in concentrated doses and periodically. Since good speakers on sex education are found infrequently, most communities do not have any. The foregoing arguments are against using the outside speaker as a method of sex education in preference to other possible methods.

If the question is whether to utilize a lecturer or do nothing, then the choice should be to use the lecturer. Some lecturers do excellent work and achieve good results provided proper arrangements are made in advance.

Problem-Solving Techniques. Problem solving is the technique of arriving at the best solution to a problem having more than one possible answer, which point applies especially to sex behavior as based on a value system. The use of this method stimulates the development of deeper values, understanding, judgment, and decision making. It promotes group discussion and provides for practice of democratic procedure. Methods in which problem-solving techniques are used include projects, surveys, exploration, demonstrations, laboratory experiments, and field trips.

The use of science experiments is given more consideration in Chapter 6, "Integration and Correlation."

Vocabulary Emphasis. It is important that the class develop a good vocabulary in this field, as well as in other areas. Textbooks often italicize new words or list them at the end of a chapter or in other ways call attention to them. Teachers can also list important words on the blackboard. Correct spelling as well as meaning should be stressed.

This topic is sufficiently important to the development of programs in sex education in the schools and at home that a separate chapter is being devoted to it (Chapter 8).

MATERIALS OF SEX EDUCATION

Materials as here used mean all instructional aids in the form of printed and multisensory materials and objects of various kinds which can contribute to the development of a sound program of sex instruction. Visual and printed material, while valuable, ought to be supplementary to a complete educational program.

Selected *teaching devices* are often needed to open the way for discussion, particularly early in a course or unit, and before the students have gotten over some of their initial reticence. Educational films are very helpful—especially if they deal with the human-relations aspect of sex behavior or with physical development. Current news items and episodes in movies and plays often provoke worthwhile introductory discussions.

Certain procedures help in obtaining the maximum value from books, pamphlets, literature, and films. Any printed material or film used in teaching should first be read or seen by the school authorities and, most of all, by the teacher. These people can then, if it is found acceptable, adapt the material to the level of the pupils and develop teaching devices to fit the content.

A book, pamphlet, or film may appear to be too far advanced for a particular school or community. In such cases, however, the question of readiness usually involves the school authorities and the parents rather than the youth. Even with readiness on the part of adults, the need for taste and discrimination in the selection of material still exists. One would wish to use material which would contribute to the long-time good adjustment of youth, and serve to stabilize marriage and family life.

Materials for Reading Assignments. Reading assignments, as a method of teaching and learning, is probably the one most commonly used in the schools today in most subjects.

Assignments can be adapted to individual ability and can be geared to individual learning speed. Printed material is especially necessary for learning in the more technical areas. It promotes and stimulates thinking and understanding. Such material can be classified as follows:

Textbooks and readers.
Supplementary reading materials including:

Reference books	Leaflets	Workbooks
Magazines	Guides	Newspapers
Pamphlets	Handbooks	Comics
Bulletins		

The use of one of the fine texts written for adolescents on education for family living is recommended for the high school level. There are also a number of helpful, well-written pamphlets for this age level. Extensive use of additional reading and reporting on books and articles which stimulate thinking in this area is strongly recommended.

In order to assure a wider use of the books, definite procedures for popularizing their circulation is desirable. The English teacher can include the books on recommended reading lists. The school librarian and the city librarian can also compile a joint bibliography of books on sex education, dating, marriage, and family life, and make them available to all pupils. Librarians should call the attention of both teachers and pupils to available books, pamphlets, and periodicals.

Committees of pupils at the secondary level can be used in making selections of books and pamphlets in sex education. Pupils might announce the arrival of new books in the library.

Once pupils realize that books relating to sex education and pertinent subjects are readily available and that interest in them is regarded as natural and normal, they will be accepted and used freely. The likelihood of the books being undesirably marked or stolen will be reduced.

Books recommended for various age levels are listed in the Appendix.

Visual Aids. Materials classified as visual aids, often used simultaneously with verbal presentation by the teacher, include the following:

Blackboard	Posters	Health mobile
Charts	Filmstrips	Microscopic slides
Graphs	Flash cards	Lantern slides
Tables	Cartoons	Mirrors
Maps	Comic strip drawings	Bulletin board
Drawings	Exhibits	Flannel board
Pictures	Displays	Magnetic board
Photographs	Museums	Collections
Paintings	Fairs	Opaque projection

Audiovisual (Multisensory) Aids. Under this heading are those educational methods which help learning through the senses of seeing and hearing by the use of projection and recording equipment.

Motion pictures	Radio programs
Filmstrips with sound recordings	Television programs
Tape recordings	Puppets

Films often are used without any attendant instruction. These media, which leave the school authorities personally uninvolved, are sometimes made to carry the whole program. It would, however, be a very incomplete program if all of the other ways of teaching the subject were not also used.

Models and Objects. Included here are objects that can be seen, handled, and examined. They are three dimensional and are commonly used in science teaching. The more common examples are:

Models—anatomical and others	Specimens
Mannequins	Make-ups
Real objects	

Models and charts of the reproductive and endocrine systems are very desirable teaching aids. Preserved specimens of animal embryos are used in many biology laboratories and might be borrowed for use in other classes.

Sources of such materials of instruction are listed in biological equipment catalogs. A list of such commercial companies is included in the Appendix.

INDIVIDUAL COUNSELING

Individual student problems cannot all be considered in regular class situations. Therefore, there is great need for opportunity for individual conferences to deal with unique circumstances. Undoubtedly, every pupil could benefit by such help.

The interview or conference with an individual for the purpose of offering information and guidance is one of the most effective teaching methods. The individual has the opportunity to state his problems, fears, and symptoms and has the benefit of personal consideration of them by an expert. Thus, he feels that the counsel or guidance is definitely fitted to his personal problems and, as a result, is more apt to follow such teachings or counsel. This method should be an integral part of any program in sex education.

As the only method, individual counseling has some very serious limitations: only a small number of pupils can be reached because of inadequate time; some pupils who need help may be excluded for a variety of reasons. Often the instructor does not recognize those most in need of help, or is not able to establish a satisfactory rapport so that the needed discussions can take place. Some who need help do not recognize it themselves. And some who do realize that they need such counseling are hesitant to come to the teacher.

Pupils also benefit considerably from the interchange of ideas that occurs through *group* discussions—and this applies particularly to the topics of sex behavior, dating, and preparation for marriage.

Regardless of the advantages of group education about sex and sexuality, there is need for some provision for pupil counseling. For teachers who desire to help pupils with their individual, personal problems, there are several points to consider:

1. The teacher needs to acquire an adequate understanding of the psychological and sociological aspects of sex as well as the biological.
2. With counseling, the pupil is more able to understand his own sexual adjustment and will settle his own individual problems to the extent that he is not in emotional conflict.
3. The pupil gets the experience of talking over his problems of sex adjustment with an objective, mature teacher.

Through these several procedures, the pupil will develop his own ability to talk more objectively with his peer group.

It is also desirable that the teacher have this ability, because if he speaks haltingly and with confusion and embarrassment regarding sex, he should avoid counseling in this field. If, on the other hand, he teaches well a class in which sex adjustments and preparation for marriage are discussed, that teacher will be sure to have requests from individuals in the group.

In order that a pupil be willing to discuss freely such intimate matters of personal adjustment, he must feel that the teacher, in the role of a counselor, is friendly toward him, is attempting to understand him, and will accept him as an individual in the situation in which the counselor finds him.

The counselor should not make the pupil feel forced to discuss a personal problem about which he is too sensitive, at least for the time being. He should also not give the pupil the feeling that he is being hurried. The counselor, instead, should help the pupil to feel that it is not unique for him to have his given problems of personal adjustment. The pupil should be able to feel that the counselor understands such problems based on previous experience with other pupils.

Sometimes, the discussions with a counselor can be supplemented by offering the pupil a book or pamphlet on the problem as a way of looking at the problem more objectively. However, reading, as here suggested, although it is helpful in establishing good rapport, should not substitute for counseling. Readings or viewing certain films can help to open the way for objective discussion, in reducing feelings of shame or guilt, and for changing attitudes to some degree—but counseling is still greatly needed.

Finally, since adjustment to sex and sexuality is not a function at a particular stage in growth and development, but instead is a process which continues throughout life, it becomes important that the individual concerned be able to talk freely with someone when the need arises.

Through the processes of counseling, discussion, and class instruction, the schools can help youth to obtain an understanding and poise which, hopefully, will help them as adults to face their own problems wisely.

Good training in general counseling would be very valuable to all teachers and especially to those who also are in the field of sex education.

SEGREGATED VERSUS MIXED CLASSES

A very common error in the teaching of family life occurs when students are unnecessarily and conspicuously separated on the basis of sex. Coeducational classes are essential so that members of the opposite sex may better understand one another's viewpoint. Except when the division is a natural one and one with which the students are familiar and to which they are accustomed, it is unwise to segregate by sex for such teaching. A topic deemed desirable to teach separately can be presented in, for example, the physical education or home economics class.

One school for example, is coed through sixth grade in the teaching of sex education. Then, in seventh grade, films and lectures are together but the sexes are separated for questions.

Many teachers find it difficult or even impossible to teach about some of these topics to a mixed class. However, it has been shown that confidence comes with practice for both men and women teachers in teaching such a mixed group.

THE FUNCTION OF THE TEACHER

It is the function of the teacher in the education of the learner (1) to assist him to select objectives that are socially and individually desirable and that are attainable by him; (2) to help him to realize that these objectives are valuable to him and to lead him to accept them; (3) to guide him in choosing those activities and experiences that will enable him to attain the objectives set up; and (4) to help him to know when he has attained the objectives.

The content, methods, and activities used by the teacher, as well as the physical and social environment and the personality of the teacher, are all part of a unified experience. A child learns not only intellectually and verbally, but emotionally, physically, and socially. It is unrealistic, therefore, to seek an isolated "method" on the supposition that it can answer equally well for all phases of a child's learning experience.

Sex problems and their solutions need to be presented in a meaningful context that will eventually help the learner to see the biological, social, cultural, economic, and ethical implications of his actions in regard to sex and sexuality.

It is also important to realize (a) that nothing has been taught until something has been learned and (b) that learning will manifest itself in changed behavior.

Personal Example of Teachers. Children learn habits and attitudes including those related to sex and sexuality by observing adults and adult practices—including their teachers. Examples set by school staff members serve as one of the major instructional procedures of the school. In the same way, the physical and emotional environment of the school must be considered as a major learning aid.

The Teacher of Family Life Education. The feeling is held by those with experience in this field that a large proportion of people who are otherwise good teachers of children would also be good teachers in the area of family life education, if they were prepared. However, many teachers feel that they are unqualified to give such instruction to a mixed group, either from personal uneasiness over the subject or because they have acquired the idea that it is a highly technical subject for which they are ill-prepared.

Properly prepared teachers can approach the matter of teaching family life with a greater degree of objectivity and without embarrassment. Often the pupils are embarrassed for their teacher as much as by the topic under discussion.

Many teachers colleges are today offering courses in this field for the classroom teacher. Also many schools give in-service courses in this area.

The reason for inadequacies in sex education is to be found in the teachers themselves. Many teachers and school administrators are emotionally unprepared or unable to teach the subject or administer programs concerning it. It is obvious that teacher selection cannot be based solely on the teacher's capacity to deal with one or more controversial subjects. It seems that the ability to handle such subjects—correlated with emotional maturity, his own beliefs, and preconceptions—must be criteria used as important aspects in the selection of teachers.

It would seem that the way or manner in which teachers handle such a subject as sex education is a better test of their capacity to teach in this area.

We must have teachers who can handle this subject either without revealing their own biases and their own fears, or without imposing these on their students. How to accomplish this is a problem yet to be adequately faced in teacher candidate selection and preparation.

The teacher of sex education might have the potential for promoting as much harm in the area of child mental health as good if this sensitive area is not well understood and approached with the caution, respect, and delicacy which it certainly deserves.

Teachers dealing with sex instruction in the school are in a critical position to establish or undermine the true success of the sex education curriculum.

The individual teacher must possess knowledge of the feelings of the clergy, the school administration, and the people of the community.

No matter how scientific and impartial the material on sex education in present-day textbooks may be, it is manifestly impossible to present objective data wholly objectively. In fact, it is not open to question as to whether it is desirable, particularly at early school-age levels, to present data and to permit the students to draw conclusions from the data. The students find it difficult to handle and to interpret the new data. It is the place of the teacher to enlighten the students to the desirable interpretation and the action which they should follow in order to be good citizens. This, of course, places an enormous burden and challenge on the teacher.

The teacher must be in possession not only of material knowledge but also the correct ethical and moral concepts of the material knowledge in the light of the religions involved, or rather represented, in the class in which he teaches. As far as sex education is concerned, the moral issues should contribute and aid in alleviating problems which the adults and community leaders have been trying to face.

Activities

1. Collect a list of questions about sex and sexuality which children and youth ask.

2. From one of the questions from Activity 1, prepare your idea of what to answer the child or youth. Include some background about the child such as age, sex, degree of maturity, grade in school, his previous background in sex education, and the parent relationships which determine the setting in which the question is asked and might be answered. State whether your answer would be to the individual or to him as part of a group such as his class.

3. Investigate what outside speakers might be available in your local teaching area to speak on some selected topics of sex education. What would you do to prepare the class for such a visit?

4. Prepare a list of readings (books and pamphlets) for a specific class or age level. Rank these in the order in which you recommend their use by the pupils. Also prepare a short annotation of twenty-five to fifty words about each.

5. Review several motion pictures or filmstrips that deal with some aspect of sex education. Prepare a report giving full information about the audiovisual aid and your judgment as to the age or grade range for which you think it is suited. Do you recommend that the parents see it as well?

6. As in Activity 5, review a recording in sex education and prepare a report.

References

American Association of Colleges for Teacher Education, *Teacher Education and Media—1964* (a selective annotated bibliography), 1201 Sixteenth Street, N.W., Washington, D.C., 1964, 49 pp.

Edling, Jack V., *The New Media in Education,* Office of Education, U.S. Department of Health, Education, and Welfare, Washington, D.C., 1960, 99 pp.

Erickson, Carlton W. H., *Fundamentals of Teaching with Audiovisual Technology,* The Macmillan Co., New York, 1965, 384 pp.

Humphrey, James H., Warren R. Johnson, and Virginia D. Moore, *Elementary School Health Education: Curriculum, Methods and Integration,* Harper & Row, New York, 1962, 390 pp.

Lobb, M. Delbert, *Practical Aspects of Team Teaching,* Fearon Publishers, Palo Alto, Calif., 1964, 60 pp.

Mann, Hannah, *The Use of Psychodrama in Health Education,* Carlton Press, New York, 1961.

Patter, David, J. Joel Moss, and Herbert F. A. Smith, *Photosituations: A Technique for Teaching,* Burgess Publishing Company, Minneapolis, 1963, 114 pp.

School Health Education Study, *Sample Teaching-Learning Guides and Supplementary Instructional Materials,* Washington, D.C., 1965.

8

The Vocabulary
for Sex Education

The development of a scientific vocabulary is one of the important ob-jectives of sex education. Sex education has its own language. It includes the names of the reproductive organs and their functions and products, words to describe sexual behavior and relations, and many other names pertaining to sexuality.

Learning the correct words should be as easy as learning the correct names for other parts and processes of the human body, such as those related to digestion, respiration, or circulation. Learning the vocabulary of sex edu-cation should be no more difficult than learning the correct names for the parts of an automobile.

There is, however, one important difference between developing and using a correct vocabulary in sex education as compared to a vocabulary for other parts of the body. We have strong feelings about sex, including the feeling that some words are distasteful or "dirty" and that it is not "nice" to talk about sex.

These feelings are likely to put an emotional note into our discussion with our children which causes embarrassment and even inhibitions to both the adults and the children involved. This difference arises from the attitudes which we as parents and teachers acquired in our own childhood.

One fact cannot be escaped. Children will ask questions and they will learn—that is, they will develop some kind of a vocabulary, even though limited, of sex terms and meanings. How do children acquire a sex vocabulary?

How Sex Vocabularies Are Acquired

Most children and youth develop their vocabularies from some combination of the following four ways:

1. They coin their own words for various parts and functions of the reproductive and excretory systems as well as for other systems of the body. Occasionally this language is considered "cute."
2. Fathers and mothers, in answering children's questions, use words with meanings which they themselves acquired as they grew up. Most adults (ourselves), including parents, learned the popular language of sex, and even today the words of proper sex language sound strange to them (us) and they (we) don't know their meaning with certainty.
3. As children begin to associate with other children, they pick up new words, many of which are not socially acceptable or correct in meaning.
4. Parents may teach children the correct (or scientific) and commonly accepted terms.

Experts in childhood education and in sex education feel that the fourth method is the preferable one.

Reasons for Learning the Correct Terms

The use of correct scientific terms seems, in the long run, to be the most logical and desirable method. Here are several reasons for this view:

1. If children are to learn to respect (an attitude) their bodies and body functions and organs, they will need to know respectable and dignified words to use as they speak and ask questions.
2. Normal body functions—particularly as related to urination and defecation—are less likely to acquire undesirable, shameful, and dirty connotations if words which are associated with objective, unemotional discussion are used in the instruction about them.
3. Teaching the right words and the right facts early saves a lot of unlearning later. Even while they are still young, it is well that children know that there are correct words which can be used and which are not silly or "dirty."
4. When the child enters kindergarten or first grade and comes into contact with

many children, his baby talk applied to bodily parts and functions may embarrass him. The ability to use correct terms should make the transition from home to school a little easier. Children get along better after they have a common vocabulary.

5. It makes it easier for young people (and adults) to bridge the language barrier in talking to adults about sex matters. The inability to use correct language is illustrated by the twelve-year-old girl who confided to her mother that she was afraid to visit the doctor because she didn't know how to tell him about personal problems —she didn't know the words to use.

6. Parents and children can usually be much more objective—and therefore less emotional—about sex and its vocabulary if the correct terms are learned *before* the children have formed an emotional attitude toward sex. It is much easier to begin early with correct terminology than to wait until the children are entering puberty and adolescence.

7. When children are accustomed to calling the parts of the body by names accepted by their elders and to speaking of the body's functions from the very beginning as a matter-of-fact, decent thing, it becomes easier for them to ask—and the parents to answer—their sex questions.

Developing a Desirable Vocabulary

Here follow some suggestions for teachers and parents in the process of developing a better sex vocabulary for themselves and their children.

1. When dealing with our children's inevitable sex questions, we should employ the same open manner we use in answering questions about food, automobiles, or airplanes. Call the sex organs and other bodily parts and their functions by their right names, and speak of them as casually as you do about your arms, legs, hands, and face. The child may not always understand all these terms but they can be explained on a simple elementary level.

2. The most important thing of all is that the parents should feel comfortable and relaxed with the vocabulary they use. Some parents may feel more at ease with the expressions they used in their own childhood or with nursery terms. If you find that you are introducing a note of discomfort into your own talks with your children when using scientific words, perhaps you need to compromise by using the terms that you and your child feel at ease with while you gradually acquire the recommended vocabulary.

3. An unlearning process has to take place. As the teacher, the parent, or the pastor introduces new terms, care will have to be taken to use explanatory phrases and illustrations so that new words are correctly understood. The phrases and illustrations will have to be carefully selected and practiced.

4. Introducing synonyms gradually and using both the old term and the new one for a while, may help to make the transition more relaxed for all concerned. The "cute" word can often be used as one also describes and encourages the use of the proper words. The procedure is helpful when pairing such words as urinate with

"wee wee" and navel with "belly button." There is no harm actually in using both babyish talk as well as the scientific. This combination may be the simplest one for you as a teacher when you grow in this area of understanding. Some go so far as to advocate the use of such synonyms, regardless of how filthy or obscene they might be, when in the process of first teaching the new correct terms, but this seems questionable except possibly with a professional group in sex education.

5. One procedure in building attitudes is to *discuss* with children and youth the *reasons* for developing a scientific sex education vocabulary. It implies a more mature and objective attitude toward the topic of sex. Furthermore, pupils readily see that these abilities are called for under circumstances such as reading a scientific article, a visit to a doctor, the education of children, to hold a discussion with informed people, and to contribute to the solution of the problems of premarital and marital adjustment.

6. One method for building vocabulary, suggested by Kirkendall, is to use an anatomical chart to point out the various physical parts as the anatomical terms are used. The charts, being medical in nature, carry a certain prestige and make for objectivity. At the same time some behavior terminology can be taught. For example, in tracing the route of the sperm cells and explaining the production of semen, one might define masturbation by saying, "These sperm cells are ordinarily discharged in three different ways, by seminal emissions at night, often called "wet dreams," sexual intercourse, and masturbation. Masturbation occurs when the sexual organs are moved and stimulated by hand until semen is discharged." Thus the definition is given in a relatively objective setting, and not in reference to a particularized discussion of behavior. Later the glossary of terms might be mimeographed and given to the pupils.

7. Since some adults find it difficult to use new terms and expressions, it has been suggested that this problem be overcome by repeatedly using these terms in private. Reading sex education books aloud to self and to others will help teachers and parents verbalize words that they hesitate to use in talking to each other. Gradually a person comes to feel less shy and more comfortable. Children and teenagers will more likely lose their own shyness more quickly if their teacher displays an "at home-ness" in this kind of conversation.

8. With some parents, the most comfortable choice of language varies with the child's age. Parents may prefer to use the nursery terms when their children are younger and the more scientific ones later on. In any event, parents will want their children to learn the correct terms as the children gradually mature and need them.

9. Parents who have practiced using correct terms—such as navel, buttocks, vagina, and penis—in bathing and dressing their babies find that they lose their own self-consciousness as they practice using these words.

In conclusion, parents and teachers need to build a sex education vocabulary that is suitable for the age group with which they are concerned. Thereby they will be able to function more adequately and effectively in their respective roles.

TABLE 5. VOCABULARY CHECKLIST IN SEX EDUCATION

Word	Ages	1–3	4–5	6	7–8	9–11	12–14	15–17	18–22				
	Grade	PRE	K	1	2–3	4–6	7–9	10–12	COL-LEGE	ELEM. TEA.	PAR-ENTS	OTHER
Abortion													
Adolescence													
Adoption													
Adultery													
Afterbirth													
Amniotic sac													
Androgen													
Aphrodisiac													
Artificial insemination													
Autoerotic													
Bigamy													
Birth													
Birth control													
Birth marks													
Bisexual													
Bladder													
Breast													
Caesarean birth													
Castration													
Celibacy													
Cervix													
Chancre													
Change of life													
Childbirth													
Chromosomes													
Circumcision													
Climacteric (see menopause)													

It is here assumed that it is desirable that the following list of terms be understood by the average lay adult. The question then is that of determining the age (and the circumstances) at which the term should *first* be introduced to the average child or youth. The next need is that of determining the ages (and grades) at which the term should *progressively* be given more meaning and usage.

This table should be filled out as follows:

0—The term is not suitable for this age period because it is not pertinent, or because it is too difficult, or for other reasons.

1—The term can now be used on occasion in its simplest meaning within the comprehension of the child.

2—The term can be used more regularly by the individual with more technical meaning being given to the term.

3—The term should now be understood correctly to the extent that a lay person needs to understand the term for his own reading and for possible use with his own (and other) children and youth.

TABLE 5 (continued)

Word	Ages	1–3	4–5	6	7–8	9–11	12–14	15–17	18–22				
	Grade	PRE	K	1	2–3	4–6	7–9	10–12	COL-LEGE	ELEM. TEA.	PAR-ENTS	OTHER
Clitoris													
Coitus													
Colostrum													
Common law													
Conception													
Condom													
Congenital													
Continence													
Contraception													
Copulation													
Corpus luteum													
Courtship													
Criminal abortion													
Defecation													
Delivery													
Diaphragm													
Divorce													
Douches													
Dysmenorrhea													
Ectopic													
Egg													
Ejaculation													
Electra complex													
Emasculate													
Embryo													
Emission													
Endocrine gland													
Engagement													
Epididymis													
Erection													
Erogenous zone													
Erotic													
Estrogen													
Eugenics													
Eunuch													
Exhibitionism													
Extramarital													
Fallopian tubes													
Family planning													
Feces													
Female													
Femininity													

TABLE 5 (continued)

Word	Ages 1–3	4–5	6	7–8	9–11	12–14	15–17	18–22			
Grade	PRE	K	1	2–3	4–6	7–9	10–12	COL-LEGE	ELEM. TEA.	PAR-ENTS	OTHER
Fertile											
Fertility											
Fertilization											
Fetishism											
Fetus											
Follicle											
Foreplay											
Foreskin											
Fornication											
Frigidity											
Gene											
Genitals											
Germ cell											
Gestation											
Gland											
Glans penis											
Gonad											
Gonorrhea											
Graafian follicle											
Gynecologist											
Heredity											
Hermaphrodite											
Heterosexuality											
Homosexuality											
Hormones											
Hymen											
Hysterectomy											
Illegitimacy											
Implantation											
Impotence											
Impregnation											
Incest											
Infertility											
Intercourse											
Interstitial cells											
Invert											
Labia majora											
Labia minora											
Labor											
Lactation											
Lesbian											

TABLE 5 (continued)

Word	Ages	1–3	4–5	6	7–8	9–11	12–14	15–17	18–22	COL-LEGE	ELEM. TEA.	PAR-ENTS	OTHER
	Grade	PRE	K	1	2–3	4–6	7–9	10–12					
Libido													
Love													
Maidenhead													
Males													
Mammary glands													
Marriage													
Masculinity													
Masochism													
Masturbation													
Maternity													
Meiosis													
Menarche													
Menopause													
Menstrual cycle													
Menstruation													
Miscarriage													
Mitosis													
Monilia													
Monogamy													
Mons veneris													
Multiple births													
Mutation													
Narcissism													
Navel													
Nocturnal emission													
Nursing													
Nymphomania													
Obscene													
Obstetrician													
Oedipus complex													
Onanism													
Oophorectomy													
Oral eroticism													
Orgasm													
Ovary													
Oviduct													
Ovulation													
Ovum (pl. ova)													
Parents													
Paresis													
Parthenogenesis													

TABLE 5 (continued)

Word	Ages	1–3	4–5	6	7–8	9–11	12–14	15–17	18–22			
	Grade	PRE	K	1	2–3	4–6	7–9	10–12	COL-LEGE	ELEM. TEA.	PAR-ENTS	OTHER
Parturition												
Pederasty												
Pedophilia												
Penis												
Perversion												
Petting												
Pituitary												
Placenta												
Polyandry												
Polygamy												
Polygyny												
Pornography												
Postpartum												
Potent												
Precocious sexuality												
Pregnancy												
Premarital relations												
Premature birth												
Prenatal												
Prepuce												
Progesterone												
Promiscuous (Promiscuity)												
Prophylactic												
Propagation												
Prophylaxis												
Prostate												
Prostitute												
Prostitution												
Prudish												
Puberty												
Rape												
Reproduction												
Rhythm method												
Sadism												
"Safe period"												
Scrotum												
Secondary sex characteristics												
Seduction												
Semen												
Seminal vesicles												
Seminiferous tubules												

TABLE 5 (continued)

Word	Ages	1–3	4–5	6	7–8	9–11	12–14	15–17	18–22 COL-LEGE	ELEM. TEA.	PAR-ENTS	OTHER
	Grade	PRE	K	1	2–3	4–6	7–9	10–12				
Sex												
Sex drive												
Sex gland												
Sex hormone												
Sex organ												
Sexual inadequacy												
Sexual intercourse												
Sexual outlet												
Sibling												
Sodomy												
Somatic												
Sperm (spermatozoon)												
Sperm duct												
Spermatogenesis												
Spermatozoon												
Spirochete												
Sterility												
Sterilization												
Sublimation												
Syphilis												
Tampons												
Testicle												
Testis (pl. testes)												
Testosterone												
Transsexualism												
Transvestism												
Trichomoniasis												
Twins												
Umbilical cord												
Umbilicus												
Urethra												
Urination												
Urologist												
Uterine tube												
Uterus												
Vagina												
Vaginitis												
Vas deferens (ductus deferens)												
Vasectomy												
Venereal disease												
Virginity												

TABLE 5 (continued)

Word	Ages	1–3	4–5	6	7–8	9–11	12–14	15–17	18–22				
	Grade	PRE	K	1	2–3	4–6	7–9	10–12	COL-LEGE	ELEM. TEA.	PAR-ENTS	OTHER	
Voyeurism													
Vulva													
Wassermann test													
"Wet dreams"													
Womb													
X chromosome													
Y chromosome													
Zygote													

Vocabulary Arrangements in This Book

Attention is given in this book to a sex education vocabulary in the following ways:

1. Table 5, "Vocabulary Checklist in Sex Education," contains over 200 words. Included are simple words for preschool and elementary school children, more difficult words for the secondary school level, and a few less commonly used words that at least the parents and teachers might be expected to understand and be able to use.

2. A glossary for use by the readers is included in the Appendix. It consists of most of the words in Table 5. Omitted are some of the obvious words used with small children.

3. Less common technical words, used in Part II, are described there.

4. The index makes reference to all terms used in this text.

Activities

1. Using Table 5, check in the column marked "Other" those terms which you personally do not fully understand. Then check their definitions by means of the glossary or some other source.

2. In the column marked "Elementary Teacher," check all the terms which you believe such a teacher ought to understand and be able to use when the occasion arises.

3. In the column marked "Parent," check all the terms which you believe parents ought to understand and be able to use with their children as they grow up.

4. Prepare a word list with its appropriate definitions for a particular age group or grade.

5. Prepare a lesson plan which concerns the development of vocabulary in sex education for a specific grade level.

6. Prepare a list of terms used by children at home and match them with the correct and scientific counterparts.

References

Witty, Paul, and Edith Grotberg, *Developing Your Vocabulary*, Science Research Associates, Chicago, 1968, 96 pp.

CHAPTER

9

Evaluation of
Sex Education Programs

In this chapter, attention will be given to the measurement and evaluation of the educational outcomes of the school sex education program since they are primarily the responsibility of the teacher. These educational outcomes are grouped into the three areas which have been stressed—namely, knowledge, attitudes, and behavior, as discussed in Chapter 2.

Evaluation is here defined as the process of determining the value or amount of success in achieving a predetermined objective. Evaluation should be based on the objectives of the program. Included are usually the following steps: formulation of the objectives, identification of the proper criteria to be used in measuring success, determination and explanation of the degree of success, measurement, implications for replanning and reevaluation.

Of the three types of educational outcomes of sex instruction, the most important one to achieve is the development and practice of desirable behavior, habits, and conduct. It is important that evaluation techniques be used to determine progress in this area, although it should be recognized that it is difficult for teachers to measure objectively the effect of education on the development and improvement of behavior. Attitudes are even more difficult to measure objectively. It is only knowledge that can be tested with a fair degree of accuracy. We must assume that the best we can do for the present is to test the effectiveness of our teaching of facts in the hope that we, as teachers, can furnish through these facts combined with our method of instruction, the incentives which will lead to correct and desirable attitudes and behavior.

Measurement in Relation to Evaluation

Evaluation of the effectiveness of an instructional program is a complex task which may involve the use of many kinds of evidence from different sources. Evaluation is impossible without the use of some kind of measurement. In its most elementary form, it involves nothing more than the observation that Student A possesses more of a defined characteristic than does Student B. If this statement can be verified independently by another observer, a useful measurement has been made.

Evaluation first requires the use of measurement techniques, and then adds a value judgment concerning the worth of the quantity or quality measured. Measurement may tell "how much"; evaluation may tell "how good." We cannot say *how good* an educational program is without knowing *how much* it has achieved of certain objectives. Evaluation goes beyond measurement in another respect—it sets different standards for different individuals and different standards for different schools. What represents a high achievement for one student may represent a low achievement for another and a relatively mediocre achievement for a third. But we have no basis for deciding whether a pupil's achievement is "good" or "poor" without knowing first *how much* he has achieved.

It is important to realize, in evaluating the educational outcomes of pupils, that one cannot be sure to what extent the sex education program should be credited with any or all improvements, since other factors are involved such as home and community environments.

Techniques for studying changes in pupils vary depending upon whether the teacher is primarily concerned with changes in knowledge, attitudes, or behavior. Although these aspects of learning are closely related, certain procedures measure one aspect more effectively than others. The more informal and subjective methods have a place in evaluating individual and group progress toward many goals of the educational program, as well as the objective methods.

Perhaps the simplest and most direct approach to the measurement of personal-social adjustment is to *ask* the student about his sex behavior, feelings, and attitudes. Such approaches, however, involve several assumptions: (1) that sufficient *rapport* has been established to permit him to describe and explain his behavior, feelings, and attitudes frankly and honestly; (2) that his responses are not distorted or misinterpreted because of difficulties in *communication;* and (3) that he has *insight* into his own behavior, feelings, and attitudes.[1]

The most common evaluation and measuring instruments or procedures used by teachers include observation, surveys, questionnaires, rating scales, self-evaluation scales, personal health inventory lists, interviews, diaries, and other autobiographical records kept by students, health records, case studies, and objective tests.

Tests of educational achievement provide an important basis for evaluating the effectiveness of an instructional program. The quality of a testing program depends upon the relevance of the tests chosen to the educational objectives of the school. Locally constructed tests are necessary to evaluate the specific and unique aspects of a local school's instructional program. Standardized tests or wide-scale testing programs can be used to evaluate progress toward the basic objectives which most schools have in common.

After the tests have been given and scored, the results must be interpreted competently and critically. *Norms,* reflecting what is true in general, must be distinguished from *standards,* which indicate what ought to be true in a particular case. It is as true of schools as it is of individuals that a performance which represents commendable achievement in one school (or class) may be a cause for serious concern in another.

Values of Measuring Sex Education Outcomes

The findings or interpretations obtained through a program of measuring the sex education outcomes can be of value in several ways. Most of those here presented apply especially to knowledge testing. However, with more refined procedures for determining sex attitudes and behavior, these same values of a testing program will also largely apply.

FOR MEASURING NEEDS AND PROGRESS OF PUPILS

A test can be administered at the beginning of a unit in a given grade to determine individual or group abilities or weaknesses in knowledge.

[1] George S. Adams, Theodore L. Torgerson, and Ernest R. Wood, Editors, *Measurement and Evaluation for the Secondary School Teacher,* Holt, Rinehart & Winston, New York, 1956, pp. 152–153.

Specific analysis of individual test items will identify concepts that are in need of special attention.

FOR MOTIVATING PUPIL LEARNING FOR HEALTH

An education test administered at the beginning of a course may help to show students that they are in need of learning certain facts and of applying them. Discussion is usually an important result of such testing procedures.

FOR EVALUATING TEACHING

An evaluation of sex instruction outcomes really becomes an evaluation of teaching. The teacher may use the difference between preliminary test results and final test results as a basis for appraising his own teaching efficiency.

Improvement in performance by students in knowledge, without a corresponding improvement in application, would suggest the need for greater teaching emphasis in the utilization of information already acquired by the students.

FOR GRADING STUDENTS

Test results of health knowledge may be used as a *partial* basis for pupil's marks. The thoughtful teacher will also use subjective judgment of the quality of each student's participating in class activities. Some teachers also consider his improvement in attitudes and habits as additional criteria for determining progress.

Some teachers consider marks in sex education as somewhat inappropriate, since they introduce an artificial element into a phase of education that is essentially concerned with attitudes and behavior.

FOR PROGRAM PLANNING

The aforementioned uses of testing procedures are all adaptable to program planning, including area emphasis, grade placement, time allotment, and teaching procedures.

Pupil needs and interests should be a basis for determining what is to be taught them. Information tests may be used to help determine what units of sex education should be stressed or excluded.

Evaluating Sex Knowledge

It is possible, and not too difficult, to measure objectively the knowledge of an individual. And, as previously indicated, since it is relatively difficult to measure attitudes and behavior, it becomes that much more important to understand that desirable attitudes and desirable behavior are in general the result of information and understanding.

Of the several areas of sex education considered in this book, those that have a substantial body of factual content, such as anatomy and physiology of human reproduction, conception and growth, eugenics, and venereal disease, lend themselves most readily to knowledge testing. By contrast, it is more difficult to prepare knowledge tests for areas such as boy-girl relationships, dating, and marriage, since they have a minimum of factual content.

If a teacher has the special training and, particularly, the time and interest, he should develop education tests for his own classes. Local norms can be established and test results from other similar classes can be compared. If comparisons of local test results are made with national norms, careful interpretation is needed.

TYPES OF TESTS

Standardized sex knowledge tests are made up of various types of test items, of which true-false, multiple-choice, matching-type, and completion-type items are the most common.

True-False Tests. This type of test is especially useful for questions involving just two alternatives, such as are found in physiology, anatomy, and heredity. They are difficult to prepare in areas which have less scientific content. Here are given a few examples of true-false tests (several additional examples of tests, scales, and inventories are included in the Appendix):

A True-False Test for the Kindergarten Level
(Prepared by Mrs. Evelyn Strum, a kindergarten teacher)

Answer yes or no to slow reading of each question.

  Yes   1. All babies have mothers and fathers.
  Yes   2. Twins have the same birthday.
  No   3. The father produces eggs.
  Yes   4. A human baby needs nine months to grow in the mother.
  No   5. Girls become men.
  Yes   6. Fish eggs are called roe.
  Yes   7. Babies need special care to grow.

A True-False Test for the Upper Elementary Grades
(Prepared by Marie Sedutto, a sixth-grade teacher)

If a statement is true, circle the letter T at the left of the statement. If the statement is false, circle the letter F.

T (F) 1. Males carry XY chromosomes in the sperm cell.
T (F) 2. Your glands have nothing to do with your growth.
(T) F 3. Your emotions can affect the way your body works.
T (F) 4. Mammals lay eggs.
(T) F 5. Cells store food as energy.
T (F) 6. Egg cells ripen in the human male three times a month.
T (F) 7. Cells cannot reproduce.

A True-False Test for Secondary Schools on
Preparation for Marriage
(Prepared by Nicholas Mangelli, a senior high school teacher)

1. __T__ Similarity of social and cultural background is one of the most important single factors in the lifelong enjoyment of a mate.
2. __T__ When "going steady," a couple develops a deeper level of friendship.
3. __T__ The fact that your parents are happy together and raised you in a "good home" is more likely to make your own marriage happy and successful.
4. __T__ Well-educated people much more often make a success of marriage than poorly educated people.
5. __F__ Mixed racial marriages can succeed very easily in today's liberal society.
6. __F__ Sex relations during engagement are acceptable to society.
7. __T__ In most marriages surveyed, it was found the husband was older than the wife.
8. __F__ The only function of the father in a family is that of a breadwinner.
9. __F__ The honeymoon is a traditional but useless prelude to a happy family life.
10. __F__ The husband should dominate the wife if the family is to be successful and happy.

Multiple-Choice Tests. This is the most common type of knowledge test. In this type of test item, a direct statement, situation, or question is followed by a number of possible responses (usually four or five) from which the examinee selects the one he considers correct or best. However, the younger the pupil, the fewer should be the choices.

A Multiple-Choice Test in Sex Education
(Prepared by Adeline Levin, an elementary school teacher)

1. Human reproduction is more like that of:
_____a. Snakes.
_____b. Birds.
__X__c. Guinea pigs.
_____d. Fish.

2. Growing up and adjusting socially are important because:

_____a. Your family wants you to.

_____b. Because the crowd is striving to do so. (Jim is growing a mustache like his dad. Joe drinks every weekend, etc.)

_____c. Because your girl friend wants you to.

__x__d. Because it is compatible with your future aims and objectives.

3. The pituitary, an endocrine gland necessary to growth and development, is located:

__x__a. At the base of the brain.

_____b. On the pancreas.

_____c. In the neck below the thymus.

_____d. In the abdomen.

4. Since an important function of family life is to provide moral and religious training for children, it is therefore least likely to be a problem if:

_____a. The father and the mother are of different religions.

_____b. The father and the mother do not have a religion.

__x__c. The father and the mother's religion are alike.

_____d. None of these apply.

5. One of the most important expressions of love and desire for permanence in a marriage is:

_____a. A new home.

_____b. A new car.

__x__c. Reproduction of children.

_____d. None of these.

6. In order to produce a male, the egg of the female must unite with the male germ cell which has:

_____a. X chromosome.

_____b. AB chromosome.

__x__c. Y chromosome.

_____d. None of these.

7. The human race may be biologically improved by:

_____a. Euthenics.

_____b. Eugenics.

_____c. Improving the environment.

__x__d. All of these.

8. If after a number of years no children are conceived by a happily married couple, the fault may lie with

_____a. The male.

_____b. The female.

__x__c. Either of the above.

_____d. It is not known.

9. If a mother is struck by a harp during pregnancy, the child:

_____a. Will be a musician.

_____b. Will get to heaven sooner.

_____c. Will have a birthmark.

__x__d. None of the above.

10. A contraceptive is a device or procedure to prevent:

_____a. Sterility.

__x__b. Conception.

_____c. Venereal disease.

_____d. Menopause.

Sentence-Completion Tests. In this type of objective test, the student completes a statement by writing in a missing word or phrase. This type of test is relatively easy to construct. It lends itself more readily to use in those areas containing considerable content. An example test follows:

*Completion Test for the Secondary School
on the Endocrine System*

(Prepared by Peter Marshall, a secondary school teacher)

Directions: Complete the following statements with the word or words that best fit.

1. The name of the hormone that can make a person temporarily stronger is called   (adrenalin)
2. The gland called the master gland is the   (pituitary)   gland.
3. Diabetes is controlled by the hormone   (insulin)
4. The larger the pituitary gland, the   (more)   growth producing hormone it makes.
5. The sex glands are also known as   (gonads)
6. The hormone that causes a mother to produce milk comes from the (pituitary) gland.
7. The gland which regulates the speed with which you burn food is the (thyroid) gland.
8. The hormone ACTH is produced by the   (pituitary)   gland.
9. In order to make its hormone, the thyroid gland must have   (iodine)
10. The development of the mammary glands in females is due to the functioning of the   (ovaries)
11. A person born with a small thyroid is likely to be   (small)   and   (dull)
12. The development of a beard in males is due to the functioning of the (testes).
13. A nervous, restless, excitable person may have an overactive   (thyroid) gland.
14. The endocrine glands are also called   (ductless)   glands.
15. The development and functionnig of the sex glands is controlled by the   (pituitary)   gland.

Matching-Type Tests. This type of test item is really a more complicated version of the multiple-choice question. One list of statements, terms, or phrases is matched against those in a second list. Matching-type items are suitable for use in large subject areas but are difficult to prepare where the content is limited. They are also more difficult to score and grade.

Examples of matching-type questions follow:

Matching: Following are two separate lists of terms (Group A) and their definitions (Group B). Put the letter of the correct answer in Group B in
front of the term in Group A which it identifies. (The answers have
inserted.)

Group A		Group B
1. A antibody		A. A substance produced in the body as a result of the action of antigens.
2. B gynecologist		B. A doctor who treats diseases peculiar to women.
3. G sarcoma		C. The food necessary for the building and repair of body tissue.
4. C protein		D. Needed to supply the body with a solid food is best able to alleviate hunger.
5. E antitoxin		E. A specific type of antibody.
		F. A substance causing the production of anti-bodies.
		G. A malignant tumor of connective tissue.

A Matching Test for Grade Six on the Male and Female Reproductive Organs

(Prepared by Elizabeth Goss, a fifth-grade teacher)

After the review of the reproductive system, the following quiz may be given.
Find the word in the left column which fits a definition in the right column.

Question A

1. B Fallopian tubes	A. The storage place for the immature egg cells.
2. D Uterus	B. The passageway through which the mature egg travels from ovary to uterus.
3. A Ovaries	C. Formed by the fertilization of two eggs by two sperm.
4. C Fraternal twins	D. The organ in which the embryo forms.

Question B

1. B Conception	A. The process of the egg leaving the ovary.
2. D Chromosomes	B. The moment of the uniting of the sperm with the egg.
3. F Gestation	C. Formed by the fertilization of one egg by one sperm.
4. A Ovulation	D. Carriers of hereditary characteristics.
5. C Identical twins	E. The release of sperm cells during sleep by the male reproductive system.
6. E Seminal emissions	F. The period from fertilization to birth; also called pregnancy.

Evaluating Sex Attitudes

It is difficult to measure sex attitudes since they are abstractions and consist chiefly of emotional factors. Furthermore, it is difficult to distinguish between (1) the examinee's real attitude and (2) his knowledge of what response society approves. Similarly, a person's actions or behavior may not give a true picture of his feelings. For these reasons, there are few techniques that actually are able to objectively measure the student's real attitude toward a given topic. Therefore, one usually has to depend upon subjective evidence for measuring attitudes.

In the field of sex and sexuality, we are concerned about such general attitudes as the *satisfaction* of having correct practices; the *dislike* for unsanitary or unhygienic conditions; a *respect* for the human body; a *liking* for good literature; the *enjoyment* of certain family group activities; a *preference* for some people; and many other similar attitudes toward the factors that influence our behavior.

The teacher's own evaluation, based on pupil observation, interviews, and diaries—subjective as these methods are—can adequately serve to indicate the predisposition of youngsters to react to situations and values. Items such as the pupil's likes and dislikes, his interests, and his emotional relationships to fellow pupils might be included.

Similar observations and records made by parents in the home would also contribute to attitude evaluation. However, parent participation in such a program of attitude evaluation is not to be recommended as a dependable measuring device, but may be valuable educationally to parents and children.

Attitudes in the sense of expression of opinions may be studied by means of questionnaires, scales, or checklists. Degrees of preference may be used, such as indicating whether one "agrees," is "uncertain," or "disagrees" with the viewpoint represented; or absolutes, such as "yes" and "no," can be employed.

Another technique used in securing pupil attitude reactions is the story test in which the pupil underlines those words indicating procedures or things that he considers as good or desirable and crosses out those items that are bad. It is thought that attitudes of young children are measured by these story tests primarily because of the lifelike situations to which pupils are required to react.

Little has been done with attitude measurement as compared with the use of standardized knowledge tests. A series of instruments is needed that can be used from kindergarten through the adult level to determine the prevalence of various attitudes in family life education.

COMMERCIAL ATTITUDE TESTS AND SCALES

There are some real attitude tests available. It needs to be stressed that there are a number of so-called sex attitude tests, or scales, that actually measure our knowledge about attitudes—that is, whether we know which attitude is the one that is generally accepted. Such tests are included in the discussion of health knowledge tests.

Examples of Attitude Scales

The following examples of attitude scales have been prepared by teachers for use in their own classes. A three-point scale is used for the sixth-grade scale whereas a five-point scale is suggested for the secondary school students who are more mature in taking such evaluation instruments.

Scale for Sixth Grade
(Prepared by Henry M. Adams, a sixth-grade teacher)

If you agree (A), are undecided (U), or disagree (D) about the attitude expressed in each sentence, circle either A, U, or D.

1. It's right for boys and girls to go steady in the sixth grade.	A	U	D
2. Parents really don't understand their children.	A	U	D
3. A person should express his emotions as he wants to.	A	U	D
4. Girls should date boys of the same age.	A	U	D
5. Parents should tell their children all about sex.	A	U	D
6. Children can find out all about sex without any outside help.	A	U	D
7. Sex is physical only.	A	U	D
8. A girl should remember that she is a lady, and should never participate in vigorous sports.	A	U	D
9. When a boy is going out with a girl, the boy should be the "boss."	A	U	D
10. Children should be able to tell their parents everything.	A	U	D

Scale for the Secondary School
(Prepared by Nicholas Mangelli, a secondary school teacher)

Read each of the following statements; then tell if you strongly agree (SA), agree (A), are undecided (U), disagree (D), or strongly disagree (SD) about the opinion expressed in each. Circle either SA, A, U, D, or SD.

1. A girl should allow a boy to kiss her on the first date.	SA	A	U	D	SD
2. A boy could not get serious with a girl who has a reputation of being promiscuous.	SA	A	U	D	SD

3. Teenagers who go steady are more apt to become involved in sexual problems than those who "play the field."   SA   A   U   D   SD

4. I would marry a boy (girl) who had previous sexual relations with others.   SA   A   U   D   SD

5. Petting is all right if the boy and girl stop short of intercourse.   SA   A   U   D   SD

6. It is better to get a divorce than to stay with a partner you do not love.   SA   A   U   D   SD

7. I would marry someone of a different race than my own.   SA   A   U   D   SD

8. Most of my sex education should come from discussions with my friends.   SA   A   U   D   SD

9. A young married couple should get established and have money in the bank before having any children.   SA   A   U   D   SD

10. Indecent and immoral books and pictures should be banned from public sale.   SA   A   U   D   SD

Evaluating Sex Behavior

It is important to determine pupil behavior, habits, practices, and conduct to measure the extent to which changes have occurred since they were last appraised. Direct observation of habits of pupils by the teacher promises best results in habit evaluation. Those having the most favorable opportunities for doing this include the elementary schoolteacher, the physical education teacher, and the homeroom teacher. Observation reveals such practices.

Practices can also be surveyed by *orally* asking the class to indicate how many drank milk for breakfast, how many brushed their teeth after breakfast, what time they went to bed, and so on. Group discussion will usually follow the tally, and group motivation can be utilized to considerable advantage following the summarizing. Tact will be needed in handling such class activities. Successive surveys will reveal the extent of group progress. Such information can also be supplemented with anecdotal records, pupil diaries, and case studies.

A more formal approach to the observation of student behavior is through the use of a checklist. It can be prepared cooperatively by the children and the teacher. Such self-appraisal devices are useful in arousing pupil interest and in helping pupils to see where an education program is leading them (see form shown on pp. 157–58). Checklists, inventories, and questionnaires relating to behavior must be used skillfully if accurate results are to be obtained. Students must be informed that the procedures are for obtaining information and not to test their knowledge or to provide a basis for marking. Unless this is done, they will give answers which they think are wanted.

It may be felt that it is desirable to enlist the parents to aid in the evaluation program by keeping a record of home habits practiced by their children. Some teachers develop a short practice questionnaire for such a purpose. However, it is doubtful that parent reports concerning such observations constitute valid and reliable measures of pupil habitual conduct. Probably the principal value of such a parent-observation program would be in the development of increased interest by the parents in the program.

CRITERIA

There are some criteria of behavior in family living which lend themselves to evaluation through observation by the classroom teacher.

1. Interpersonal relationships with peers.
2. Overt sexual behavior.
3. Covert sexual behavior.
4. Choice of reading materials.
5. Choice of free-time or recess-time activities.
6. Behavior in lavatories.
7. Reaction to classroom discussions.
8. Participation in discussions.
9. Discretion employed in speech, dress, and behavior.
10. Self-discipline.
11. Correct use of terminology.
12. Responsibility to self and to others.
13. Frequency of pornography brought to class.
14. Incidence of toilet markings with obscene theme.
15. Respect for and cooperation with members of the opposite sex.

Inventory Form for Behavior
(Prepared by Peter Marshall, a high school teacher)

If the statement is true, circle the T preceding the statement. If it is false, circle the F.

1. T F I blush when we discuss sex in class.
2. T F I have never been in love with anyone.
3. T F I have never been in trouble because of my sex behavior.
4. T F I never worry about my looks.
5. T F I do not talk much during the lessons on sex education.
6. T F I am easily embarrassed.
7. T F I daydream very little.

8. T F I take frequent baths.
9. T F I get embarrassed at dirty jokes.
10. T F I treat others fairly.
  Note: The above test can also be rated on a three-point scale using Always, Sometimes, and Never; or on a five-point scale of Never, Rarely, Sometimes, Usually, and Always.

Evaluation of Programs in Family Life

In addition to examining the overall school curriculum to determine the extent to which family life education is included, the following type of evidence can be used to indicate the relative effectiveness of such programs.

1. Freedom in asking about and discussing personal problems.
2. A growth in attitudes of respectfulness and concern for the welfare of the other sex.
3. A lessening of pornography, obscenity, wall markings, and lewd jokes.
4. Freedom in raising questions or pertinent points in class.
5. Objective reactions to class discussions.
6. The type of requests for books from the library.
7. Direct appraisals from pupils and parents.
8. Former students returning for help and discussion.
9. The kind of questions asked.
10. Spontaneous pupil expressions.
11. The ability to consider problems and issues in a comprehensive setting.

Here follow two evaluations of certain aspects of the programs in a classroom and an entire elementary school, as prepared by graduate students in a course taught by the author. These reports might serve as partial guides to others in appraising or evaluating their own school's program.

AN EVALUATION OF PUPILS IN A THIRD-GRADE CLASS BY ITS TEACHER

This program was submitted by a prekindergarten teacher.

I usually evaluate a child on the amount of learning he uses when he is playing with other children. If he remembers to wash his hands when he comes out of the bathroom or to say excuse me when he steps on someone's toe, I feel that some worthwhile habits are being formed. I can more or less determine his attitudes toward school, toward me, and toward the others with whom he comes in contact. The amount of knowledge that he has gained from home and in the class I can judge from his responses and his questions.

Last year, when I remarked on how nice a child's hair looked, the mother wrote a note thanking me because it was very difficult getting this child to have her hair washed. Whenever her hair was done, her mother wrote me a little note and sent it by her older sister and by the end of the term this particular child showed no resistance to having her hair done or looking nice and behaving better. Between the home and the school, habits like these can be a pleasing learning experience.

AN EVALUATION OF THE FAMILY LIVING PROGRAM IN AN ELEMENTARY SCHOOL

This program was submitted by a school nurse whose school now has a model program.

Strengths

1. The children are given many opportunities to learn to live together harmoniously in the classroom and in after-school activities, to report on their own family parties and excursions, to carry on projects of their own choosing, and to develop their interests in worthwhile use of leisure time.

2. A very active school-home public relations program is being carried on to explain the interest of the school in helping the child to develop to his fullest capacity.

3. The services of a school physician, school psychologist, and a nurse-teacher are available to those children seeking help.

4. The Elementary Science Curriculum meets the basic requirements of the curriculum suggested in the University of the State of New York Bulletin #1224 on Science for Grades 1–6.

Weaknesses and Recommendations

1. Discussion of adolescent growth and development and human reproduction are not provided for in either the elementary or high school curriculum. This is partly due to community pressure, but with in-service education of teachers in this area, a smooth transition from the discussion of lower animal to human growth and development could be achieved. The elementary school teacher spends the entire day with the same group of children and has the opportunity to integrate family living education into the daily program in many subject-matter areas.

2. The nurse-teacher had sought to introduce a program on menstruation for fifth-grade girls but the request was denied on the basis of community pressure. Under the sponsorship of the PTA, this program could be made available after school hours to the interested mothers and daughters.

3. Nothing is being done at present with animal breeding at school because of danger of animal bites. The setting up of a live animal museum in the building which the children could visit might be one way of introducing animal projects into the curriculum. Many schools have found this an invaluable method of building a scientific vocabulary.

4. While much is being done to develop good school-home-community relations, there is at present no opportunity for group meetings of parents for discussion and advice on the sex education of their children. From my experience in speaking

with mothers who have come asking for help in explaining menstruation, it is apparent that much could be done in parent education. This might be done through the Adult Education Program and would eventually result in a better informed student body.

5. Library books on human growth and development suitable for the elementary level should be made available to the children who wish this type of reading matter just as other books on other topics are made available to the children.

The American Social Health Association tells us that basic to the whole question of the role of the school in sex education is the need for parental understanding of the parents' own responsibilities. There is need for parents to understand just what it is that the school views as its share in this mutual home-school educational effort. There is need for guidance from the churches on moral training. In short, there is need for the three major influences in the child's life—home, school, and church—to work as a unit, as partners in an important and profitable enterprise.

Activities

1. Make a study of the commercial knowledge tests in family life education. Determine for each test the types of objective questions used, the age level for which the test is intended, the length of time needed to take the test, and the validity and reliability of the test.

2. Prepare an original objective test using various types of questions—true-false, multiple-choice, matching-type, and completion-type for a given grade level.

3. Prepare a sex-attitude test or scale for a specific grade level comprising ten or more items. For answer choices, use the degrees of preference, such as "Agrees," "Uncertain," and "Disagrees," or one of the other plans discussed in this chapter.

4. Prepare a scale for measuring personal practices for a given grade level.

5. Make a checklist of twenty items for evaluating the overall sex instructional program in either an elementary school, junior high school, senior high school, or college.

6. Administer one of the tests in this chapter or in the Appendix to a class or group of pupils.

7. Administer the Information Test on Human Reproduction to a group of teachers or to some parents.

References

Adams, Georgia Sachs, Theodore L. Torgerson, and Ernest R. Wood, Editors, *Measurement and Evaluation for the Secondary School Teacher,* Holt, Rinehart, and Winston, New York, 1956, 658 pp.

Buros, Oscar K., Editor, *The Seventh Mental Measurement Yearbook,* The Gryphon Press, England Park, N. J., 1968.

Educational Testing Service, *Selecting an Achievement Test: Principles and Procedures,* Princeton, N. J., 1961.

Edwards, Ralph, "An Approach to Health Attitude Measurement," *J. School Health,* September 1956, pp. 215–219.

Flanagan, John Clemens, et al., "New Tool for Measuring Children's Behavior," *Elem. School J.,* Vol. 59, December 1958, pp. 163–166.

Green, John A., *Teacher-Made Tests,* Harper and Row, New York, 1963, 141 pp.

Greene, Harry A., Albert N. Jorgensen, and J. Raymond Gerberich, *Measurement and Evaluation in the Elementary School,* Longmans, Green and Company, New York, 1953, 617 pp.

Gronlund, Norman E., *Measurement and Evaluation in Teaching,* The Macmillan Company, New York, 1965, 464 pp.

Kilander, H. Frederick, "A Survey of the Public's Knowledge of Certain Aspects of Human Reproduction," *J. School Health,* June 1959.

Sliepcevich, Elena K., *School Health Education Study,* American Association for Health, Physical Education, and Recreation, Washington, D.C., 1964, 74 pp.

Stanley, Julian C., *Measurement in Today's Schools,* Prentice-Hall, Englewood Cliffs, N. J., 1964, 512 pp.

Sutton, W. C., "Misconceptions About Health Among Children and Youth," *J. School Health,* Vol. 32, May 1962, pp. 347–349.

10

Teaching Units
and Lesson Plans
in Sex Education

In previous chapters, attention has been given to the curriculum in sex education by grade levels. When this area is broken down to that which should be taught for a particular school level such as the junior high school, or for a particular course or student group, it is often referred to as a teaching unit. When a teaching unit is divided among a specific number of class periods, the teaching plan for one of these days is known as a lesson plan.

In this chapter we shall briefly consider the teaching unit and then at length discuss and illustrate lesson planning in sex education.

The Teaching Unit

A course in any field usually consists of several units for study, investigation, and discussion. Ordinarily the number of units will be determined by how many broad topics are to be included in a given course. Some of the longer teaching units can in turn be divided into subunits. Since much of sex education is correlated into other courses, it may be that one of the units in a biology course, for example, will be on certain biological content in sex education. See Chapter 5 for topics for units.

It will be helpful again to examine those outlines in sex education for the secondary school that are shown in Chapter 5. Each course consists of a number of units, and each unit is further divided into a number of daily lesson topics for which a lesson plan will be needed.

Units differ widely in scope and content. Some may be short, lasting one period to a few weeks, whereas others may be long and cover a span of months or a whole semester. Some units may be focused on subject matter content, whereas others may consider problems that need to be solved. Units that lend themselves to integration may even cut across several teaching areas; such a plan requires coordination through, for example, the school health committee. The following suggested outline [1] prepared by the Society of State Directors of Health, Physical Education and Recreation might be used as a guide.

A SUGGESTED OUTLINE FOR DEVELOPING HEALTH UNITS

A. Finding the problem.
   In a brief paragraph, explain how the problems happened to be brought to a focus, or enumerate the methods used for discovering the health needs or problems, such as:
   1. Observations in the classroom or during play periods.
   2. Survey of school or community environment.
   3. Interviews with nurse, parents, and pupils.
   4. Studying health examination records.
   5. Studying accidents or epidemics occurring in school and community.
B. Objectives.
   List goals or desired outcomes.
C. Procedure.
   Describe procedure followed for attaining goals, including such items as:
   1. Approaches used for arousing pupil interest in the work.
   2. For study in connection with the unit, list specific:
      a. Content items.
      b. Questions.
      c. Problems.
   3. Activities selected and learning situations provided for helping students answer their questions and solving their problems related to the main problem. Explain how activities were selected.
   4. Other steps taken, if any, for attempting to solve the problem, such as:
      a. Cooperation with the home and community and other school personnel.

[1] Committee on Health Instruction of the Society of State Directors, "Health Teaching Units, Part I," *J. Health, Phys. Educ., Rec.,* June 1953.

      b. Examining and improving the daily program.

      c. Making changes designed to improve the school environment.

      d. Providing essential materials and equipment necessary for solving the problem.

D. Teaching aids used:

1. Reading materials.	5. Demonstrations.
2. Audiovisual aids (multisensory).	6. Field trips.
3. Resource people.	7. Work projects.
4. Experiments.	8. Others.

E. Evaluation.

Describe briefly outstanding accomplishments as a result of the teaching of this unit in terms of original purpose.

LESSON PLANS

A logical step now is to consider the lesson plan as a natural outgrowth of unit planning. Preparation of the lesson plan is a responsibility of the individual teacher.

It is essential that the unit be broken down on a day-to-day basis. However, it is possible that a lesson may cover less than one class period or may extend into more than one class period.

The lesson plan should be modest rather than too large and too detailed if the lesson objectives are to be met. The lesson plan does not necessarily include all of the steps or procedures recommended for a unit plan; it has, in a sense, less scope but more detail. Its form and pattern vary with the teacher. It should be so flexible as to allow for recognition of spontaneous pupil interest and activity; and it should allow for pupil participation in the planning of daily instruction. Bringing the pupils into the planning of a lesson or unit increases their interest in the subject under consideration. When pupils develop, or help the teacher to develop, the plans for their own work, the work is more meaningful, and their motivation is consequently increased and learning is facilitated. A sense of self-direction is developed for the students in that classroom.

ELEMENTS OF GOOD LESSON PLANNING

There are a number of elements which make up a good lesson plan. These elements may not be applicable to all lesson plans but, in general, consideration needs to be given to most of them for any given day or week of teaching on a narrow, selected topic.

Objectives or Aims. All of the objectives or aims of the course or unit will not be repeated in the daily and weekly lesson plans. However, short-term objectives should be indicated daily, and these should fit appropriately into the broader and long-term objectives of the unit.

Specific objectives in sex education for a specific lesson plan should include some from each of the broad educational objectives, namely, the acquisition of desirable knowledge, attitudes, and behavior.

It is essential to keep in mind that the continuity preserved from one class period to another should be such that the objectives of the teaching unit are realized. Therefore, the teacher, in planning the daily lesson, should have a clear perspective of the total learning that is expected from the unit.

Content. The content of the topic to be considered may need to be outlined in detail as a guide for the teacher and the pupils. The extent of detail will be determined by the nature of the topic and by the relative need for the teacher to have much or little help in recalling the content when presenting the lesson.

Methods and Activities. The lesson plan needs to be very specific in regard to the methods and procedures to be used in light of the topic to be taught, the age level, the background and experience of the pupils, the amount of time available for treating the particular topic, and the experience of the teacher.

The lesson plan should show very specifically the activities in which the pupils are to be involved. It is these activities which in part determine what methods are to be used; they provide for the learning experiences. To have meaning, any activity, task, or assignment must be understood, have relevance, and have or imply a purpose.

Since the time element varies considerably with the use of various teaching aids and materials and with other factors such as the age level of the group and with different pupil activities, it is important to carefully plan the use of time when setting up the lesson plan.

It may be desirable to list several alternate teaching methods to provide for flexibility in the handling of the class.

Materials. The teacher needs to ask himself: "What tools do we need in order to get the job done?" The use of materials is implied in certain of the methods and activities listed in a lesson plan. It is essential, therefore, that the teacher know exactly what materials, including textbooks, are needed for the teaching for that specific day on that specific topic. Having such a list prepared in advance helps to minimize the possibility of some item not being available just at the time that it is needed.

Evaluation and Follow-up. Another question that needs to be raised is: "What results have we obtained and how can we use or apply these results?"

What needs to be done in regard to evaluation for a single lesson plan may need to be slight. However, even if it may be brief, it needs to be there. It may consist only of questions that the teacher may raise with the class to be answered during or at the end of the class period, or at a later date when other related topics have been completed.

The evaluation may also be in the form of a summary of what has been done on that day. Such a review can serve as a background for leading into the next assignment or suggestions for "next steps."

References. Two separate lists of references may be desirable—one for the teacher and one for the pupils. The latter may be the assignment given previously for the day's preparation. Having such specific references listed will be of help the next time that the same lesson plan or a related one is to be used.

STRUCTURING A LESSON PLAN

Although there are many ways of structuring a lesson plan, each plan should give recognition to the following elements:

1. Grade and ability level of class.
2. The topic to be selected from the unit.
3. The place in the course or unit; for example, it should be noted that the lesson plan is the third of four topics on human reproduction.
4. A description of the teaching situation, such as the characteristics of the pupil group and that it is in a regular classroom or is a field trip.
5. The amount of time available for the specific lesson.
6. A statement of the objectives to be sought: general objectives as well as specific objectives—knowledge, attitudes, and behavior to be attained.
7. An outline of the subject-matter content.
8. The methods and materials and pupil activities to be included, and suggestions for initiating the lesson plan such as review, orientation, or introduction.
9. Teacher and pupil references and related reading.
10. Evaluation procedures.
11. An explanation of the assignment for the next class session.

AN EXAMPLE OF A UNIT

A teaching unit is presented here as an example of what a unit in sex education might comprise. This particular unit can be taught in one to five lessons, the number depending upon student interest and the available time. It may be helpful to the teacher to break the unit into individual lesson plans if more than two lessons are to be devoted to the unit.

See Part II for further help in developing units in sex education. It gives, in outline form, the content on many topics which can be adapted into units and lesson plans.

Examples of Lesson Plans

1. A LESSON PLAN FOR PREKINDERGARTEN

SPECIFIC TOPICS: 1. Does life come from life?
2. Does like come from like?

PLACE IN PROGRAM: As a lesson in science.

GENERAL OBJECTIVE: To stress knowledge, using experimentation.

SPECIFIC OBJECTIVES

1. To teach that lima beans will reproduce lima beans, and only lima beans; they are alive.
2. To teach that pebbles will not reproduce at all; they are not alive.
3. To demonstrate more care and reverence for a living plant than for the inanimate pebble, in hopes of eventually instilling a reverence for life among the children.
4. To teach incidentally the fine auditory discrimination between "life" and "like."

DEVELOPMENT OF THE LESSON

1. Review chart of plants which has been posted on the tin board for several days in anticipation of this review of plant parts: root, stem, leaf, flower, fruit, and seed.
2. Motivation: The children themselves have planted lima beans and pebbles in separate labeled pots, and have given identical care to both; they are already eager to see what has developed within the lima bean seed.
3. Procedure:
   a. Break open a lima bean seed pod in a reverent, gentle, careful manner.
   b. Allow children to examine seeds.
   c. Encourage comparison to original parent lima bean seeds planted months ago showing children dried lima beans from same or similar box.
   d. Draw from the children that the size and shape are the *same.*
   e. Draw from the children that the color and the "feel" is different—greener and wetter.
   f. Draw from the children the name of the parent seeds—lima beans.
   g. Try to draw from the children the fact that if they plant these new seeds they will not get corn, carrots, or apples, but lima beans.

    h. Encourage children to plant the new seeds, to see what they get.

    i. Unearth pebbles; dump them with no particular care because they are not alive.

    j. After the children have examined them, plant some more to repeat the first experiment.

EVALUATING ACTIVITIES
1. Small group oral questioning about what will grow from:
   a. Lima bean seeds.
   b. Tomato seeds.
   c. Carrot seeds, etc.

Prepared by Mrs. Marilyn Perry, Head Start teacher.

2. A LESSON FOR PREKINDERGARTEN

SPECIFIC TOPIC: How can we all help welcome the new baby?

PLACE IN PROGRAM: Unstructured.

GENERAL OBJECTIVE: To develop attitudes, using demonstration.

SPECIFIC OBJECTIVES
1. To develop a feeling of self-worth and accomplishment in siblings.
2. To reduce sibling rivalry.
3. To demonstrate the care and handling of new babies.
4. To diaper baby, thereby giving opportunity for observation of body parts.

DEVELOPMENT OF THE LESSON
1. Review: Discuss at circle time the changes a new baby brings to the home.
2. Motivation: Introduce cooperative parent who has brought in young baby for demonstration (be very ceremonious to enhance interest).
3. Procedures:
   a. Teacher allows children to question parent freely, but she answers the embarrassing queries herself.
   b. Teacher demonstrates caution, gentleness, and love when handling baby but clearly indicates that the children watching the demonstration are just as important.
   c. Parent feeds the baby.
   d. Baby is bathed and dressed.

EVALUATION ACTIVITIES
1. Watch children playing in housekeeping corner and note any changes in bathing and dressing of dolls.
2. Observe children with class pets.
3. Observe children with those members of the class who are more helpless than they.

ASSIGNMENT: None.

TEACHER REFERENCE: De Schweinitz, Karl, *Growing Up*.

Prepared by Mrs. Marilyn Perry, Head Start teacher.

3. LESSON PLAN FOR KINDERGARTEN

GENERAL TOPIC: Developing masculinity and femininity.

SPECIFIC TOPIC: Sex identity through use of bathroom.

PLACE IN PROGRAM: Unstructured and continuous.

GENERAL OBJECTIVE: To help develop awareness of one's sex identity.

SPECIFIC OBJECTIVES
1. To establish a proper code of conduct in the use of the school bathroom.
2. To reinforce hygienic habits such as washing one's hands before leaving the toilet.

TOPICS FOR DISCUSSION
1. Boys and girls use separate bathrooms.
2. Anatomical differences between the sexes.
3. Safety in the school bathroom.

SPECIAL ACTIVITIES
1. A tour of the school building, pointing out the locations of bathrooms.
2. A demonstration of the best way to wash and dry the hands.

Contributed by Mrs. Evelyn Strum, kindergarten teacher.

4. A LESSON FOR PREKINDERGARTEN

SPECIFIC TOPIC: How to discourage public masturbation (nonpathological) or other sex-play without causing guilt or shame in the child.

PLACE IN PROGRAM: Unstructured.

GENERAL OBJECTIVE: To stress desirable sex behavior.

SPECIFIC OBJECTIVES
1. To discourage public masturbation or sex-play.
2. To encourage socially acceptable behavior.
3. To avoid damage to either the child's self-concept or his respect and pleasure in his body parts.

DEVELOPMENT OF THE LESSON
1. Review: None.
2. Motivation: One of the few instances in which pleasing the teacher is the motivation.
3. Procedures:
   a. Teacher prepares acceptable rhythmic substitutes, such as (1) workbench with saw or (2) rocking boat or see-saw.
   b. Teacher gently suggests to child or to children that their activity is personal and private, that sometimes people may get upset when they see children playing with genitalia (name the appropriate body part), and that this must not be done in public.
   c. Teacher offers a choice of activities in a cheerful, friendly manner.
   d. Teacher repeats this procedure whenever the need arises, always explaining that this is a private, not a public activity.

EVALUATING ACTIVITY: If, by observation, the incidence of public masturbation or sex-play by the specific child or children in question lessens, and if the child can gradually progress from rhythmic to intellectual or creative activity returning less and less frequently to masturbation, the intervention is successful.

TEACHER REFERENCE: Johnson, Warren H., *Masturbation,* SIECUS Publication G03, 1966.

Prepared by Mrs. Marilyn Perry, Head Start teacher.

5. LESSON PLAN FOR KINDERGARTEN

GENERAL TOPIC: The role of the family.

SPECIFIC TOPIC: The role of animal parents to their babies.

PLACE IN THE PROGRAM: As a part of the science teaching about animals.

GENERAL OBJECTIVE: To learn about the relationship of baby animals to their parents.

SPECIFIC OBJECTIVES: To instill the knowledge:
1. That some baby animals need to have their parents take care of them.
2. That some baby animals do not need to have their parents take care of them.

TOPICS FOR DISCUSSION
1. The young of mammals:
   a. Are milk fed by their mother.
   b. Are trained to varying degrees by their parents.
   c. Are sometimes carried on the back or tail or in the pouch of the mother.
   d. Are often protected from predators by their parents.
2. Some baby animals resemble their parents in looks.

  a. In which ways do human babies resemble their parents?
  b. Does a kitten look something like its mother or like its father?

SPECIAL ACTIVITIES
  1. Discuss the way babies and children are cared for by their mothers and fathers. Why do parents care for their children? Do some animals take care of young too?
  2. Make a collection of pictures showing animals and their young: a cat and her kittens, a dog and her puppies, a horse and her colt, a duck and her ducklings, a bird and her nestlings, etc.
  3. Bring in pictures showing mothers and fathers helping children.
  4. Start a large Animal Album for the classroom. Add pictures as they are discussed. Place the album on the library table for children to review.
  5. Read to the class the story *Baby Animals* by Garth Williams.
  6. Teach the following songs from *The Kindergarten Book* (Ginn and Company):
     a. "Birds, Bees, and Bugs," pp. 105–109.
     b. "Animals," pp. 114–118.

Contributed by Mrs. Evelyn Strum, kindergarten teacher.

6. LESSON PLAN FOR KINDERGARTEN

GENERAL TOPIC: Developing masculinity and femininity.

SPECIFIC TOPIC: The differing roles of the sexes.

PLACE IN THE PROGRAM: Unstructured and continuous.

GENERAL OBJECTIVE: To compare the abilities and duties of men and women.

SPECIFIC OBJECTIVES: To develop an awareness of the facts:
  1. That there are physical and social differences between the sexes.
  2. That there are certain jobs that usually only men or only women do.
  3. That there are certain jobs that both men and women do or can do.

TOPICS FOR DISCUSSION
  1. Men are big and strong.
  2. Women are not as strong as men.
  3. Women become mothers and take care of the family.
  4. Men become fathers and provide for the family.
  5. There are different types of work a father may do; not all daddies have the same kind of jobs.

SPECIAL ACTIVITIES
  1. Boys act out fathers' jobs. Class guesses what they are.
  2. Members of the class act out the various family roles in the housekeeping corner.

3. Children cut out pictures from magazines showing men and women at work.
4. Read to the class the story *The Little Family* by Lois Lenski.

Contributed by Mrs. Evelyn Strum, kindergarten teacher.

7. LESSON PLAN FOR GRADE TWO

GENERAL TOPIC: Unit on understanding physical and social growth.

SPECIFIC TOPIC: The many ways we grow.

PLACE IN THE PROGRAM: An introductory topic on the broad one of physical and social growth.

GENERAL OBJECTIVE: To develop the concept of how we grow.

SPECIFIC OBJECTIVES
1. To show the various ways we grow.
2. To develop a better understanding of growth.

MOTIVATION: By means of a picture set, show illustrations of:
1. Children helping themselves by:
   a. Taking a bath.
   b. Tying own shoes.
   c. Making own sandwich.
2. Children discovering for themselves by:
   a. Using a dictionary.
   b. Asking questions.
3. Children doing things they have learned how to do such as:
   a. Playing baseball.
   b. Playing the piano.
   c. Making a model plane.

PROCEDURE
1. Let children study the pictures.
2. After silent study, let pupils describe what each child is doing.
3. Question children about the pictures:
   For example: What is the girl in the first picture doing? In what way do you think she is growing?
4. Continue questioning until the following is realized:
   a. We grow in knowing how to help ourselves.
   b. We grow in knowing how to find out things for ourselves.
   c. We grow in knowing how to do things.
5. Finally, help the children to reflect on advantages of growing in the ways emphasized in this lesson.
   Question and raise discussion on:
   a. How might it help a girl to know how to play a piano? (She can play songs she likes; she can play while others sing.)

b. How might it help a boy to know how to throw and bat a ball? (He can play ball with others; it is satisfying to be able to do things others can do.)
c. How do you feel when you can do things and find things all by yourself? (You feel "big," happy, pleased, and so on.)

CULMINATING ACTIVITY AND EVALUATION
1. Draw picture of some aspect of growth. Children always enjoy drawing and it often tends to be a good evaluation exercise.

Contributed by Miss Donna Mollica, second-grade teacher.

8. LESSON PLAN FOR GRADE TWO

GENERAL TOPIC: Unit on understanding physical and social growth.

SPECIFIC TOPIC: Animals and their babies.

PLACE IN THE GENERAL TOPIC: A topic that might follow the introductory lesson.

GENERAL OBJECTIVE: To learn about animals and their babies.

SPECIFIC OJECTIVES
1. To understand that animals reproduce young replicas of themselves.
2. To observe the similarities and differences between animals and their babies.

PROCEDURE
1. Have children observe pictures of animals.
2. Let children identify animals.
3. Ask whether they know what babies of different types of animals are called, for example:
   a. dog—pup.
   b. lion—cub.
4. Let children tell about animal babies they have seen.

ASSIGNMENT
1. Have children collect pictures of animals and their babies.
2. Use pictures of animals and babies for a bulletin board display.

EVALUATION: A simple completion test such as the following:
1. A baby lion is called a _____.
2. A baby cat is called a _____.
3. A puppy will be called a _____ when he grows up.
4. A baby chicken is called a _____.
5. A lamb will grow up to be a _____.

Contributed by Miss Donna Mollica, second-grade teacher.

9. LESSON PLAN FOR GRADE THREE

GENERAL TOPIC: Reproduction.

SPECIFIC TOPIC: Reproduction in animals.

PLACE IN THE GENERAL TOPIC: One of the early lessons on reproduction.

GENERAL OBJECTIVE: To learn about reproduction.

SPECIFIC OBJECTIVES
  1. To help the children establish the use of proper terminology in reference to the body and its natural processes.
  2. To help children develop wholesome attitudes toward sex.

REVIEW: Plants grow from seeds or ovum inside plants.

MOTIVATION: Show film, "Kittens—Birth and Growth," Bailey Films.

PROCEDURE: A discussion following the showing of the film on topics such as:
  1. All things, whether plant or animal, start as seeds or eggs. We can see the eggs of birds for they are outside the body. Other animals have their eggs inside the mother.
  2. The new fetus takes different lengths of time to grow in the mother.

EVALUATION: A question-and-answer period follows on the material covered.

ASSIGNMENT: Make a chart listing the length of time required from conception to birth for two types of animals.

Contributed by Miss Bonnie Kennedy, third-grade teacher.

10. LESSON PLAN FOR GRADE THREE

GENERAL TOPIC: Reproduction.

SPECIFIC TOPIC: Introduction to reproduction.

PLACE IN THE GENERAL TOPIC: The first of several lessons.

GENERAL OBJECTIVE: To learn about reproduction.

SPECIFIC OBJECTIVES
  1. To impress that life begets life.
  2. To show how the life force works in animals.

DEVELOPMENT OF THE LESSON
  1. View the film, "Biography of the Unborn." This film traces the process of human reproduction from conception to birth.

2. A question-and-answer period follows the film. Stress vocabulary: sperm, egg, fertilization, conception, etc.
3. Discussion:
   a. The male and female roles in reproduction.
   b. How eggs are fertilized.
   c. The development of the fertilized egg.
   d. The different types of fertilization:
      (1) Inside the body.
      (2) Outside the body.

SUGGESTED ACTIVITIES
   1. Mating class pets, mice, hamsters, etc.
   2. Incubation of fertilized hen's eggs.
   3. Reading *How Life Begins* by Powers.

Contributed by Mrs. Irene Sessa, third-grade teacher.

11. LESSON PLAN FOR GRADE FIVE

GENERAL TOPIC: Human growth.

SPECIFIC TOPIC: The difference in growth between boys and girls.

PLACE IN UNIT: The first lesson for this grade on this general topic. It is assumed that the topic has been considered in earlier grades as well.

GENERAL OBJECTIVE: To understand how growth occurs in boys and girls.

SPECIFIC OBJECTIVES
   1. To learn about individual differences in the rate of growth.
   2. To learn about the influence of the endocrine glands and their hormones on growth.
   3. To broaden their vocabulary with words such as endocrine gland, hormone, and pituitary.

MOTIVATION
   1. The night before, have the children cut out several pictures of men and bring them to class.

PROCEDURE
   1. Discuss the differences in size and body build for the men in the pictures.
   2. Compare the differences of rates of growth of boys and girls in class.
   3. Discuss that bodily functions affect the rate of growth.

SUMMARY AND EVALUATION
   1. Teacher's question: Can boys and girls who are the same age be quite different in height and still be growing in a way that is right for them?
   2. Teacher's question: What have you learned about the growth patterns of girls from nine to sixteen? About boys of approximately the same age?

ASSIGNMENTS
1. Magazine pictures can be collected for a bulletin board display which would illustrate the differences in size and physiques among adults.

Contributed by Elizabeth Woods Goss, fifth-grade teacher.

12. LESSON PLAN FOR GRADE SIX

GENERAL TOPIC: Menstruation.

SPECIFIC TOPIC: Female sex organs.

OBJECTIVES: To understand and learn to use the correct terminology for the female reproductive organs.

MATERIAL: Each student will receive
1. A mimeographed sheet of the illustration on p. 238. (Parts are not to be labeled.) This illustration can be transferred to a transparency to be used with an overhead projector.
2. A three dimensional (mannequin-like) figure or model which displays those areas found in the illustration on p. 238.
3. A mimeographed sheet containing the terms (anus, cervix, etc.) and definitions found in the subunit.

METHOD
1. Using the overhead projector, the teacher will indicate and discuss those parts of the body found on the first illustration.
2. In turn, the students will locate and label each portion of their own mimeographed diagram of that illustration, as that portion is discussed.
3. Using the three-dimensional model, the teacher will name a body part and ask a student to locate it. (Pupil may use his mimeographed sheet as an aid.) Once the student locates the part, he may call on another student to give the definition or function of this part. (Students may use definition sheets as aids.) This continues for the entire twelve body parts mentioned above.

CULMINATION: Ask the following of the class:
"In the future, it would be useful to use the correct terminology for those parts learned today. What method do you consider helpful in retaining that which was learned?" Students may suggest memorizing, or further reading on the topic as reinforcement, or constant referral to those pertinent mimeographed sheets whenever discussing female genitals. Consensus will dictate which technique or techniques will be employed.

EVALUATION: Several lessons later, while discussing the same overall topic of menstruation, the students can be given the test on p. 368.

Note: Boys and girls should not be separated for above lesson.

Suggested by Lucille Mattiola, sixth-grade teacher.

13. LESSON PLAN FOR GRADE SIX

GENERAL TOPIC: Menstruation.

SPECIFIC TOPIC: Menstruation: A step toward womanhood.

OBJECTIVES: To understand menstruation as a process whereby the girl is readied in a physical sense for the future role of wife and mother.

MATERIAL: Show the film "Girl to Woman."

METHOD
1. Class discussion. Write objective on the board. Ask students whether they agree or disagree with the statement.
   Purpose of the discussion: Teacher can observe the discussion to discover which children in the class are knowledgeable and which are quiet and hesitant to participate. If the teacher is available after class, she can encourage all students (with the hope of getting the shy ones) to ask questions in private.
2. Teacher will also raise questions when necessary and play back ideas into the group for clarification to discover whether students have grasped the information.
3. Discussion should continue until misconceptions are cleared. Avoid over-emphasizing topic so children do not become preoccupied with subject.

Suggested by Lucille Mattiola, sixth-grade teacher.

14. LESSON PLAN FOR GRADE SIX

GENERAL TOPIC: Menstruation.

SPECIFIC TOPIC: Menstrual hygiene.

OBJECTIVES: To make students aware that a woman should maintain the same good health habits during menstruation as she does at any other time.

MATERIALS: A health chart consisting of pictures illustrating activities that are performed daily (the chart can be compiled by the teacher).
1. Bathing—daily use of soaps and deodorants.
2. Brushing teeth two or three times a day.
3. Washing hair once or twice a week.
4. Eating three meals a day.
5. Receiving sufficient rest.
6. Performing physical activities that improve muscle tone and blood circulation.

METHOD: The following methods are suggested:
1. Instruct students to formulate individual charts of daily health activities. This can be done in word form.
2. Place teacher's chart on bulletin board. Have students compare their own

chart to that of teachers. Students should insert omitted information on personal charts.

3. Discussion through questions such as:
   a. Why do we bathe daily?
   b. Why do we brush our teeth daily?
   c. What does food do for us?
   d. Why do we need rest? Exercise?

CULMINATION: Ask:
1. Are the activities on the health charts prescribed for the daily schedule of a healthy person?
2. Knowing that menstruation is a normal process that occurs in a healthy woman, would there be any logical reason for altering her daily program on the days when she menstruates?
3. Why would it be even more important for her to maintain her normal hygiene program on the days she menstruates?

EVALUATION: Since hygiene is very personal, it would be difficult to formulate a method of evaluation. It would be necessary to hope the student would execute the practices taught.

Note: The above lesson is intended for female students only.

Suggested by Lucille Mattiola, sixth-grade teacher.

15. LESSON PLAN FOR JUNIOR HIGH SCHOOL

GENERAL TOPIC: Youth problems.

SPECIFIC TOPIC: Going steady.

PLACE IN COURSE: One of early topics on youth problems, for two class periods.

AIM: To show what going steady means and what particular advantages and disadvantages there are.

METHOD
1. The class is divided into two groups by sexes. Arguments are presented by both sides in the form of a debate.
2. Topics for debate:
   a. Reasons girls do or do not want to go steady.
   b. Reasons boys do or do not want to go steady.
   c. Advantages and disadvantages for girls in going steady.
   d. Advantages and disadvantages for boys in going steady.

RELATED ACTIVITIES
1. Show the following films:
   a. "Dating, Do's and Don'ts."

 b. "Going Steady."
2. Student discussions with parents.

Readings: Books on dating.

Suggested by Mr. Woodrow Chisena.

16. LESSON PLAN FOR JUNIOR HIGH SCHOOL

Topic: Appropriate emotional levels.

This lesson plan is for the purpose of determining the emotional levels considered appropriate for different age levels. It is an activity that is also useful as a get-started technique in a new unit or class.

A. Make five charts with headings:

 Appropriate for children.
 Appropriate for teenagers.
 Appropriate for teenagers *sometimes*.
 Appropriate for adults.
 Never appropriate.

B. On a table, place 3-by-5 cards, each bearing one of the following phrases:

 1. Cuddles teddy bear.
 2. Kisses mother in private.
 3. Kisses mother in public.
 4. Kisses father at home.
 5. Kisses father in public.
 6. Kisses brother.
 7. Kisses sister.
 8. Cries if hurt.
 9. Does not cry in public.
10. Holds hands in public.
11. Walks down street with arm around partner.
12. Hits back if hit.
13. Joins group tearing down football goalpost.
14. Climbs trees.
15. Uncomfortable sitting with opposite sex.
16. Talks freely with opposite sex.
17. Dresses to attract opposite sex.
18. Asks opposite sex for date.
19. Participates mostly in groups of the same sex.
20. Dates persons older than self.
21. Dates persons younger than self.
22. Obeys parents.
23. Dates a number of different people.
24. Feels desire to relate to opposite sex—not always sure of how to do it.
25. No awareness of opposite sex as boy/girl.
26. Untidy appearance acceptable.
27. Competes to win.
28. Wants to be tucked in bed by parent.

29. Argues about points where he doesn't agree with others.
30. Disagrees with others inside but keeps it to himself.
31. Flirts with opposite sex.

C. Ask teenagers to place each card in its appropriate category on the chart. If it fits more than one, make extra cards.

D. Examine the lists the teens have made on each chart. Frequently they list the major number under the *sometimes* category, pointing up their transition stage from child to adult. Parents who make similar charts may tend to be less rigid on what is expected of adults than teens can be from their limited perspective.

17. LESSON PLAN FOR SENIOR HIGH SCHOOL

GENERAL TOPIC: Youth problems.

SPECIFIC TOPIC: Relationship of parents to teenagers.

PLACE IN COURSE: One of the last topics under "youth problems" for one class period.

OBJECTIVES
1. To consider the responsibilities of parents with respect to their children.
2. To consider the responsibilities of teens toward their parents.

METHOD
1. Dramatization
2. Setting
   a. Teenage girl: A dispute arises when the daughter comes home late from a date.
   b. Teenage boy: A dispute arises when the boy is refused the use of the family car because he failed to perform some chores around the house.
3. The dramatization develops certain questions and the students are then asked to discuss the problems which have arisen.

PROBLEMS TO CONSIDER
1. How late should a teenage boy or girl be allowed to stay out?
2. What responsibilities do teenagers have within the family circle?
3. How would you treat your children under the same conditions?
4. Are most parents equipped to deal with the normal problems of raising children?
5. Should parents be liberal or strict with their children?

ASSIGNMENT: Selecting readings.

Suggested by Mr. Nicholas Mangelli, senior high school teacher.

18. LESSON PLAN FOR SENIOR HIGH SCHOOL

GENERAL TOPIC: Youth problems.

SPECIFIC TOPIC: Dating practices.

PLACE IN COURSE: Scheduled for two class periods in the beginning of the general topic of youth problems.

OBJECTIVES
1. To consider basic attitudes in our society toward dating practices.
2. To consider attitudes of teenage boys and girls toward dating practices.

METHOD
1. The plan is to put boys against girls in a class discussion by raising various questions concerning dating practices. The boys can learn how girls feel about certain practices and vice versa. The discussion—which may turn into a heated debate at times—must be supervised by the teacher.
2. Questions to discuss:
   a. Should a girl allow advances on the first date?
   b. Would a boy date a girl again if she is "cold" to his advances?
   c. What opinion do boys have toward a girl who allows sexual relations (intercourse) on a date?
   d. Would you marry a girl who has a reputation of promiscuity?
   e. Would you tell your husband or wife of your premarital sex experiences?

ASSIGNMENT: Appropriate readings on subject of dating.

Suggested by Mr. Nicholas Mangelli, senior high school teacher.

Activities

1. Prepare a unit on sex education for a specific grade—preferably the grade which you are planning to teach or are now teaching.

2. Prepare several lesson plans for the unit indicated above.

3. For one of the lesson plans included in this chapter, make it more complete by listing specific class readings for the pupils and another list for the teacher. What additional teaching aids can you list?

References

American School Health Association, *Report of the Elementary Health Education Committee on Teaching Units,* Kent, Ohio, 1963, 103 pp.

Gilbaugh, John W., *How to Organize and Teach Units of Work in Elementary and Secondary Schools,* Fearon Publishers, Palo Alto, Calif., 1957, 104 pp.

Haag, Jessie Helen, *School Health Program,* Holt, Rinehart and Winston, New York, 1965, 395 pp.

Hanna, Lavone, Gladys L. Potter, and Neva Hagaman, *Unit Teaching in the Elementary School,* Holt, Rinehart and Winston, New York, 1963, 608 pp.

Humphrey, James H., Warren R. Johnson, and Virginia D. Moore, *Elementary School Health Education,* Harper and Brothers, New York, 1962, 390 pp.

Irwin, Leslie W., James H. Humphrey, and Warren R. Johnson, *Methods and Materials in School Health Education,* The C. V. Mosby Company, St. Louis, 1956, 367 pp.

New York City Board of Education, *The Unit in Curriculum Development Instruction,* The Bureau of Curriculum Research, New York, 1956.

11

Venereal Disease Education

A separate chapter is here being given to the topic of venereal disease education because of several aspects which make this desirable.

1. It is here being given special attention because it is very important and because it often is not given its due attention in the schools.

2. There is considerable content to the subject of venereal disease.

3. Venereal disease is a communicable disease problem as well as a problem in psychosocial sex relations.

4. There has been a marked increase in the rate of VD among the youth of our country since 1957, which situation makes it desirable to focus special attention on this topic at the junior and senior high school levels.

5. Many educators feel that the nature of the details about VD make it preferable *not* to give full consideration to the topic when other aspects of sex education are being discussed. Instead, such details can more appropriately be presented in the communicable disease context in such courses as health education, general science, and biology where communicable diseases are normally considered. Some attention, of course, needs also to be given to the topic in other subject areas.

So that the reader who is especially interested in VD education may obtain maximum use of this text, we wish to here indicate how VD education is presented in this book.

1. This chapter considers the aspects of venereal disease and education about venereal disease which otherwise have not been adequately highlighted in other chapters of the book. For example, in Table 2, which lists all the major topics in sex education, venereal disease is one of over fifty such topics.

2. Much that has been covered in earlier chapters also relates to VD education. It is desirable that the reader has read these previous chapters so as to better see how VD education fits into the broad area of sex education. VD is so closely related to sex attitudes, sex behavior, sex knowledge, and sex morals that a study of such areas prior to and concurrently with that of VD education is desirable.

3. In teaching about sex education, methods of instruction have been discussed in Chapter 8. Many of these methods also apply to VD education. Therefore, in this chapter only special methods will be considered. The same statement applies to lesson plans, evaluation procedures, and other educational features.

4. The content of VD education, similar to that for other topics, is given in Part II of this text. In this chapter, reference will only be given to the broad headings of VD.

5. The bibliography on sex education in Appendix A gives VD education a separate heading so that such references can be located more quickly by interested teachers.

6. A multiple-choice test of venereal disease is included in the Appendix.

The Extent of the VD Problem

Venereal diseases are those that are usually contracted through sexual relations. In the United States *syphilis* and *gonorrhea* are most common. Less common in our country are three other venereal diseases: *chancroid, lymphogranuloma venereum,* and *granuloma inguinale.*

The venereal diseases constitute public health problems of major national significance, ignoring state boundaries in their spread throughout the United States.

In recognition of the seriousness of the VD problem, school administrators, teachers, parents, and youth have strongly endorsed the inclusion of VD education in the curriculum of the schools.

A CONCERN OF HEALTH DEPARTMENTS

In view of the fact that statistics indicate an average of one VD infection in every 224 teenagers (ages 15–19) in the United States, health authorities strongly recommend that state and local departments of education consider VD education for teenagers as an emergency need, particularly in geographical areas of high incidence; they further recommend that state and local health departments assist schools in the provision of teaching materials and in the preparation of teachers.

Also recommended is an aggressive and continuous program of education among the civilian population, and a sound program of education about the venereal diseases as a part of the training of all military personnel.

Many health departments report greater public awareness of the VD problem as reflected by an increase in coverage of the subject by mass media, requests for VD information, requests for educational materials, self-referrals to clinics, cooperation of private physicians, and requests for information and talks from professional physicians' societies.

A CONCERN OF MANY HEALTH ORGANIZATIONS

Further concern is illustrated by a joint statement [1] by the American Public Health Association, the American Social Health Association, and the American Venereal Disease Association with the cooperation of the American Medical Association and the Association of State and Territorial Health Officers. It reads as follows:

> Increasingly effective programs of education about the venereal diseases in school and community must be developed to support the work of state and local health departments, and of private physicians who treat infected patients.
>
> Research to develop new approaches to control, and to find immunizing agents for syphilis and even gonorrhea (which looks more difficult), appear essential for the eventual eradication of these diseases.

FACTS ABOUT VENEREAL DISEASE

Some selected facts about venereal disease are here listed. More detailed information is available on pp. 311–21.

1. Venereal diseases are caused by germs from an infectious person. These germs may be passed from one person to another through intercourse or other kinds of skin-to-skin contact.
2. The first sign of syphilis may appear sometime between ten and ninety days after the germ first entered the body.
3. Someone with syphilis may pass the disease along to someone else before he realizes there is anything wrong with him.

[1] The American Social Health Association, *Today's VD Control Problem,* January 1968, p. 7.

4. *Whether or not a person feels anything, the syphilis germs multiply in the blood, and cause an antibody (reagin) to develop which only a blood test can reveal.*

5. Proper treatment by a doctor is the only cure for syphilis.

6. Ordinarily, a person with syphilis may pass the disease along to others at times up to two years after infection; but mothers may pass the disease on to their unborn babies indefinitely.

7. About the only thing you can always depend on among the signs and symptoms of syphilis is a positive blood test about three months after infection.

8. If a pregnant woman is treated for syphilis, her baby probably will be born without syphilis. However, if the treatment comes late in pregnancy, the baby may have syphilitic damage to its body, even though it does not have active syphilis.

9. Syphilis is more likely to cause serious damage to its victim *after* he is no longer able to pass the disease on to anyone else.

10. Syphilis may look like a lot of things, and a lot of things may look like syphilis. Only a doctor can tell the difference.

11. Since the symptoms of syphilis disappear even if untreated, self-medication does not mean a cure and should never be relied upon.

12. The surest way to stop the spread of syphilis is to treat everybody who has had contact with an infectious person.

13. Accordingly, one of the most important ways to control syphilis is to trace contacts who might be infected from persons known to be infected.

14. It is important that all persons who have had contact with *infectious* syphilis be treated by a doctor as soon as possible.

15. Gonorrhea may cause sterility by blocking the passage of eggs or sperm.

16. Most men develop painful symptoms of gonorrhea between three and eight days after they become infected. Many women have no symptoms until the disease has done serious damage.

17. Many women realize they have gonorrhea only after a man becomes infected from them and helps get them to treatment.

18. Anyone who suspects he or she may have syphilis *or* gonorrhea should go to a doctor and ask to be examined for syphilis *and* gonorrhea.

19. Most states require that "drops" be put in the eyes of *all* newborn babies to prevent blindness from gonorrhea.

20. All persons exposed to known infectious cases of syphilis or gonorrhea should be treated for the disease as soon as possible.

THE HISTORY OF THE VD CONTROL PROGRAM

It has only been since the 1930's that serious attempts have been made to control venereal disease in our country. Prior to that time, VD was a taboo subject as far as the American public and press were concerned.

In November, 1934, Dr. Thomas Parran, as New York State Commissioner of Health, was to discuss "Public Health Needs" over the CBS network. His script included the following paragraph:

We have made no progress against syphilis, though its end results crowd our jails, our poorhouses, and our insane asylums. Yet, there are specific methods of controlling syphilis. We need only to do what we know how to do, in order to wipe out syphilis as a public health problem.

CBS, fearing to offend its listeners, demanded that the word *syphilis* be dropped. Dr. Parran refused. Music was substituted for the program. The suppressed script was printed in newspapers across the country, and Dr. Parran had a running start on his campaign to provide scientific treatment for venereal diseases which, until then, had been cloaked in Victorian prudery and ignored.

In 1936, two other events occurred which contributed to a breakdown in the public's outmoded attitude on the subject of VD control. In that year the first article on venereal disease in a periodical for the lay public—namely, the *Readers Digest*—was published. It shocked many people. Others, however, applauded the periodical for its contribution to the eradication of this problem.

Also, in 1936, the First National Conference on Venereal Disease was held which brought together interested people. This conference received publicity through the public press. It was the same Dr. Thomas Parran, then U.S. Surgeon General, who sponsored this conference. He stated at that time as follows:

It cannot be repeated too often that first and foremost among American handicaps to syphilis control is the widespread belief, from which we are only partially emerging, that nice people don't have syphilis, and nice people shouldn't do anything about those who do have syphilis.

Such attitudes on the part of the American public toward this problem have been changing for the better during these past thirty years.

INFECTION AMONG YOUNGER AGE GROUPS

The information on infection among younger age groups points definitely to the need for VD education in the community, and the schools must do their share. Here are some figures concerning the VD rates for the school-age population in the United States in 1966. (See Table 6.)

1. For children in the ten-to-fourteen-year-old age group, the rate of infectious syphilis was 1.1 per 100,000 and for gonorrhea it was 14.3.
2. The rate of infectious syphilis among teenagers (fifteen to nineteen) was 22.5 per 100,000 population, or more than twice the national rate of 10.9 for all age groups.

3. Gonorrhea among teenagers reached a rate of 424.9 per 100,000 in 1966, considerably more than twice the national rate of 178.6 for all age groups.

4. There has been an increase in the rate of infectious syphilis for teenagers of from 19.1 to 22.5 per 100,000 over the six-year period.

5. The teenage gonorrhea rate also increased, rising from 398.4 to 424.9 per 100,000 in the same period.

6. In contrast, rates for infectious syphilis in the twenty-to-twenty-four-year-old age group have remained almost static since 1960 with a rate of 42.9 in 1966.

7. Gonorrhea infections in the twenty-to-twenty-four-year-old age group increased sharply, however, from 790.1 per 100,000 in 1960 to 899.4 in 1966.

8. The fifteen-to-twenty-four-year-old age group, representing 16.2 per cent of the total U.S. population in 1966, accounted for 46.1 per cent of all reported primary and secondary syphilis and 57.5 per cent of all reported cases of gonorrhea in the nation.

9. The case rate per 100,000 for the same group for infectious VD was three and one-half times the rate for all age groups.

VD AND PROSTITUTION

While open prostitution is no longer tolerated in any but a few American cities and in only a few developed countries, the actual extent of prostitution is unknown, as is the degree to which prostitutes are now a source of VD infection.

However, from 10 to 15 per cent of persons with infectious syphilis named prostitutes among their sex contacts and 5 per cent infected with gonorrhea have similarly indicated prostitutes as contacts.

Today, promiscuity—sex relations with several or many partners—adds to the spread of venereal disease.

VD AND HOMOSEXUAL BEHAVIOR

The percentage of persons infected with primary and secondary syphilis who named contacts of their own sex has remained at almost the same level for the past four years. Homosexually acquired infectious syphilis represents 11 to 12 per cent of the total reported infections in 1966.

The importance attached to VD infection in homosexuals is related to two factors: (1) the known high promiscuity of this group; and (2) the reluctance of the homosexual to identify his sexual contacts because of fear of exposing both himself and his contacts.

A MORAL QUESTION

The control of venereal disease is not only a medical problem but also a moral problem. Since we know the cause of syphilis and gonorrhea and how they are transmitted, and since we have simple tests to aid in their diagnosis and have effective cures, why have we not been able to stamp them out? With that same amount of knowledge of other communicable diseases, we have been able to eliminate them completely or nearly so.

When it comes to syphilis and gonorrhea, unfortunately, man's moral behavior stands in the way of really effective control. Sexual promiscuity, homosexuality, and prostitution are the main causes for the spread of these diseases and tend to cancel out to a large extent the benefits of our medical knowledge.

Those young people whose morals are high, whose character is well developed, and who are adequately informed will not desire to expose themselves to venereal disease. In brief, the real control over venereal disease must spring from a sense of moral responsibility and self-discipline in matters of sex behavior.

A STUDY OF TEENAGE VD PATIENTS

The findings of one study [2] conducted by the American Social Health Association should be of interest to those who deal with youth. It involved a study by means of interviews of the attitudes of 600 teenage venereal disease patients attending the social hygiene clinics of New York City, and visits to the homes of 100 of them.

From the beginning of the study, the response of the teenagers was friendly, interested, and cooperative despite initial resentment at having to prolong a visit to the clinic that sometimes took up to three hours. The young people seemed eager to make a contribution to the study.

While all the teenagers interviewed had had sexual relations, only 63 per cent were found by the study to have had one or more venereal infections. Of these, 70 per cent were boys and 30 per cent girls. Among the infected group, numbering 379 teenagers, 159 reported one previous infection and fifty-five reported two or more.

Promiscuity—defined as casual, frequent, and depersonalized sexual relations—was a predominantly male phenomenon in this study group.

It should come as no surprise that promiscuity correlated significantly with venereal disease, especially among the boys.

Homosexuality was also much more prevalent among boys, with only nine girls so involved out of a total of 115 teenagers who reported homosexual activity.

Although nonwhites accounted for 71 per cent of the group studied,

2 Celia A. Deschin, "Teenagers and Venereal Disease," *Children,* July–August, 1962.

Puerto Rican teenagers, 16 per cent, and other whites, 13 per cent, promiscuity was found in all three groups with no essential difference.

Over two-thirds of the teenagers reported that their parents were interested in knowing where they went, expected them to be home at a certain time, and set standards for their behavior even if unable to assure that these were carried out at all times.

Most of the parents who were interviewed expressed concern over the behavior which had resulted in their child's illness, though often they did not seem to know about other socially deviant aspects of his or her behavior.

Almost half the young people reported that their parents attended religious services, while slightly more than 25 per cent of the teenagers did so.

The educational and cultural levels of most of these young people can only be characterized as impoverished. While nearly 75 per cent had entered high school, only 15 per cent had graduated. However, 3 per cent were attending college.

The major school problems reported were lack of interest in subjects, reading difficulties, failure to achieve promotion, and lack of interest on the part of the teachers. Many of the teenagers had been involved in truancy before becoming involved in sexual activities. Repeated truancy was reported by 80 per cent.

When asked what they did in their spare time, 509 replied: "Nothing!" Having nothing to do—in the sense of having few meaningful and socially useful responsibilities—means essentially to be nothing. To what extent this lack of role may be related to promiscuity can only be raised as a question for further investigation.

The indices of social control of most importance as related to promiscuous and socially deviant behavior were psychological atmosphere of the home (rated as favorable if the teenager spent considerable time there, took his friends there, and did things with his family); teenagers' religious attendance; and whether or not the teenager was still in school. School status reflected the most statistically significant influence.

Despite their involvement in sexual activities, these young people exhibited little understanding of the meaning of sex. Peers constituted the source of sex knowledge for 64 per cent of these youth, while parents were the source for 21 per cent, and other adults, for 15 per cent. Relatively fewer of the teenagers who obtained their sex knowledge from parents or adults with whom they had a positive identification were promiscuous.

While many of the teenagers had been involved in "delinquent" behavior, the group as a whole could not be characterized as delinquent.

Consider the contrasts in the young people who were interviewed in the social hygiene clinics:

1. A shy, withdrawn, guilt-laden honor student of eighteen, who lives with his grandmother, had his only sexual experience with a prostitute to test his "virility."
2. An eighteen-year-old drug addict, who lives with both parents, had had at least twenty-five sex partners toward whom he felt no personal attachment. He felt sorry only for having been "caught."

One need that all these young people in this study had in common was for better education about sex and venereal disease. On the surface, this should present little or no problem. However, the issue is beclouded by emotionally charged, conflicting, and controversial attitudes toward sex in society at large, as well as among the teenagers who have contracted the disease.

Constructive sex education requires a point of view and sanctions for codes of behavior to which society expects its youth to adhere.

The director of the study concludes the report by stating as follows:

Teenagers like those in this study have been held responsible for conduct traceable to the failure on the part of adults to facilitate and sanction controls. Twentieth-century psychological theories that have been exploited to support sexual license, almost to the debasement of human values and personal relations, need to be reexamined if followup studies and experimental clinics confirm the findings of this study. Conduct, not treatment, is the key to control.

THE STORY ABOUT JOAN AND JACK [3]

What do parents do when a loved child, a "good child who never gave us a moment's trouble," contracts a disease that "*nice* people don't have"? Here is how two typical families met the problem many are faced with today. We'll call them the Walkers and the Rosses.

THE STORY

The Walkers live in a comfortable home on an attractive street in a pleasant suburb. Their oldest child, fifteen-year-old Joan, is in high school. She is pretty, popular, and this year, for the first time, she has been going steady. Her parents have not been happy about this. They have felt that she is too young. But Jack Ross, seventeen, comes from a "nice" family too. And, like millions of other

[3] Celia A. Deschin, *Another Epidemic of Teen-Age VD?* U.S. Public Health Service, 1963.

parents, the Walkers and the Rosses have found it hard to argue down that teen-age cry, "Everybody else goes steady!"

When the telephone rang in the Walker house one afternoon, Mrs. Walker answered in her usual cheerful tone. But as she listened, her face paled. The caller was a doctor, not their family physician, but one whose name was known to Mrs. Walker. "It must be a mistake, doctor," she protested. "It can't be my daughter. What is she doing in your office?"

The doctor assured her that Joan *was* in his office. She had been brought there by Jack. Jack suspected that he had contracted syphilis and had exposed Joan to it. Tests had confirmed his suspicions. Would Mrs. Walker permit Joan to be examined?

Convinced that what he was saying was impossible, Mrs. Walker managed to say, "I'll be there right away." She drove to the doctor's office, trying not to think through the implications of what he had said. Joan could not be involved in anything like this. But Joan's white, frozen face told her that there had been no mistake. Mrs. Walker could not bring herself to look at Jack or speak to him.

The doctor asked Jack to wait outside and told Mrs. Walker the story Jack had told him. It was not, he said, an unusual story: A group of boys in a car, some drinking, and a pickup of several girls from another suburb. None of the boys had met the girls before, and (they said) would not recognize them again. One of the girls said, "My mother and father are away. Why don't we all go to my house?" They picked up some beer, and at the house there was more drinking. Sexual intimacies grew out of half-drunken goading and taunts of "don't be chicken!"

Joan had not been at this party. But later Jack discovered that he had contracted syphilis, and might have infected Joan. He asked her to accompany him to the doctor's office. There, hearing the whole story for the first time, Joan was too upset to telephone her mother. She asked the doctor to do it.

It would be necessary to examine Joan and make some laboratory tests, the doctor went on. Did Mrs. Walker prefer that it be done by their regular family doctor? It was Joan who said no to this. She did not feel that she could go through the painful, humiliating explanation again.

When the examination was finished, Mrs. Walker asked to speak to the doctor alone. "What can we do?" she asked helplessly. "Is Joan going to be all right?"

The doctor outlined the treatment Joan would require if tests proved positive. It was simple and effective. Since Joan had sought medical help so early, there should be no lasting harmful effects. Then he added bluntly but kindly: "I have teen-age children of my own, Mrs. Walker. I know how you feel. If I were you, I would not ask Joan too many pressing questions right away. Joan is deeply shocked. She feels frightened and guilty. She cannot bring herself to admit that she has had sexual relations with Jack, though Jack admitted it to me privately. Joan insists that they just 'petted heavily.' But she will tell you the truth, I'm sure, if you do not arouse her resentment with too many questions and accusations. Believe me, it will work out better in the long run." He concluded: "I will telephone you as soon as I have Joan's laboratory reports."

Mrs. Walker nodded, thanked him for his kindness, and left the office. In the car she patted Joan's hand with a calmness that she was far from feeling. At home, Joan went silently to her room and stayed there for the rest of the afternoon.

Remembering the doctor's advice, her mother fought back the questions she wanted so desperately to ask. One question, however, would not be stilled. Joan's father had to be told. How was it done, and who was to do it? Joan decided that. She would tell him herself—after dinner when the younger children were in bed.

It was not an easy story, and it was not told without tears and hesitations. But Joan told it. This shocking and bitter experience taught her a lot, she said. "A lot that I should have known—did know, really." As they listened, heartsick, her parents realized that they, too, were hearing things they should have known—had known, really. Their failure had been in not using their knowledge to protect their daughter.

Joan admitted having sexual relations with Jack. "He said it was all right, we were going steady. It was just proof that I loved him. If I didn't love him, there wasn't much point in our going steady, was there?"

"Joan is too young to go steady," Mrs. Walker remembered protesting only a few weeks ago. Why had she let herself be argued down when she knew she was right?

The first time was here in their house, Joan went on. "You and mother went out to play bridge," she told her father. "Jack and I were listening to records. We had argued about things before, and I knew how it would be, so I hoped you wouldn't go out."

It happened several times after that in Jack's car. "I wasn't ever happy about it," Joan said. "I knew it was wrong. I talked to other girls about it, and most of them felt it was wrong too. But nobody knew how to say no. The boys wouldn't want to go steady any longer if we said no." Her tone told them what a serious, humiliating loss of status this would have been among her contemporaries.

Joan paused. Then she went on with resolute determination to show them that she really had learned. "Boys just try that 'prove your love' to see if it will work. Girls shouldn't be fooled by it. I don't blame Jack any more than I blame myself, but right now I don't ever want to see him again—or any other boy!"

Next day the doctor told Joan and her mother that laboratory tests were positive. Joan paled, but took the diagnosis quietly. The doctor started treatment with antibiotics immediately. "The *right* medical treatment is vital," he stressed. "Sometimes teenagers foolishly rely on 'drug store treatment' with penicillin obtained surreptitiously. The amounts obtained this way are not sufficient to cure the disease; they only mask the symptoms temporarily." He explained that Joan would have three or four treatments, and that she would come in for regular checkups over a period of six months.

Joan asked only one question, her voice very serious. "Does this mean that when I marry I can't have babies?" The doctor assured her that it did not.

HOUSE RULES SET UP

That night Joan and her parents drew up a set of what they called House Rules. It listed clearly and simply what was expected of Joan, from household tasks to the number and kind of dates she could have and the time she must be home. All parties at the Walker house would be chaperoned, and Joan would attend no unchaperoned parties at homes of friends. "I'll talk to the other mothers in the neighborhood," Mrs. Walker said. "If we all agree on certain standards of behavior—and stand firm—the children won't be able to gang up on us with that 'everybody else does it' cry."

It was agreed that Joan had a right to expect certain things from her parents. More thoughtful, serious attention to questions that troubled her, for one thing. And more effort to be good examples of the sort of person they wanted her to be. They would also try to make clear to her the standards and values which they would most like to have her hold.

A little to her surprise, Joan's friends were enthusiastic when they heard about the House Rules. "It's a lot easier when you *know* what your parents expect of you," one said honestly. "Most of the time they just say 'Be good,' without ever telling us *how* to be good, or just what 'good' really means to them."

Jack and his parents worked out their own set of rules, as each family must, since no single formula could possibly be successful for all. But the first and most important step toward success was made when they faced the problem honestly and together.

SUGGESTIONS BASED ON THE STORY

In general, the following suggestions might help:

Adolescents need to know what behavior is expected of them, especially in the area of sex. Parents should provide this guidance. Accurate sex and health education in schools could help protect children against VD.

(In the New York City teen-age VD study which I conducted, 64 per cent of the teenagers said that all of their information about sex and venereal disease came from friends their own age. They displayed pitiful ignorance of even the most basic facts. Only 10 per cent knew what VD is, and that it is almost never contracted except through sexual intercourse.) People who oppose sex education in schools argue, "If you teach a child about sex, he'll be out experimenting with it!" I would say that the exact opposite is true—the more *accurate* information a child has, the less likely he is to get into trouble. True knowledge does not corrupt, it protects.

Parents should limit the number of dates a teenager is permitted and set a definite time for coming home. They should be at home and visible when their teenagers entertain.

Parties (at home, in schools, churches, teen-age clubs, and so on) should be chaperoned by responsible adults. Adolescents may complain, but they really do feel more secure with adult guidance and supervision.

Group activities—sports, music, drama, lectures—should be encouraged to replace the present practice of too-early dating and going steady and to discourage pairing off of boys and girls under conditions which favor sexual intimacy.

Adolescents should be weaned away from the "happiness ratrace," which, after a while, becomes a bore. Work (paid or volunteer) provides happiness too. Personal accomplishment lends confidence and self-reliance.

Like the Walkers, parents should try to be good examples. They should not "preach one thing and live another." They should also try to define the standards they want their children to live up to.

On the community level, parents can work for more public-health clinics and more programs of health education. In 1957, Federal funds for these services were cut. It is no coincidence that we find 1957 the year that the VD rate began its current spectacular rise.

Curriculum Planning for VD Education

The goal of VD education is to eradicate VD from among our youth and, ultimately, from the nation and the world.

It is hoped that this purpose can be accomplished by effective teaching about:

1. The nature of venereal disease.
2. How it is spread.
3. How it can be cured.
4. Above all, how it can be prevented.

Since the VD problem for adolescents is so serious, the following recommendations concerning education on this topic need to be stressed: [4]

1. VD education per se should consist of the presentation of a body of information about syphilis and gonorrhea which may be expected to motivate the recipient.
2. VD authorities should recognize that their primary educational focus is VD education per se. Nevertheless, they should endorse related programs of sex education, character guidance, and family life education when appropriate.
3. VD education per se should be initiated not later than the seventh grade and be continued at least through senior high school.
4. Whenever possible, the facts about VD and their implications should be taught routinely in existing conditions without segregation of sexes or any other imposed conditions which would tend to place VD in a special category other than as one of a number of intolerable diseases.
5. Every effort should be made to have additional VD-related content of

[4] Public Advisory Committee on Venereal Disease Control, *Venereal Disease Education,* U.S. Public Health Service, Atlanta, Georgia, 1964.

greater depth included in health-related textbooks for use in grade and secondary school.

EXTENT OF VD EDUCATION IN THE SCHOOLS

VD education was included in 1967 in various courses in the curriculum of 2,275 out of 3,719, or 61.2 per cent, of all junior and senior high schools in a sample of 107 urban areas. In twenty-six areas, VD education was reported as being included in the curriculum of *all* junior and senior high schools in the area. In eighteen other areas, VD education was not included in *any* school. In many instances, the replies indicated that the inclusion was very recent, and that, while included in the curriculum, courses given were not yet of satisfactory quality.

As of 1967 reports, the establishment of working relationships between state health departments and departments of education, as a first step in bringing about the inclusion of VD education in the schools, had been made in all except eight of the states.

Further, approval of the inclusion of VD education in the curriculum of junior and senior high schools has been given by state education departments in thirty-four states and in ninety-seven urban areas.

GRADE LEVELS FOR VD EDUCATION

We have to begin our teaching about VD at the age and grade level at which statistics indicate that trouble begins—which is somewhere in the fifth or sixth years of elementary school. Accordingly, some beginning should be made in the sixth grade within the framework of communicable diseases.

The Educational Subcommittee of the National Advisory Committee on Venereal Disease has recommended that the subject be covered thoroughly and repeatedly between the seventh and twelfth grades in health or science classes.

It is further recommended that the biology, pathology, prevention, and treatment of venereal disease be presented as early as possible since potential dropouts might be expected to be more in need of and concerned with these aspects than they would be with others.

It is recommended, therefore, that these areas be covered at the eighth grade level. For those students who have received such a background in these aspects of VD, it is suggested that the social and public health aspects be covered in the eleventh or twelfth years of the secondary school.

It is further recommended that possibly three class periods be devoted to VD education at each of these two levels.

CONTENT OF VD UNIT

The following suggestions for course content are suggested by the New Jersey State Department of Education.

Where a limited amount of time is to be devoted to the topic, important facts about syphilis and gonorrhea under these headings can be included:

1. Causes.
2. How transmitted.
3. Signs and symptoms.
4. Whether it is hereditary.
5. Course of the diseases.
6. Treatment and cure.

If the class is studying communicable disease, and venereal diseases are included, the same outline that is used for any other disease is useful for VD. Thus, another outline, and in more detail, might be:

1. Trends in morbidity.
2. Trends in mortality.
3. The age levels attacked most commonly.
4. How disease is spread.
5. Causative organism, if known.
6. Control of the disease.
7. Diagnostic test.
8. Possible immunization.
9. Early symptoms.
10. What a person with early symptoms should do.
11. What people who are associated with this person should do.
12. Treatment in general.
13. Research now being carried on.

QUESTIONS FOR DISCUSSION

The following questions can be discussed with a secondary school class after going over the facts about venereal disease.

1. Why is untreated syphilis among the worst of infectious (or communicable) diseases?

2. In syphilis eradication, why is treatment almost useless without contact tracing?

3. Why does syphilis eradication require the closest cooperation between the health department and the private doctor?

4. Why is speed so important in finding venereal disease cases for the sake of *both* the infected person and the community?

5. Considering the reasons for the spread of syphilis in the sixteenth and seventeenth centuries, which of the same reasons may be partly responsible for the increase of syphilis in our age, and are there any new reasons?

6. Why do we say that venereal disease is *everybody's* problem?

7. Why have syphilis and gonorrhea always been a problem among the military?

8. Why do we say that *everyone* can help in some way to eradicate venereal disease? What are some of the ways different kinds of people might help (students, teachers, parents, clergy, doctors, businessmen, others)?

CORRELATION AND INTEGRATION OF VD EDUCATION

The courses and grades in which VD is taught are listed in Table 8 for 107 local urban areas that were surveyed. Ranking first by local areas was health education with the following ranking in descending order: physical education, family life education, biology, and home economics. Many other courses were mentioned, including science, psychology, social studies, health and safety, sex education, and VD education.

Suggestions for correlating the topics of venereal disease into various subjects is shown in Table 7.

In an integrated program of VD education, English literature can also contribute since references to VD appear in literary works. Sometimes it is the theme of a play, a story, or a poem, and sometimes there is just passing reference to it. Since literature reflects the health, history, and social climate of the time, the discussion can be centered about this core.

Sources that might be discussed include Ibsen's "Ghosts," Marlowe's "Dr. Faustus," Voltaires' "Candide," Shakespeare's "Love's Labour's Lost," and "All's Well That Ends Well."

The statement, "To know syphilis is to know history," by William F. Schwartz of the Venereal Disease Branch of the U.S. Public Health Service, refers to historical figures whose lives were affected by syphilis, which in turn affected the course of history. Some of the people who might be investigated by interested history students include Henry VIII of England, Christopher Columbus of Italy, Charles VIII and Francis I of France, and Ivan the Terrible of Russia. (See "VD and History" on pp. 312–14.)

**TABLE 7. SUGGESTIONS FOR CORRELATING INFORMATION
ABOUT THE VENEREAL DISEASES IN SELECTED
AREAS OF THE CURRICULUM ***

Area of Correlation	HEALTH INSTRUCTION	SCIENCE	SOCIAL STUDIES	HOME ECONOMICS	FAMILY LIVING	GUIDANCE
1. In relation to other communicable diseases, their cause, spread, symptoms, control and prevention	X	X	X	X	X	
2. In relation to public health and the health department's methods of controlling and preventing the spread of communicable diseases.	X		X		X	X
3. In relation to causes of mental illness.	X		X		X	X
4. In relation to organisms which cause disease such as the spirochete and syphilis, and the gonococcus and gonorrhea.	X	X				
5. In relation to scientific methods of detecting disease. a. The blood test for syphilis. b. Microscopic examination for syphilis and gonorrhea.	X	X			X	
6. In relation to the discovery and use of antibiotic drugs.	X	X				
7. In relation to scientific discoveries dealing with disease.	X	X				
8. In relation to the effects of venereal disease on the history of the world.	X		X		X	
9. In relation to public health laws. a. The premarital and prenatal blood tests. b. Blood tests for food handlers. c. Laws against prostitution.	X		X	X	X	
10. In relation to the future health and happiness of the family, with reference to freedom from communicable diseases.	X			X	X	X
11. In relation to congenital syphilis and children.	X	X		X	X	X
12. In relation to disease statistics and the incidence of various communicable diseases.	X	X				

* Topics from Donald A. Campbell, "Education About Venereal Disease," *J. Health, Phys. Educ. and Rec.,* April 1962, p. 32.

**TABLE 8. COURSES AND GRADES WHICH INCLUDE
VD INSTRUCTION**

Courses	No. of States	No. of Local
Biology	26	58
Family life education	29	68
Health education	32	80
Home economics	20	32
Physical education	34	77

Grades	No. of States	No. of Local
6th	4	8
7th	20	44
8th	30	60
9th	32	74
10th	33	86
11th	32	78
12th	31	77

PARENTAL CONSENT AND MIXED CLASSES

In planning for venereal disease education in the curriculum, consideration needs to be given to (1) the matter of parental consent and (2) whether or not the sexes should be separated.

The need for obtaining parental consent is related to the overall question of whether parental consent is needed in the teaching of sex education. In areas where such consent has been asked for, few parents have objected; and in many areas where no effort has been made to obtain parental consent, there has been no adverse reaction.

Concerning teaching VD to mixed or segregated classes, the answer is that already given for sex education in general (see pp. 128–29). Furthermore, since general science and biology is taught to mixed groups, there is little reason for changing this procedure. Health education classes are usually separated by sex because of the scheduling of health classes to alternate with physical education. Where health classes are mixed, there is little value in separating them when VD education is to be taught.

The Educational Subcommittee of the National Advisory Committee on Venereal Disease recommends as follows:

Whenever possible, the facts about venereal disease and their implications should be taught routinely in existing classes under existing conditions without segregation of the sexes or any other imposed conditions which would tend to place venereal disease in a special category other than as one of intolerable diseases.

METHODS OF TEACHING IN VD EDUCATION

The various methods discussed in Chapter 8 apply in general to the teaching of venereal disease. Of these methods, those of using student questions and film are especially recommended.

Student questions. One of the soundest approaches to VD education is that of starting with the questions of young people themselves. Some of their questions can then be answered directly. Certain questions, which for a variety of reasons cannot be resolved in the classroom, can be handled in other ways. Private discussions or appropriate referrals can be utilized at the teacher's discretion.

Pupil's questions can be used in *group* activities where each member of the class has an opportunity to recognize that he may be seeking a solution to the same problem.

A visit to a physician. A discussion could be held about what a visit to the physician would entail in case a student had, or suspected that he might have, a venereal disease. Such a discussion could be planned in several ways:

1. The film, "The Innocent Party," in which procedure in a doctor's office can be viewed, could be shown to the class.

2. Some students might get information from doctors whom they know.

3. Or a physician could be invited to explain such procedure to the class. The class should understand that whatever information is given to the doctor is considered confidential. In anticipation of the doctor's visit, students might be encouraged to prepare questions they may wish discussed by him.

A play. The showing of the play, "You Never Told Me," at a PTA meeting might be one way of getting parents interested in VD control. Copies of the script may be obtained without charge from the Bureau of Public Health Education, Department of Health, 125 Worth Street, New York. This play is about VD and teenagers. It explains how VD "can happen" to *anyone's* child, and how the family must share responsibility for VD education. The script has directions for production, and includes a list of questions at the end for guiding discussion.

Films. The use of at least one of the excellent films on venereal disease is strongly recommended—for example, the film, "The Invader," which traces the history of the disease and how it can be controlled. Students can be told before the film showing that the following questions will be discussed.

1. How did syphilis affect history?
2. Why did syphilis spread rapidly in the sixteenth and seventeenth centuries?
3. How did earlier scientific discoveries make it possible for later scientists to discover the germ, the test, then the cure of syphilis?
4. What contributions were made by Schaudinn, Hoffman, Wassermann, Bordet, Ehrlich, Parran, Fleming, and Mahoney?
5. How was knowledge about syphilis and its cure kept from people?
6. What were the Rapid Treatment Centers?
7. What evidences can you find to indicate that the film was more optimistic than the present situation justifies?

In light of the belief that nice people do not have syphilis, show the film, "A Respectable Neighborhood."

PROGRAM EVALUATION

The results of VD education are difficult to evaluate. The following report, however, sheds some light on the subject. A study of the effectiveness of VD education in the Los Angeles schools after four years showed the following results:

1. *Decreased incidence of VD.* In Los Angeles, by the end of 1966, teen-age syphilis case rates had been reduced by 72 per cent. During this period, both teenagers and all other age groups had been exposed to a variety of "awareness" programs. However, only teenagers had the benefit of school education programs.

2. *Increased volunteer reporting rate.* Recognition of VD symptoms and motivation to seek immediate medical attention are prerequisite to an eradication program. Speed in volunteering to report reduces the likelihood of spread. It is also an illustration of an informed patient practicing preventive measures in the interest of others.

That the Los Angeles teenagers became more knowledgeable is evidenced by the increased number of patients reporting without prompting from the Health Department and by a reduction in the number of days elapsed before reporting.

3. *Sex pattern alteration.* A reduction in promiscuity was reported. This change reduces the number of sex contacts, which in turn reduces the possibility of VD infection.

Effect of VD Education on VD Incidence. A question in a study in 1967 as to the effect of VD education in the schools on the problem of teen-age VD brought comments from 118 local health departments, as follows.

Four positive measurable effects on teen-age VD were reported by forty-six (39 per cent) local health departments:

1. Sixteen health departments noted increased student awareness of VD.
2. Fifteen stated that more teen-age students came to VD clinics for examination.

3. Fifteen reported that infected teenagers sought earlier diagnosis and treatment.

4. Two commented that, as a result of VD education, students were uninhibited in revealing their problems to teachers and in seeking advice or treatment.

Judgment on the effect of VD education was reserved by thirty-five other health departments, with nineteen stating that it was too early to judge, twelve that the effect was impossible to evaluate, and four that it was not known.

Another fifteen health departments commented that VD education had little or no measurable effect on teenage VD. The remaining health departments did not reply to the question.

Activities

1. Concerning venereal disease in your state, find answers to the following questions:

   a. What are the rates for syphilis and gonorrhea?
   b. How does this rate compare with that of other states? (See Table 5.)
   c. Is there a law requiring a premarital examination?
   d. Is there a law requiring a prenatal examination?
   e. Is the teaching about VD permitted? Required?

2. Prepare a lesson plan around the use of the article "Another Epidemic of Teenage VD" in a high school class.

3. Make a list of the patterns of today's teen-age behavior which lead to VD. Suggest how they might be changed.

4. Determine whether working relations have been established between your local health department and your local department of education to consider the inclusion of VD education in the school curriculum. If the answer is "yes," obtain information about the program recommended.

6. By means of the objective test on venereal disease included in the Appendix, determine the knowledge or lack of knowledge of a group of high school students on the subject. Report to the class your findings and observations.

7. Where VD education is included in the curriculum of some junior or senior high school, determine in what grades and courses it is taught.

References

American Association for Health, Physical Education, and Recreation, *Facts About Syphilis and Gonorrhea* (student's manual), National Education Association, Washington, D.C., 1965, 154 pp.

American Association for Health, Physical Education, and Recreation, *Teacher's Manual on Venereal Disease Education* (prepared by William F. Schwartz, U.S. Public Health Service), National Education Association, Washington, D.C., 1965, 152 pp.

American Association for Health, Physical Education, and Recreation, *VD Re-*

source Unit for Senior High Schools, National Education Association, Washington, D.C., 1965.

American Social Health Association, *Today's VD Control Problem,* New York, 1968.

Burton, John, "VD: A Behavioural Disease," *Internat. J. Health Educ.,* January–March, 1968, pp. 13–17.

Deschin, Celia A., *Another Epidemic of Teen-Age VD?,* U.S. Public Health Service, Washington, D.C., 1963.

Deschin, Celia A., "Teenagers and Venereal Disease," *Children,* July–August, 1962.

New York City Board of Education, *A Resource Guide on Venereal Disease Control,* Curriculum Bulletin 1967–1968, New York, 1967.

New Jersey State Department of Education in cooperation with the N. J. State Department of Health, *Venereal Disease: A Teaching Reference Guide,* Trenton, N.J., 1966, 87 pp.

Public Advisory Committee on Venereal Disease Control, *Venereal Disease Education,* U.S. Public Health Service, Atlanta, Ga., 1964.

Webster, Bruce, *What You Should Know About VD—and Why,* Scholastic Book Services, New York, 1967, 64 pp.

12

The Dissemination
of Offensive
and Obscene Material

The topic of obscenity is one that merits a separate chapter because of its impact upon American children and youth. It is not a topic about which one teaches children. It rather is a topic which teachers, parents, and others interested in the welfare of children need to be aware of. Such awareness should contribute to a better understanding of this sordid problem in our society.

It should further strengthen the desire of adults to do something to reduce and prevent the spread of obscene ideas and literature to the immature in particular. It should also contribute to a better understanding of the psychological, sociological, and moral factors in our society which need to be strengthened or changed, as the case may be, in the interest of our children and youth.

Specifically for the field of sex education, such better understanding of obscenity will give us a broader insight into what needs to be done through sex education, appropriate to grade and age levels, to develop the pertinent knowledge about sexuality and attitudes and behavior related thereto—as a counteraction to the smut industry.

Material gathered for this chapter has largely been derived with adaptations from the *Report of the New York State Joint Legislative Committee to Study the Publication and Dissemination of Offensive and Obscene Material* published in 1962 after a year of hearings on the subject. This report is one of the most recent and extensive exposés of the character and extent of the dissemination of obscene materials. It also includes the opinions on, and viewpoints concerning, the relative effects this has on the developing attitudes and resulting conduct of children and youth, as presented by knowledgeable individuals—clergymen, sociologists, psychiatrists, educators, and law-enforcement people.

The Committee has focused its attention upon the mass media of communication. Through its reports to the Legislature, it has consistently warned that great quantities of lewd, lascivious, and obscene books, magazines, films, and articles were being distributed throughout the State of New York. It has registered its findings, year after year, that much of this material was reaching the hands of minors. The Committee has exposed and detailed those mass media practices of advertising which sensationalize, glorify, and condone immoral acts or which describe lurid, illegal, or unnatural sex practices.

The Committee has specifically concluded that dissemination of this type is contributing to juvenile delinquency, inciting to sex crime, leading to perversion, and posing a serious threat to our standards of morality.

Also used has been the material from the hearings of the Senate Juvenile Delinquency Sub-Committee, Senator Thomas J. Dodd, Committee Chairman.

Reference is also made to the role of laws—federal, state and local—on the control of the distribution of obscene literature, the school's role in the reduction in the availability of such materials, and a reduction in the reading of it by children and youth through programs of better reading materials.

Explanation of What Constitutes Pornography and Obscenity

It is difficult to set down a satisfactory definition of the word *obscenity,* although the term itself has been in use for centuries. In the old English Hicklin case, the test of obscenity was whether the tendency of the material was to deprave or corrupt those whose minds are open to such immoral influences and who might come into contact with it.

The Supreme Court of the United States defined obscenity as follows: "Whether to the average person, applying contemporary community standards, the dominant theme of the material taken as a whole appeals to the prurient interest."

The word *pornography* is often loosely used. "Outright pornography" (as used here) refers to pictures and motion pictures which show acts of sexual intercourse and sexual perversion.

Large quantities of such motion pictures, playing cards, colored slides, and similar material continue to appear throughout our country. There has been a steady increase in the volume of material dealing with perversion. Particularly repulsive have been those publications or materials which describe or otherwise show sadistic, masochistic, or deviate sex acts or practices.

Pornography has reportedly become a five-hundred-million-dollars-a-year business.

The nature of pornography and obscenity can further be described as a concern with presenting a wish-fulfillment fantasy. The object is hallucinogenic, and it serves either as a substitute for experience or to satisfy an insatiable craving.

It is rare for pornography to present anti-erotic aspects of sexual activities such as venereal disease, pregnancy, and contraceptive devices.

There is little or no development of character or of theme besides an attempt towards sexual stimulation.

The Legal Testing of Obscenity

Here follow the landmark obscenity laws and decisions:

1. The Hicklin Rule (1868): The tendency must be to deprave or corrupt minds.
2. The Comstock Law (1873): It declared that obscenity was unmailable.
3. The Halsey Case (1922): The entire work must be considered as a whole.
4. James Joyce's *Ulysses* was ruled not obscene (1934).
5. The Roth Case (1957): Obscenity must be "utterly without redeeming social importance" and appeal to "prurient interests." This ruling knocked out the Hicklin Rule.
6. The Supreme Court (1962) clarified the Roth ruling by stating that a work must have the quality of "patent offensiveness" as well as appeal to "prurient interest" in order to be considered obscene.
7. In further clarification (1964), the Supreme Court declared that obscenity must be judged by "national" community standards and not by individual local standards.
8. The *Fanny Hill* case (1966)—the first obscenity case in America involving a book—is now the basis for current rulings.
9. The Congress enacted legislation (1967) designed to protect the public from receiving unsolicited mailings of "pandering advertisements."

This ruling concerns whether the material is *utterly* without social redeeming value, and whether to the average person, applying contemporary national standards, the dominant theme is prurient interest, and whether the material is patently offensive. The heart of the ruling is the belief that obscenity motivates certain people to commit antisocial acts, but there is little statistical support either way.

Authoritative Viewpoints

During these past years, there has been a steady and frightening increase in juvenile delinquency. Even more alarming are the number of juvenile court cases which relate directly to sex and violence. The Federal Bureau of Investigation shows a shocking increase in juvenile prostitution. Rape and venereal disease are on the increase. At the same time, records show a large increase in the crimes of aggravated assault and murder.

That there is a relationship between such statistics on rates of sex crime and the widespread dissemination of obscene, immoral, and amoral materials has been challenged. It is believed that J. Edgar Hoover best answers this and similar challenges when, referring to such statistics, he states as follows:

> This truly shocking and shameful state of affairs is made even more deplorable by the knowledge that sex crime and obscene and vulgar literature often go hand in hand. . . . I believe pornography is a major cause of sex violence. I am convinced that if we can eliminate the distribution of obscene material among impressionable school-age children, we can reduce the current sex rate. . . . This diabolical business is costing the nation much more than money. It is robbing our country and particularly our younger generation of decency—it's a seed-bed for delinquency among juveniles and depravity among all ages.

In forums and debates and reports or articles relative to this subject, those who disagree with the position of the New York State Committee, or that of Mr. Hoover, normally point to the testimony of one or more psychiatrists who contend that obscenity or pornography does not cause crime. Admittedly, there is a difference of opinion as to the direct causal relationship. Nevertheless, few of the experts will deny, when pressed, that the widespread dissemination of lewd and obscene materials contributes to delinquency.

In assessing the situation, the Committee has been most impressed with the testimony of the police who fight crime as professionals. These men and women face the offenders; they interrogate them and know their motivations. Almost without exception they rank obscenity high among the factors contributing to crimes of sex and violence.

Dr. Nicholas G. Frignito, the Chief Neuropsychiatrist and the National Director of the Philadelphia Municipal Court, has daily opportunity to study and evaluate the effects of obscenity and pornography on the conduct of youthful offenders. In testifying, the doctor has stated in part as follows:

Anti-social, delinquent, and criminal activity frequently results from sexual stimulation by pornography. This abnormal sexual gratification creates such a demand for expression that gratification by vicarious means follows. Girls run away from their homes and become entangled in prostitution. Boys and young men who have difficulty resisting the undue sexual stimulation become sexually aggressive and generally incorrigible. The more vicious delinquent or psychopathic type may become an exhibitionist, a rapist, a sadist, a fetishist. He may commit such anti-social acts as arson, pyromania, or kleptomania, which are often symbolic sexual acts. The Philadelphia Municipal Court has case histories in which sexual arousal from smutty books has led to criminal behavior ranging from vicious assaults to homicide. Sexual stimulation by printed material does not always lead to crime, but it is always an inducement to impurity and in the more suggestible individual leads to aberrant forms of sexual misconduct.

"It is no overstatement to say that obscene literature is a threat against the moral fiber of the next generation of Americans. There can be no doubt that, unless action is taken quickly, this vast and lucrative business will become a major department in the empire of organized crime," stated former Senator Keating of New York before Congress.

Among the national organizations which have raised their voices in support of the link between crime and obscenity, none is better acquainted with the problem, nor speaks with more authority, than the National Association of County and Prosecuting Attorneys. This organization has stated:

The publication of literature designedly devoted to exploration of moral perversion, lust, vice, physical violence and crime has become increasingly prevalent during the past decade. This appeals not only to the base and depraved instincts of adults, but also presents a highly distorted image of adult manners and morals to the grave detriment of the common good and welfare.

Freedom of the Press and Obscenity

Whenever a committee of this type deals with the problems of obscenity, or of purported obscenity, it deals with the avowed advocates of freedom of the press. Admittedly, freedom of the press is the key safeguard of civil liberty. As such it is to be respected, safeguarded, and defended. However, it is the New York State Committee's position that liberty is not to be abused, or construed as a license to contaminate for profit. All too often, it has been found that it is license which is coveted, rather than freedom which is protected. The courts and the American public must either learn to distinguish between them or suffer the consequence of an amoral society.

The United States Supreme Court has clearly held that obscenity is not within the area of constitutionally protected speech and press. Obscenity, however, must be defined, and in practice the Supreme Court has become increasingly liberal in interpretation. State Courts have followed the trend.

The New York State Committee has stated:

> If government is to be powerless to prohibit the general public dissemination of material void of social value, "dedicated to coarse sexual titillation" and "containing stories of sexual seduction devoted to little other purposes than sexual stimulation," it must at least find a means of protecting children from the evil inherent in material of this kind. . . . In the battle against obscenity, moral standards will rapidly deteriorate if the public is content to accept as morally inoffensive all that we are unable to legally curtail.

Dr. Carl F. Russ of the American Lutheran Church has stated as follows:

> No matter how "emancipated" and modern persons may believe their views to be, the history of mankind demonstrates, at least to me, that the areas of sex, marriage, parenthood, the sacredness of human life, protection of person, property, name, reputation, and peace of mind and the upholding of authority are so basic that they cannot be left to the whims of personal freedom, imagined emancipations from restraint, and the dangers of license and anarchy. Sound, sensible, proven customs and mores must control these areas of life. Self-seeking cannot be allowed to corrupt and degrade the quality of our social living under protections intended for nobler purposes.

The Role of Mass Media

Here follows a review of the role of various forms of mass media in the dissemination of undesirable materials and programs.

MAGAZINES

The so-called "girlie," "sex," and "sophisticated" magazines are on the increase as to number and variety. The contents, like the cover, exhibit the same attempt to pander and commercialize upon man's taste for the bawdy and the ribald behind a bare disguise of aesthetic respectability.

Thus, together with short stories of apparent literary merit, reprinted with permission from standard editions of the authors' works, which are inoffensive under any standard of sexual sensitivity, there appear the usual staples of this form of sexual provocation, including "artistic" photographs, salacious cartoons, and short stories of sexual seduction.

BOOKS

The public market place continues to abound in both hardcover and paperback books dealing with and exploiting sex. Advertisements for many of these publications appear in the best of our newspapers.

The current attitude is evidenced by an ad for a book entitled *Confessions of a Spent Youth* which appeared in one well-known paper. In bold letters the ad read: "THE LIBERATION OF OUR NOVELIST TO WRITE FREELY OF SEXUAL MATTERS IS FINALLY PAYING OFF." The ad goes on to state that the book "will startle the staid, titillate the suggestible," and that it is one of the "tenderest, funniest, most shocking and disturbing books in years."

Another newspaper carried an advertisement for a book entitled *McCafferty,* which stated that the book is "a sensational new novel about a furious young man who burns away his poverty and his past by plunging into a life of depravity."

He is McCafferty, bright, good-looking and gifted with a certain fatal charm. One dark night he moves from a tenement in New York's Yorkville to a plush Greenwich Village brothel. In the oldest profession, he is an innovator. No act is too sordid for McCafferty, no wealthy woman too old or too fat, no male customer too demanding. Then a remarkable man named Bentley—suave, sophisticated, unnatural—introduces McCafferty to genuine luxury and horror. McCafferty lives in his penthouse, learns the savage rites of perversion, attends the parties where thirty people make thirty kinds of love. He finds himself sinking into a well of decadence so deep that only the most violent crime can save him.

This is a rare book. It deals with the degradation of sex in our society and is one of the most controversial novels of recent years. *Lady Chatterley's Lover,* for readers old enough to know where babies come from, is really a dull book. Nobody can say that about *McCafferty.*

PAPERBACKS

The paperback book has become commonplace. Many of these books provide interesting, amusing, or educational entertainment. A large number deal with illicit sex and perversion, neatly wrapped in covers which loudly proclaim their dedication to titillation. These books are displayed in great quantity on newsstands, in drug stores, and in supermarkets. Many of them describe sexual conduct and attitudes believed to be most harmful to the mental health and moral standards of our people.

MAIL SOLICITATION

The volume of obscene and near-obscene material flowing through the mails continues to increase in an alarming manner. Children and adults alike are bombarded with mailed advertisements for sex publications: nude, pornographic, or near-pornographic still and motion pictures, "medical" or "scientific" publications dealing with sex techniques or practices, and medicines or contraptions which purportedly serve as cures for real or imagined sexual deficiencies.

When such advertising is brought to the attention of postal authorities, the postal officials are too often without recourse, either by reason of constitutional limitations imposed upon their authority or by reason of delays and frustrations encountered in seeking to proceed under complex postal laws and regulations.

GREETING CARDS

In recent years, a thriving business appears to have developed in greeting cards of a highly questionable nature which ridicule commonly accepted standards of conduct and decency.

There are many men and women who operate card shops who have stated that "they spend half of their time fighting to keep the indecent stuff out of their stores." They fight with the salesmen who represent certain greeting card manufacturers who print a large line of pornography. There are thousands of card shops that try to and do keep the dirty stuff off their racks. But there is an equal number where anything goes.

The Greeting Card Association obviously has an obligation to reduce and eliminate the indecent stuff that they try to sell to the local stores.

RECORDS

There is a type of "risqué" record now finding favor with certain segments of the American public. Many of these recordings are obscene.

One record reviewer for a large newspaper has stated: "Most of the grime crusting the record industry draws its profits from the curiosity of young people and the juvenile sense of humor of a surprisingly large percentage of their elders. The disc world should police itself, I'm convinced."

The reviewer further adds: "Such records are indispensable equipment for college student's rooms, stag affairs, and just plain enjoyment in one's home."

TELEVISION

Crime, terror, sex, and violence in television have been spotlighted in Washington at hearings of the Senate Juvenile Delinquency Sub-Committee. Writers, producers, television executives, psychiatrists, psychologists, and criminologists have appeared and testified. In reviewing the record, it becomes obvious that within recent years there has been a sharp increase in the number of programs featuring violence, that some of this violence has been deliberately injected and highlighted in specific telecasts, and that its nature and abundance give reason for genuine alarm.

While conducting hearings of the above named congressional committee, Senator Thomas J. Dodd, Committee Chairman, stated as follows:

To the extent that there is a relationship between crime on television and movie screens and crime actually committed by our youth, we have a problem demanding immediate solution. . . . The outlook is grim. Something must be done. Sociologists, psychologists, and other scientists have pointed out in their testimonies time and time again that television programs saturated with crime, violence, and brutality are dangerous to our children and youth. The foremost experts on these problems have said that this situation is too dangerous. . . . Foreign nations have refused to accept and show our films because of their violence content, and even people associated with the television industry admit in their trade publications that the public is increasingly dissatisfied with what they see on the screen and is demanding reform. . . . Motion picture and television is a form of art created by the talent of the writers, producers, editors, and others. I believe that it is deplorable to prostitute the artistic potential of human beings by requiring them to design shows containing prescribed pre-determined amounts of violence, sex, murder, and brutality. . . . We can no longer stand by and allow the public air waves to be used to transmit inferior and demonstrably harmful entertainment in place of culturally and intellectually stimulating material.

A symposium was conducted a few years ago by the Huntington, Long Island, Township Mental Health Clinic on the subject: "Is Violence the Entertainment You Want for Your Children?" Over 400 persons in attendance heard a panel of psychiatrists, educators, TV executives, police officials, and members of the clergy discuss this subject.

Parents were admonished to exercise control over the choice of programs tuned in by children, and viewers were urged to make their views known to the television industry.

Robert Keeshan, producer and star of the excellent children's program,

"Captain Kangaroo," called upon parents to "use the on-and-off switch with more regularity" and took parents to task for using the television set as an unsupervised babysitter. Loring Mandel, a television writer, told the assembly that violence pays off for advertisers unless viewers complain when they find programs that are objectionable.

Effect on children. The debate continues to rage over the effect of such programming upon children and upon juvenile delinquency.

A number of interesting and authoritative works have now been published on the subject and among them are the following:

1. Schramm, Lyle, Parker, *Television in the Lives of Our Children,* Stanford University Press, Stanford, California.

2. Himmelweit, Hilde T., et al., *Television and the Child,* Oxford University Press, 417 Fifth Avenue, New York. It is an empirical study of the effect of television on the child.

3. Schramm, Wilbur, *Children and Television,* Television Information Office, 666 Fifth Avenue, New York. It gives some advice to parents.

4. Witty, Paul A., *School Children and Television,* Television Information Office, 666 Fifth Avenue, New York.

Reactions of fear and anxiety. The following are a few of the significant statements contained in *Television and the Child* concerning "What Frightens Children on Television?" (Chapters 14 and 15).

Westerns tended to frighten only the very young or the insecure; it is likely that the majority of children can enjoy them without fear by the time that they are about 7. On the other hand, detective, murder, and crime thrillers were often mentioned as frightening by adolescents as well as by the 10–11 year olds. Violence in these plays, unlike Westerns, is realistic, not stylized, and forms less often part of a stereotyped plot sequence.

Many children were frightened by incidents in horror programmes and space fiction. . . . On the other hand, real events of a violent nature seen on newsreels were rarely mentioned as frightening. Fiction made a deeper impact than reality.

Where children mentioned incidents that had frightened them, they often spoke of nightmares and of difficulty in falling asleep. It is in such effects as these that the disturbances caused by frightening programmes can best be seen.

Children tended to be more readily frightened when viewing in the dark and when watching programmes in the evening without an adult present.

Among types of aggression that disturb children, guns and anything to do with guns proved least and daggers and sharp instruments most disturbing, with swords somewhere in between. Fist fights and fighting on the ground were only disturbing when they occurred in sports programmes, i.e., in real life, rather than in fictional programmes.

Verbal acts of aggression, reprimand, and ridicule sometimes occasioned more unease than physical aggression, particularly when they occurred in real life situations, panel games, or sports programmes. Children were disturbed by situations with which they could identify themselves; this is a more important factor than the sheer amount of force of the physical violence shown.

Children enjoy being a little frightened; they like suspense for the sake of the relief that follows. There is a narrow margin between pleasurable suspense and intolerable fear. The children themselves made a clear distinction between exciting and frightening programmes, enjoying the former and not the latter.

MOTION PICTURES

All that applies to television programs concerning their portrayal of sex and violence can be said to also apply to motion pictures—but to a greater degree. Sex and violence are often being given unwholesome emphasis.

The Motion Picture Production Code Administration has lowered its bars to permit treatment of sex perversion. Adultery, fornication, prostitution, and perversion have become the favorite subjects for motion picture exploitation.

The findings of the New York State Committee are that "adult" films dealing with rape, perversion, premarital and extramarital relations, crime and delinquency now dominate the motion picture screen. As one views current motion picture advertisements and reviews, it becomes perfectly obvious that motion pictures are now as "adult" as they are purported to be. But the root of the problem is that a significant proportion of the audience inevitably are not adults but children and adolescents. That a need for control seems equally obvious is the conclusion of the Committee.

It was the opinion of the Committee that since the State of New York spends millions of dollars upon its educational system in an effort to properly instruct children, it was only consistent to use the existing facilities of an established department within that educational system to provide this additional guidance.

It was further the opinion of the Committee that the effectiveness of the Motion Picture Division of the New York Education Department had been seriously curtailed by recent court decisions which have narrowed the interpretation of obscenity. It is the opinion of the Committee that these presentations—legal as they may be in accordance with current court interpretations —are poisonous for impressionable teenagers.

Activities

1. Make a study of the literature available at a newsstand frequented by teenagers. Prepare a report concerning your findings as these relate to the subject of pornography.

2. Watch a television program to determine to what extent it might have adverse effect on youth. Write a short report concerning your views.

3. Watch a movie to determine similarly what its effect might be on youth and prepare a report on your observations.

4. Determine what laws or regulations your own state has on the subject of pornography and related topics.

5. Prepare a report on the topic, "The Effect of Pornography and Offensive and Obscene Literature on Children and Youth."

References

Ernst, Morris L., *Censorship: The Search for the Obscene,* The Macmillan Company, New York, 1964, 275 pp.

Kronhausen, Eberhard and Phyllis, *Pornography and the Law,* Ballantine Books, New York, 1964, 389 pp.

McClellan, Grant S., *Censorship in the United States,* The H. W. Wilson Company, New York, 1967, 213 pp.

St. John-Stevas, Norman, *Obscenity and the Law,* Secker & Warbury, London, 1953, 259 pp.

State of New York, *Report of the New York State Joint Legislative Committee to Study the Publication and Dissemination of Offensive and Obscene Material,* January 15, 1962, Albany, N. Y.

13

Parents and Sex Education

There are so many good books on the subject of parents and sex education that it might seem unnecessary to include a chapter on this topic in this book. However, of all the subjects or areas of school teaching, probably few are so closely related to the home as that of sex education, and so a brief discussion is here presented.

Parents and the Schools

It should be remembered that the school's sex education program is a supplement to that given in the home. Unfortunately, schools are expected to do more today because the home is not assuming its full share of this responsibility. In any event, it is important that the parents understand what the sex education program is in the grade and school that their child is attending. The school can help to reinforce any instruction given at home, and the home can similarly supplement that which is given at school.

The child's teacher, as well as the school librarian, can often be of real help in suggesting reading materials for the parent for his own benefit, other materials that the parent might read to the very young children, and more advanced books and pamphlets that older children and youth might be encouraged to read at home.

A parent who is also trained as a teacher, as so many are, can apply at home much from his own experience in dealing with the children in his class. Conversely, a teacher who becomes a parent, as so many do, has a helpful background both in formal education and in actual teaching experience which should make him an even better parent. To understand and use many of the teaching methods, approaches, readings, and vocabulary which a school uses can be of real help to a parent.

SOME ADVANTAGES OF SEX EDUCATION IN CHILDHOOD

1. It forms a bond of confidence between parent and child.
2. It prevents the satisfying of childhood curiosity by information obtained through unwholesome sources.
3. It enables a child to tell the parent of undesirable sex conversations or unwholesome situations relating to sex play as they may arise.

SOME OBJECTIVES OF SEX EDUCATION IN THE HOME

1. To create an atmosphere of harmony and security. This is defeated if there is constant wrangling between parents, mutual distrust, and indications that the child is a "bother" and frequently "in the way."
2. To answer the earliest questions of the child regarding the origin of life—truthfully, simply, and in a normal tone of voice.
3. To be prepared at any time to add further information, thus securing the confidence regarding sex matters on the part of the child.
4. To prepare children for their adolescent changes.
5. To guide adolescents in every field of interest, including recreation and social relationships.
6. To prepare the adolescent for independent choices.
7. To cooperate in furthering marriage opportunities.

The Role of the Home and Family in Sex Education

The fact has not changed that the home remains the most influential of all institutions in the sex education of children. Most people think that there is no sex education unless there is direct instruction. However, this is a mistake, for reactions on the part of parents toward the child's exploration of his own body, the attitudes associated with toilet training, the handling of questions, and parents' own attitudes toward their marital and individual adjustments are factors in the child's education. Such seemingly tenuous attitudes are not tenuous at all, but very substantial. Avoidance, repression, suppression, embarrassment, and shock are forms of education. Parents cannot choose whether to give sex instruction; they can only choose whether to be helpful or neglectful in this matter.

The most important contribution which parents can make toward the proper sex adjustment and later marriage of their children is to provide a happy, emotionally stable home. Adjustment has security, love, and acceptance as its foundation. Deep emotional conflicts and personality disorders can result in unsatisfactory interpersonal relationships.

Modern parents do recognize the inevitability of sex education and do teach children from infancy and early childhood wholesome attitudes toward their own bodies and reproductive processes. Hopefully, this is ongoing through adolescence. Unless the educational process begun so well continues through later years, there is sure to be a disappointment with sex education. Fine sex education at three or five or eight does not prepare entirely for sixteen, eighteen, or twenty.

What marriage and parenthood really mean, the home teaches, as these following illustrations show. Children will not grow up to see the relation of the sexes in terms of beauty unless the father and mother relationship is beautiful. The unconscious fear of sex, which is the hidden cause of so much nervous instability in later life, is engendered by quarreling parents. If a little girl is taught a puerile and incorrect name for any body part, she will always feel an embarrassment in saying the scientific name when she tardily adds it to her vocabulary. Whether in teaching or in home learning, the emotional approach to a study of sex education must be discarded for a rational approach.

CHANGES IN THE PARENTAL ROLES

The role that each parent plays in family life today is not as sharply defined as it was at the turn of the century. Traditionally, mother used to stay at home, cook, sew, and perform other clearly defined household tasks, whereas father was the breadwinner who enjoyed leisure upon his return home.

Today's home life shows a mixture of these roles. Children are becoming accustomed to seeing mother leave the house for full- or part-time work or for a schedule of community service. Father may help with household tasks or the shopping list. He has been allowed back into the nursery after having been kept out of it for several thousand years. A new family is emerging where the young father enjoys the kids and goes to parent-education classes. The kitchen is now the center of the home.

It has now been found that the parents who were concerned about their children and read books on child care and took similar courses have children turning out to be even better parents than they were. Some schools even instruct boys in homemaking and girls in industrial arts.

Today, the economic unit is no longer the family; it is much larger. Children used to support older people; today this is reversed. But confusion about the role of father and mother need not arise if families share responsibilities amiably and interpret to children any activities which are at variance with neighborhood or community standards.

PARENTS HAVE DEVELOPMENTAL TASKS

Parents, as well as children, have developmental tasks. As their kids grow older, their parental roles change. Parents have certain needs which they must accomplish during certain life periods. For instance, in the preschool years parents must be ready to sustain the child in his dependency, while gradually encouraging him to become independent. And, fully as important, parents must also accomplish their own task of learning to emancipate themselves from him so that, by the time he goes through adolescence, they will not only be ready to emancipate him but also themselves.

So it is important for parents to get an overall view of their child's growth and development—to grasp the changes that occur from infancy to adulthood. If a parent does not see the whole picture, he may feel very inadequate as a parent in the early years of his child's life, and utterly inadequate in his quite different parental role when his son or daughter steps through—or hobbles through—adolescence. Skill in parenthood requires practice, but it also calls for knowledge and understanding of one's self and children; and these may be acquired before the role itself is undertaken. The good virtues you want to inculcate in your offspring must be in you first. Continue to be a student of parenthood even after you have become a parent. You don't have to know all the answers before you can help your children with life's toughest questions. In a real sense, you help them most when you are willing to learn with them.

THE HOME'S CONTRIBUTION TO SEXUALITY,
INCLUDING SEX IDENTITY

While the influence of the home and the parents will ordinarily be powerful throughout early life, it is so nearly exclusive during the first few years that we may fairly call this the "home period." The mother with her constant services to the child brings the *feminine* aspect of sex continually to the child's attention. The father, likewise, with slight service and with *masculine* manner and voice, no less makes a sex impression but a very different one, wholly un-recognized as such by the child and too dimly recognized by the parents.

A child's image of his sex role—male or female, masculine or feminine, and later as man or woman, husband or wife, father or mother—is conditioned very early in life by the emotional and social atmosphere in his home. It is only recently that students of psychology have adequately brought our attention to the degree to which the home drama is a sex drama and the degree to which it influences the child, both in respect to general aspects of character and in the whole color and trend of the sex nature. This latter effect grows out of the fact, also poorly understood until recently, that the sex nature of the child is actively operating much earlier in life than we realize. So one may say that the sex educational work of the home is to interpret inspiringly to a child the nature and meaning of the home itself and of his own sexual development while he is a part of it and to suggest how all of it is in preparation for his own home later.

We must not forget either that we cannot separate character in sex from character in other respects. General habits influence sex habits; general tastes modify sex tastes; general ideals condition the sex ideals; and contrawise. Forming good habits and attitudes about other things does not assure sound sex controls. These must be built up carefully upon the others. There are no rewards at this period more powerful than those included in the approvals and privileges of the home relations themselves. The ideas and facts of this home which gives the start, and the later imagination about his own eventual home will, if taken together, do more to determine his sex ideals and behavior than anything else.

Those ideals and attitudes in the child which farsighted parents will seek to cultivate, both for their own value and for their relation to sex controls, will certainly include desirable attitudes toward (a) the home, (b) the child's own emotional and intellectual states, (c) amusement and use of leisure time, (d) nature and life, (e) the privileges, rights, and happiness of others such as elders, the other sex, equals, those less endowed, and (f) the elementary facts of sex, revealed in the home.

APPROACHES IN BEING A GOOD PARENT

The secret of successful child raising comes down to three simple essentials:

1. Good parents love and prize their children.
2. They are consistent; that is, they handle their children today pretty much as they did yesterday and the week before.
3. Their approach is not fretful or fearsome but relaxed and easygoing.

At the University of Chicago some years ago, Dr. Robert Havighurst made an eight-year study of discipline and reached this conclusion: How severely a parent disciplines a child (punishment) seems to bear little relation to how his character develops. Experts thus believe that hard or frequent punishment does not guarantee improvement of behavior, but that children do improve if parents make clear how far they can go and then scold or punish when they go further.

Child care specialists tell us another thing about good parents and discipline. Both parents should discipline a youngster in the same way. And each time he commits the same misdeed, he should get the same sort of discipline. What children need most from their parents—besides deep love—is to know what sort of treatment to expect from day to day.

Dr. Dale Harris studied 4,000 children at the University of Minnesota concerning the truth about good parents doling out chores to children. The salient conclusion was that youngsters were affected by how their parents approached their own responsibilities. Those parents who were conscientious workers, active in community affairs, and industrious at home had the most conscientious children.

Questions and How to Handle Them

PARENTS' QUESTIONS DEALING WITH SEX EDUCATION

Both children and parents have many questions, many of which have not actually been asked but still are there in their minds. Here is a list of questions that parents have asked on sex and sexuality. These have been compiled by the author over a number of years of talking with parents individually and in groups. Do you have any of the same questions? To what extent do you believe that you can supply a good answer?

1. At what age should children be given sex instruction?
2. I have a girl age six and a boy age four; what should I tell them?
3. Is there need for worry over a child's interest in his own body?
4. When a child asks a question referring to a sex problem, should that child's questions ever be answered by this statement, "No, you are not old enough"?
5. Is there a graded course that a mother may study in her home so that she may become a leader and helper to her friends and neighbors?
6. Just how would you begin informing a girl of eleven about sex?
7. Should her brother who is ten be given the same information?
8. Is it advisable to tell a child how the unborn child got into the mother's body? At what age does the child ask about this?

9. What is the best procedure with the child who does not ask questions?
10. Of what value is sex education to the child who shows no interest in it and asks no questions?
11. In the home where the father is incapable of or unwilling to impart necessary sex information to his boy, where and how can he (the boy) be directed to the proper source(s)?
12. If the mother feels herself incompetent to give sex education because of lack of training or her own inhibitions, to whom should she turn for help in regard to her children's education?
13. How should the parent meet the attitude in the child who says, "Oh, yes, I know all about that"?
14. How does one regain the confidence of an adolescent child who definitely gave his confidence in earlier age?
15. Should the children be allowed to discuss their questions among themselves in the mother's presence?
16. How do you go about discussing the facts of life with a child who has gone well into adolescence and when one has no idea how much the child knows?
17. I feel I have made so many mistakes but am also inspired to do better. Is it too late when my child is already fourteen, and how can I intelligently follow your program?
18. At what age should you say a boy should be advised of the physical changes which take place in the adolescent girl?
19. When in most things the value of accumulated human experience is so unquestioned, is it really wisdom to disregard the fundamental reason for reticence in dealing with the subject of sex?
20. Do difficulties between parents in any way influence the adjustment of children?
21. Do grandparents in the home have a desirable or undesirable reaction on the family life or the personality development of the children?
22. How can early emotional reactions to sex affect the child's adjustment at adolescence and in later life?
23. How can I prevent passing on to my children my inhibitions and feelings which I realize are not the desirable ones?
24. How would you answer a thirteen-year-old daughter's question about prostitution?
25. The young peoples' complaint about having received no sex education is that "My father or mother never told me." They seem to know that it is the parents' duty and not primarily the school's. Why not drive home the lesson to the parents?
26. If the children in a given family have been used to undressing with their parents and seeing their parents undress, when should this procedure be discontinued?
27. Our children are being trained correctly (so we think) along the lines of sex education. Our problem arises when neighbors object to what our children may say at times to their children. What are your suggestions?
28. Is it advisable to shorten the period of innocent childhood and awaken an interest in this topic?

CHILDREN'S QUESTIONS ASKED OF PARENTS AND OTHER ADULTS

The following questions asked of parents, relatives, and other adults are illustrative of the many that are likely to be raised by various children within a family over a number of years. How would you as a parent or teacher answer these questions?

1. Where did I come from?
2. How are babies born?
3. Did the stork bring me?
4. Did the doctor bring me in his satchel?
5. Why did I have to be born in a hospital? Were you born there?
6. Why do mothers get sick when they have babies?
7. Can I have a baby when I grow up?
8. Did you know that you were going to have a baby?
9. Can we have babies?
10. How big is a baby before it is born?
11. Can the baby breathe before it is born?
12. Where does the baby get its food?
13. How did I get into your body before I was born, Mother?
14. Why am I a boy and not a girl?
15. Does it hurt when the baby is born?
16. Where does the milk come from that the baby has for food?
17. What makes babies start to grow?
18. A girl said she did not have a father. Can that be true?
19. Can Aunt Dorothy have a baby?
20. Can people have babies if they are not married?
21. Where was I kept before you married daddy?
22. Can Blackie (a female cat) have kittens without a daddy cat?
23. I am going to marry brother when I grow up. Is that all right?
24. I want to marry daddy when I am older.
25. Why is Mrs. Blank so big?
26. Why don't Mr. and Mrs. Smith have any children?
27. Why does sister look different from me?
28. Do the little guppies have both a mother and a father?

Wrong Methods of Meeting Children's Questions. Here are four suggestions of what *not to do* when answering a child's question on a sex topic.

1. Do not postpone your answer.
2. Do not use vulgarity in your answer.
3. Do not be unnaturally solemn when answering the question.
4. Do not use a myth, such as the stork, the doctor's bag, or being purchased at the hospital, in answering a question on origins.

One guiding principle is that to the infant no question is indecent, and none should be greeted in such a way as to convey the impression that it should never have been asked. *Another* is that while falsehood should have no place in an answer, the truth need not always be given in large doses, but should be dispensed with discretion according to the degree of the child's curiosity, the extent of his knowledge, and the state of his emotions. A *third* is that replies to questions about birth no more need hushed and saintly tones than do answers to queries about billiard balls, and that the child should not be expected to receive them in any different manner. A *fourth* is that most parents, because of their own upbringing, in fact find these inquiries rather difficult to meet, and should think out well in advance just how they are going to deal with them. Indeed, discussions on sex between parent and child should be as informal in nature as those on football. And, if the home is all that it should be, teenagers will be willing to discuss these matters with their parents and will welcome their help in establishing standards of behavior for themselves. Parents must trust if they wish to be trusted, and if this means risk then risk must be accepted.

A DISCUSSION INCIDENT

Mary, eight, and Susan, seven, asked their mother at bedtime what "pregnancy" meant. She explained that it meant a mother was going to have a baby. Many questions followed the explanation and the baby's growth was charted for them. They were told that the father had a share in the production of the child. They both decided that they would be mothers when they grew up.

The next noon at the dinner table with an elderly guest present, the older girl said, "Daddy, when I grow up I am going to carry my baby right here." She pointed to her abdomen. The father hesitated a moment—started to reprimand the child, but he got a warning glance from the wife and said, "Won't that be fine!" The elderly woman was gasping but didn't say anything although her expression showed shock. The mother then smiled at the children and changed the subject by asking them what they wanted to do that afternoon.

How would you have handled the situation? How would you explain to the older woman at the table? In what other ways could the parents have reacted? Do you think the children have been adequately told of the growth of life?

ENCOURAGE A TWO-WAY TALK

Through conversation with their children, parents can get across to them what they would like to have them learn. But, what is most important, in two-way conversations parents can learn from their children as well. In sex education, it is very important for adults to know what puzzles their youngsters or to hear about the fantasies that may persist in young children's thinking often even when sound information has been given them. Unfortunately, modern family life is not always conducive to leisurely conversations.

In homes where conversations about many interesting matters can occur naturally, questions about birth and other topics are likely to come easily. When children do not ask questions of their parents, it is wise for parents to ask themselves whether there has really been the opportunity.

Sex education of a child is very properly the responsibility of both the parents, and they give their best instruction when it is incidental and from time to time. Casual conversations about sex should be as natural as discussing a book just read so that the child states, "We have always talked about this. I can't remember when we first began." Of course, we are not suggesting over-emphasis of the subject so that morbidity and unwholesome curiosity result. Yet, evidence bears down on us that objective, sincere dialogues lead to like attitudes on the part of the learner. Children, unless they have been misinformed in regard to sex matters, are not embarrassed, not lewd, not inhibited. The *trouble is not too much and too early—it is too little and too late.*

Counseling Suggestions for Parents

From an understanding of adolescents of today there comes a number of clear counseling suggestions for parents:

1. As youngsters change and grow up, adults' rules must also change.

2. Parents must relax their protection and give young people ever-increasing opportunities to do things for themselves; for the real job of a parent is to produce an adult, not to continue the child as a child. This is not easy to do since parents, and especially mothers, often have a need for dependent children. Many parents grow anxious and unhappy about their adolescents' revolt and his growing away from the family.

3. Parents need to be assured that the teenager's revolt against parental restraint is an essential preliminary to the business of getting married and founding their own family. For, falling out of love with parents is the first step toward falling in love with a mate.

4. The child or teenager to be concerned about, according to psychiatrists, is the one who remains wholly docile and affectionate during this period.

5. The role of adults is not to protect adolescents from *all* adversity and from *every* difficult experience. They must let their teenagers do their own experimenting, for without experimenting there is no learning of responsibility.

6. The teenagers are increasingly confronted with conflicting choices in matters of personality identity, career, sexual behavior, and other matters.

7. Anxieties are produced, since the making of choices today is often in a situation where there exists a lack of definite social canons, traditions, and accepted standards to serve as guides to sex values and consequently sex behavior. Therefore, a special effort must be made by parents to train their young children and teenagers for the choices that they will have to eventually make.

8. Since permitting their own children to experiment entails risks, it is the adult's role to guide and give temporary assistance when a young person is faced with overwhelming odds.

9. Children and youth still need discipline and control and cannot be left entirely to their own whims and interests.

CHILD RELATIONS

We must find a way to impress upon teenagers and young adults that freedom is much more difficult to cope with than restrictions, and that every choice involves a dilemma—a weighing of the positive and negative consequences of every course of action. It is our responsibility as parents to see that this choice is made with as much careful weighing and balancing as we are capable of, and with as much insight as we can give them considering their own stage of maturity and their own ego needs.

Each child calls for individual handling. Jack may need a liberal display of affection; Lila may need but little. What would be a reasonable standard to expect of one child would represent intolerable harshness for another. Parental love is not enough. Parental knowledge and intelligence are needed, too.

Perhaps no other way of "managing" a young person is so effective as asking their advice. The successful mother will be in her daughter's confidence, but this does not mean that the girl will tell her "all." No wise mother expects that. Most of what a girl thinks are her real secrets will go into the ear of her bosom friend only. She will never be absolutely confiding until she is a grown woman. The wise parent bides her time, watchfully waiting for the fuller intimacy of maturity, and saying to herself only, "Thank God, my daughter tells me everything worth telling. The rest I do not need to know, for I was a girl myself, and I have not forgotten."

RECREATIONAL OUTLETS FOR CHILDREN AND THEIR FRIENDS

The existence of one or more strong, absorbing interests, is important. A child with such interests has a much better chance of making a satisfactory social adjustment than the child who has unfilled time on his hands. A hobby, collections, very stimulating friendships, the Scouts, team sports, hiking, chores, arts and crafts, music, reading, and letter writing—all are social assets. Cultivating such interests has three main values: (a) they occupy one's time; (b) their accomplishments provide a basis for acceptance in a group; and (c) most vital is the fact that such abilities to express oneself provide an emotional outlet.

The greatest good fortune your children can possess during childhood and teens is a home to which all one's friends like to come, and they are equally fortunate to have good friends of both sexes. Mother is wise if she makes her front porch a club room for the neighborhood.

In one community, some parents felt that a new recreation center was needed for the youngsters. A committee was formed, being staffed by parents and young people. The center was planned for and jointly built. A trained worker and his wife were hired as directors and they as well as the facility were available day and night to the children. Many activities were a part of the program, including games, dances, and discussions. In groups, many problems of boys and girls were answered and individual conferences held to help settle sex problems. Would your community accept such a plan? Could you use volunteer leadership?

Parents need to know what their children are doing with their leisure time, whether at home or away from home. For the adolescent who now has permission to drive his father's car, or maybe his own, rules are needed—rules which are fair and expected to be followed.

Activities

1. Select one of the questions on pp. 222–23 and 224 and prepare an answer that you suggest would be appropriate. Indicate the situation and individuals involved as a setting for your answer.

2. Prepare a list of five or more books that you would recommend to parents of young children for use with these children.

3. Prepare a similar list for parents of teenagers that would help these parents do a better job with sex education.

4. Determine what opportunities, if any, exist in the schools of your community for parents to learn about the sex education program of their schools. Is the local PTA doing something in this respect?

5. Determine what community opportunities, if any, are available for parents to study through in-service courses or in other ways about raising children, including sex education.

References

Adams, James, *Understanding Adolescence,* Allyn and Bacon Company, Boston, 1968, 395 pp.

Arnstein, Helene S., *What to Tell Your Child,* Pocket Books, New York, 1964.

Baruch, Dorothy, *New Ways in Sex Education: A Guide for Parents and Teachers,* McGraw-Hill Book Company, New York, 1959, 256 pp.

Calderwood, Deryck, *Family Life Education for Adolescent Youth and Their Parents,* Emerson Books, New York, 1963.

Child Study Association of America, *What to Tell Your Children about Sex,* Duell, Sloan, and Pearce, New York, 1964.

Crow, Lester, and Alice, *Being a Good Parent,* Christopher Publishers, New York, 1966.

Curman, Hans, M.D., *What Shall I Tell My Child?,* Crown Publishers, New York, 1966, 170 pp.

Driver, Helen, *Sex Guidance for Your Child: A Parent Handbook,* Monona Publications, Madison, Wisconsin, 1960, 192 pp.

Ellzey, W. C., *Preparing Your Children for Marriage,* Association Press, New York, 1964, 159 pp.

Faegre, Marion L., *The Adolescent in Your Family,* Children's Bureau Publication No. 347, U.S. Department of Health, Education, and Welfare, Washington, D.C., 1954, 110 pp.

Schneider, Alexander A., *Counseling the Adolescent,* A Chandler Publication of Science Research Associates, Chicago, 1967, 489 pp.

Rubin, Isadore, and Lester Kirkendall, *Sex in the Adolescent Years: New Directions in Guiding and Teaching Youth,* Association Press, New York, 1968, 223 pp.

Wolf, Anna, *The Parent's Manual,* Simon and Schuster, New York, 1951, 348 pp.

Part II

Outlines of the Science Content of Sex Education

This information provides the teacher with ample material for unit plans and daily lesson plans to supplement the suggestions given in Part I.

14

The Biological Aspects of Sex

Section 1. Plant and Animal Reproduction

I. DEFINITION
   A. Reproduction is the power of living matter to reproduce itself.
   B. It is cell division resulting from protoplasmic growth.

II. ASEXUAL REPRODUCTION
   A. New organisms arise from one parent (uniparental reproduction).
   B. It is common in unicellular plants and animals.
   C. There are several types of asexual reproduction.
      1. Simple (direct) cell division (fission) (bacteria, protozoa).
      2. Budding (yeast, hydra).
      3. Spore formation (malaria parasite, some bacteria).
      4. Vegetative reproduction (algae); cuttings (geranium); regeneration.

III. SEXUAL REPRODUCTION
   A. It is biparental reproduction involving:
      1. Sex differentiation (male and female).
      2. Special reproductive organs (gonads in animals)—egg-producing (ovaries) or sperm-producing (testes).
      3. An organism bearing both types is a hermaphrodite (hydra, earthworm).
   B. It consists of fusion (fertilization) of sex cells (gametes—egg and sperm) to form a zygote.

C. It makes possible variation in offspring. Computed by formula 2^n where n represents the number of pairs of chromosomes of the species.

IV. ILLUSTRATIONS OF SEXUAL REPRODUCTION FROM PLANT AND ANIMAL LIFE
  A. Mosses and ferns.
     They reproduce by both asexual and sexual methods (alternation of generation—alternately by spores and gametes).
  B. Flowering plants.
     1. Female element (ovules) is contained in pistil of flower.
     2. Male element (pollen) is produced on stamens.
     3. Fertilization occurs through assistance (pollination) of wind and insects.
     4. Mating does not occur.
     5. Seeds are very immature new plants (embryo).
     6. Accessory parts of flower are for protection and attraction of insects.
  C. Fish.
     1. Female fish has two ovaries producing millions of eggs.
     2. Egg masses (roe) stored in egg sacs.
     3. Male fish has two spermaries producing even greater numbers of sperm (spermatazoon) which are stored in sperm sacs.
     4. Fertilization is through medium of water.
     5. Male fish pours sperm (milt) over egg masses as soon as they have been deposited by the female.
     6. High mortality rate occurs for eggs, sperm, and young (fry).
     7. Little parental interest is shown in offspring.
  D. Birds.
     1. Are egg laying (oviparous).
     2. Female gamete is known as egg or ovum.
     3. Fertilization takes place within the body of the female.
     4. Eggs usually mature singly and are fertilized singly.
     5. Birds are warm blooded; body heat is used in incubation of eggs.
     6. Family life is developed to care for eggs and young.
  E. Mammals including humans.
     1. Are animals which usually nourish young by means of mammary glands.
     2. Have hair at same stage of their existence.
     3. Type of mammals:
        a. Prototheria are egg-laying mammals (spiny anteater, duckbills).
        b. Marsupials have a pouch in which the young are carried after birth, and are without a typical placenta (opossum, kangaroo).
        c. Placentals have a typical placenta (rabbit, human).
           (1) Young are attached inside of mother's body in uterus.
           (2) Birth occurs in an advanced stage of development (viviparous reproduction).
           (3) This method offers advantages of warmth, protection, and nourishment of offspring.

V. GENERALIZATIONS IN REGARD TO REPRODUCTION IN HIGHER ANIMALS
  A. The chances of survival of offspring increase the higher up the scale of animal development represented.

B. A smaller number of egg and young consequently need to be produced among higher animals to assure perpetuation of the specie.

C. The young of higher animals are less able to care for themselves.

D. A long period of growth is required from birth to maturity giving more time for the training of young by parents.

VI. PURPOSE OF CONSIDERING REPRODUCTION OF PLANTS AND ANIMALS

A. Information serves as a background for understanding of reproduction in man.

B. It serves as illustrative material in teaching about sex and reproduction to young children.

C. It helps in the process of developing a vocabulary in a more objective way.

Section 2. Human Reproduction

I. HUMAN REPRODUCTION NEEDS TO MEET CERTAIN REQUIREMENTS

A. Produce sex cells.

B. Bring about fertilization internally.

C. Allow for a long period of development (pregnancy).

II. THE MALE REPRODUCTIVE SYSTEM COMPRISES BOTH EXTERNAL AND INTERNAL ORGANS

A. The external organs.

1. Scrotum: sac containing testes and part of spermatic cords.
2. Penis: muscular organ of copulation. Consists of three parts, the body, the glans, and the prepuce.
3. Urethra: the canal for both urine and semen; connects with urinary bladder.

B. The internal organs.

1. Testes (testicles): essential reproductive glands. Develops in pairs inside the scrotum. Produces sperm and powerful hormone called testosterone.
2. Epididymis: a coiled structure surrounding the testis. Also serves as a selection chamber, weeding out by absorption those sperm cells less equipped for fertilization and for transmitting hereditary traits.
3. Seminal ducts: connect epididymis and seminal vesicles.
4. Seminal vesicles: connect seminal ducts with ejaculatory ducts. A secretion is added to semen. Function much debated. Some think of it as a storage compartment for spermatozoa, others as a vehicle for sperm.
5. Ejaculatory ducts: formed by union on each side of seminal ducts and seminal vesicles.
6. Spermatic cords: contain seminal ducts and blood vessels.
7. Prostate gland: an accessory sex gland surrounding the neck of the bladder and the beginning of the urethra. Produces a highly alkaline substance.
8. Cowper's glands: two pea-sized structures situated slightly below the prostate at the base of the penis. During sexual excitement they secrete an alkaline fluid that neutralizes the acidity of the urethra for the passage of semen.

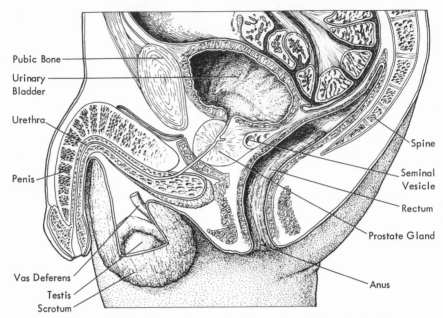

Pubic Bone
Urinary Bladder
Urethra
Penis
Vas Deferens
Testis
Scrotum
Spine
Seminal Vesicle
Rectum
Prostate Gland
Anus

Figure 14-1.   The male reproductive system (side view).

9. Semen: fluid from three sets of glands and sperm from testes.
10. Nocturnal emissions (wet dreams): occasional discharge of semen—a result of normal body activity over which the individual has no control.

III. The Female Reproductive System Comprises Both External and Internal Organs
   A. External organs are grouped under the name vulva or external genitalia.
      1. Labia majora.
      2. Labia minora.
      3. Clitoris.
      4. Hymen.
      5. Vestibule.
   B. Internal organs.
      1. Ovaries: essential reproductive glands; located on either side of the uterus. Produce both the eggs and female hormones, estrogen, and progesterone.
      2. Fallopian tubes: convey egg from ovaries to uterus.
      3. Uterus (womb): hollow muscular organ, located between the two ovaries. Place of nourishment for growing embryo.
      4. Vagina: a collapsible tube extending from vulva to the cervix of uterus.
   C. Pituitary gland: situated at base of brain, produces three gonadotropic hormones. All three secreted at puberty to stimulate the ovaries and the testes.

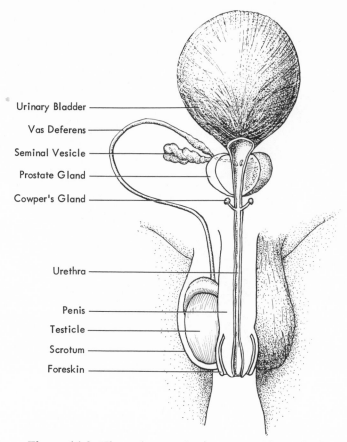

Urinary Bladder

Vas Deferens

Seminal Vesicle

Prostate Gland

Cowper's Gland

Urethra

Penis

Testicle

Scrotum

Foreskin

Figure 14-2. The male reproductive system (front view).

D. Physiology of female reproductive system.
   1. Steps in development:
      a. Formation of the egg.
      b. Fertilized egg travels down the Fallopian tube to rest in the endometrium of the uterus.
      c. If fertilized in the Fallopian tube, the egg comes to rest in the endometrium of the uterus.
      d. Formation of the amniotic sac (protective mechanism) and the yolk sac (food reservoir).
      e. Development of the embryo and organ systems for next nine months.
      f. Birth of the baby.
   2. Puberty: age at which sexual organs begin to function and secondary sex characteristics develop.
   3. Ovulation: the release of a mature, unimpregnated ovum from one of

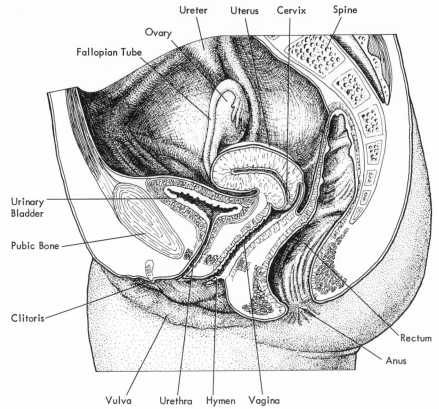

Figure 14-3. Female reproductive system (side view).

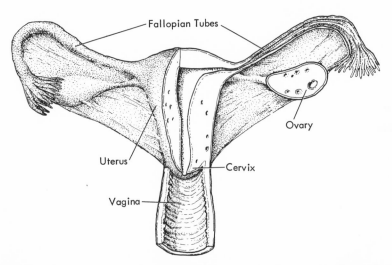

Figure 14-4. Internal organs of the female reproductive system (front view).

the Graafian follicles of an ovary. Usually occurs about fourteen days before the onset of the next menstrual period.
4. Menstruation: periodic flow of blood and other materials from the uterus for four to seven days every twenty-eight to thirty-one days.
5. Menopause: Climacteric or change of life occurs between the ages of forty-five and fifty-five, during which the ovaries become smaller, follicles disappear, the hormonal pattern is disrupted, and the nervous system is affected causing anxiety, hot flashes, and palpitations of the heart.

References for Section 2

Anderson, C. L., *Physical Aspects of Marriage,* C. V. Mosby Company, St. Louis, 1953, 234 pp.

Bowman, Henry, *Marriage for Moderns,* McGraw-Hill Book Company, New York, 1965, 603 pp.

Corner, George, *Attaining Womanhood,* Doubleday and Company, New York, 1965.

Kilander, H. Frederick, *Health for Modern Living,* Prentice-Hall, Englewood Cliffs, N.J., 1965, 400 pp.

Knepp, Thomas H., *Health and Hygiene,* Southern Illinois University Press, London, 1959, 102 pp.

Naismaith, Grace, *Private and Personal,* David McKay Company, New York, 1966, 189 pp.

Section 3. The Endocrine System

I. THE ENDOCRINE SYSTEM CONTROLS THE FOLLOWING LONG-TERM ADJUSTMENTS:
   A. Metabolism.
   B. Growth.
   C. Reproduction.

II. THE ENDOCRINE GLANDS SECRETE SUBSTANCES CALLED HORMONES
   A. Hormones are organic substances secreted in one part of the body and carried to some other part by the circulatory system.
   B. These substances go into the bloodstream rather than into ducts.
      1. Examples of ductless glands are:
         a. Thyroid.
         b. Parathyroids.
         c. Pituitary.
         d. Adrenals.
      2. Examples of glands with both internal and external secretions—the latter via ducts—are the following. They produce both hormones and some other product.
         a. Pancreas.
         b. Ovaries.
         c. Testes.
      3. Examples of glands (ectocrine) that have ducts only are:
         a. Sweat glands.

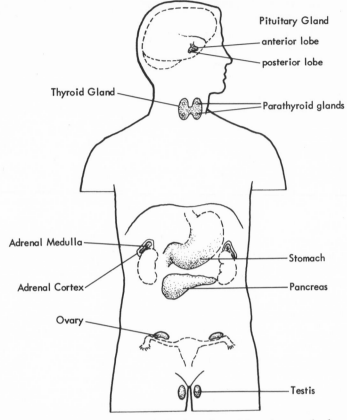

Figure 14-5. The endocrine glands (both male and female gonads shown).

  b. Stomach.
  c. Tear glands.
C. The functions of hormones are in general as follows:
  1. Regulating activities of cells.
  2. Coordinating activities of cells.
  3. Maintaining normal body functioning.
  4. Preventing functional diseases.

III. THE HORMONES AND THEIR PHYSIOLOGIC EFFECTS ARE HERE LISTED
 (Those hormones that are related to sex are indicated with an asterisk.)

Hormone	*Source*	*Physiologic Effect*
*Thyroxin	Thyroid gland	Increases basal metabolism rate; is related to growth differentiation.
Parathormone	Parathyroid glands	Regulates calcium and phosphorus metabolism.

Hormone	Source	Physiologic Effect
Insulin	Beta cells of islets in pancreas	Increases glucose utilization by muscle and other cells, decreases blood sugar concentration, increases glycogen storage and metabolism of glucose.
Glucagon	Alpha cells of islets in pancreas	Stimulates conversion of liver glycogen to blood glucose.
Epinephrine	Adrenal medulla	Reinforces action of the sympathetic nerves; stimulates the breakdown of the liver and muscle glycogen.
Norepinephrine	Adrenal medulla	Constricts blood vessels.
Cortisol	Adrenal cortex	Stimulates conversion of proteins to carbohydrates.
Aldosterone	Adrenal cortex	Regulates metabolism of sodium and potassium.
*Dehydroepi-androsterone	Adrenal cortex	Androgen; it stimulates development of male sex characters.
Growth hormone	Anterior pituitary	Controls bone growth and general body growth; affects protein, fat and carbohydrate metabolism.
Thyrotropin	Anterior pituitary	Stimulates growth of thyroid and production of thyroxin.
Adrenocorticotropin (ACTH)	Anterior pituitary	Stimulates adrenal cortex to grow and produce cortical hormones.
*Follicle-stimulating hormone (FSH)	Anterior pituitary	Stimulates growth of Graafian follicles in ovary and seminiferous tubules in testis.
*Luteinizing hormone (LH)	Anterior pituitary	Controls production and release of estrogens and progesterone by ovary and of testosterone by testis.
*Prolactin	Anterior pituitary	Maintains secretion of estrogens and progesterone by ovary; stimulates milk production by breast; controls "maternal instinct."
*Oxytocin	Hypothalamus via posterior pituitary	Stimulates contraction of uterine muscles and secretion of milk.
Vasopressin	Hypothalamus via posterior pituitary	Stimulates contraction of smooth muscles; antidiuretic action on kidney tubules.

Hormone	Source	Physiologic Effect
*Intermedin	Intermediate lobe of pituitary	Stimulates dispersal of pigment in chromatophores.
*Testosterone	Interstitial cells of testis	Androgen; stimulates development and maintenance of male sex characters.
*Estradiol	Cells lining follicle of ovary	Estrogen; stimulates development and maintenance of female sex characters. For contraceptive pill and menopausal therapy.
*Progesterone	Corpus luteum of ovary	Acts with estradiol to regulate estrous and menstrual cycles. For "Pill" and menopausal therapy.
*Chorionic gonadotropin	Placenta	Acts together with other hormones to maintain pregnancy.
*Relaxin	Ovary and placenta	Relaxes pelvic ligaments.

References for Section 3

Villee, Claude A., *Biology,* W. B. Saunders Company, Philadelphia, 1963, pp. 388–404.

Wilson, R. A., *Feminine Forever,* M. Evans and Company, New York, 1966, pp. 11–209.

Section 4. Fertilization

I. THE SPERM

   A. Sperm production.

      1. Spermatozoa are constantly formed by two testicles suspended in the scrotum.

      2. The scrotum constantly maintains the testicles at a suitable environmental temperature.

      3. Sperm-making cells are extremely sensitive to heat and rapidly degenerate.

   B. The characteristics of sperm.

      1. The sperm is 1/600 of an inch long in its entirety.

      2. The oval head is 1/6000 of an inch in diameter; the head contains all hereditary characteristics in the chromosomes.

      3. The tail—which is capable of making side-to-side lashing movements—provides motility.

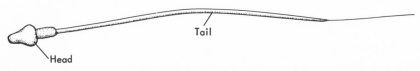

Figure 14-6. Human sperm.

4. If unobstructed, the sperm can swim one inch in eight minutes.

5. The cylindrical middle piece which connects the head to the tail provides a motor for the tail.

6. The sperm are manufactured in almost astronomical numbers with 300 million to 500 million being released to meet each egg.

C. The journey of spermatozoa up the male ducts.

1. The sperm slowly pass through the coiled tube—epididymis—which empties into the vas deferens (a wide tube).

2. The sperm mature during the fifteen-day trip.

3. The sperm do not make their own way up the male ducts; they are propelled by muscular contractions of the tube walls.

4. During orgasm, a fluid is added to the sperm by the prostate gland.

5. The sperm are thrown into vigorous movement.

6. They remain active following ejaculation for forty-eight hours in the female reproductive tract.

7. The sperm can be kept indefinitely by the addition of a glycerine compound to the semen, rapid freezing, and being kept at a very low temperature.

8. If stored sperm are used in artificial insemination, they are fully capable of causing pregnancy.

II. THE STRUCTURE AND FUNCTION OF THE MALE REPRODUCTIVE SYSTEM

A. The production of sperm cells is the primary function.

B. Another function is the depositing of sperm in the body of the female.

1. The penis is the male depository organ.

2. The urethra, a tube from which semen is ejaculated, runs through the center of the penis shaft.

3. Erection is made possible by a rapid flow of blood into special spongy tissue.

4. Blood is held in the penis by the closure of exit valves in the veins.

5. Orgasm consists of a series of muscular contractions which drive out semen in spurts.

6. After orgasm, valves of veins open—releasing imprisoned blood.

C. Male hormones are produced in the interstitial cells of the testes.

III. THE FUNCTION AND STRUCTURE OF THE FEMALE REPRODUCTIVE SYSTEM

A. The fourfold purpose of the female reproductive system.

1. It produces ovum.

2. It provides a receptacle for the male semen.

3. It serves as a trysting site for the sperm and egg.

4. It provides a place for the fertilized ovum to develop.

B. Characteristics of the egg.

1. It is round with a clear, thin shell-like capsule.

2. The capsule encloses a liquid which holds hundreds of fat droplets, proteins, and a nucleus.

3. The egg is the largest cell in the entire body—1/200 inch in diameter—so large that it is visible to the naked eye.

4. It weighs a millionth of a gram.

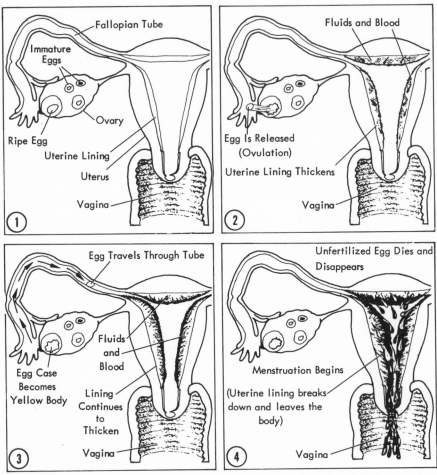

Figure 14-7. Fate of unfertilized egg. 1. Ripe egg in Graafian follicle at ovary surface. 2. Release of egg into Fallopian tube. 3. Progress of egg through tube to uterus. 4. Disappearance of unfertilized egg and breaking down of uterine lining (menstruation).

     5. The egg holds half of the chromosomes—twenty-three; the remaining twenty-three are being supplied by the sperm.

     6. The ovaries contain an estimated 400,000 eggs, of which from 300 to 400 are released during a woman's fertile years.

C. Ovulation.

     1. A ripe egg is attached to the interior of Graafian follicle, which bulges from ovary surface.

     2. The follicle bursts and the egg falls into the Fallopian tube.

     3. The tube sucks the egg into it.

     4. If not fertilized, the egg dies and is absorbed by woman's body.

    5. Ovulation occurs most often between 8 and 18 days after the onset of menses.

    6. Ovulation is totally independent of intercourse.

D. The egg's journey down the tube.

    1. The egg passes from the ovary to the Fallopian tube.

    2. The egg travels down the tube for three to five inches.

    3. Passage takes sixty to seventy-two hours.

    4. The egg is propelled down the tube by fluid currents and muscular contractions.

IV. FERTILIZATION NEARING

A. The upward journey of the spermotozoa is as follows:

    1. The cervix (passage from uterus to vagina) is filled with watery mucus three to four days before ovulation.

    2. Mucus is a good environment for the sperm.

    3. During intercourse, sperm are catapulted into the upper vagina.

    4. Sperm cells swim in all directions.

    5. Most sperm never reach the cervical canal.

    6. The sperm remaining in the vagina die in a few hours.

    7. Those sperm reaching the cervical mucus do so by accident.

    8. A small proportion of the total sperm ejaculated reach the uterus and begin the trip up its two-inch length.

    9. The sperm enter the Fallopian tubes—one on the left and one on the right (some sperm enter the wrong tube).

    10. About 2,000 of the 400,000,000 cells ejaculated reach the trysting site—the midpoint of the Fallopian tube containing the egg.

B. The process of fertilization.

    1. Sperm carry a chemical substance which breaks down the wall of the egg.

    2. Many sperm are needed to break down the egg wall.

    3. Only one sperm enters the egg.

    4. That sperm makes head-on contact with the egg and by its own swimming bores through it.

    5. The two nuclei fuse.

    6. The fertilized egg (zygote) now has a complete set of chromosomes.

    7. The sperm immediately forms a shell around the egg so no other sperm may enter.

    8. When the egg and sperm fuse, the father's contribution to his offspring is primarily in the genetic material contained in the head of the sperm.

    9. It is this contribution that determines the infant's sex.

    10. The actual process of fertilization—from the moment the sperm begin to make their way up to the uterus to the moment one unites with the egg—takes no longer than an hour.

    11. It was not until 1944 that gynecologist John Rock actually witnessed the fertilization of a human egg.

        a. A human egg had been surgically removed from a woman's ovary and put in a small dish.

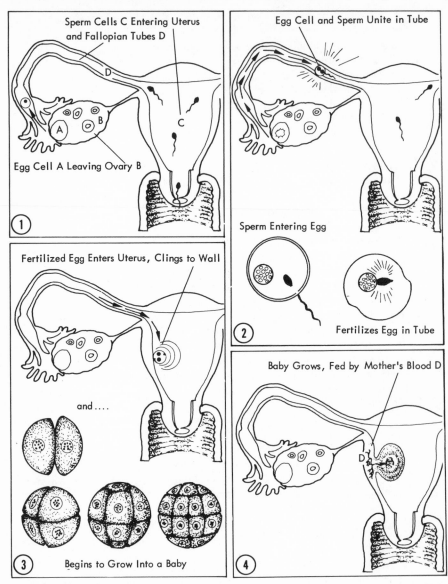

Figure 14-8. Fate of fertilized egg. 1. Ovulation. 2. Sperm fertilizes egg in Fallopian tube. 3. Fertilized egg implants in wall of uterus and begins to grow. 4. Embryo continues to grow, nourished through placenta attached to uterine wall.

    b. Some live sperm were then added.
    c. It was then placed in a culture of human blood serum.
    d. In forty hours, the single fertilized egg had split into two cells.

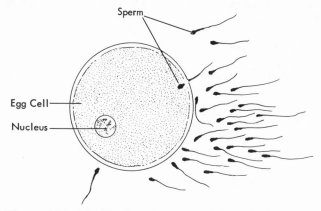

Sperm

Egg Cell

Nucleus

Figure 14-9. Fertilization of the egg cell by a single sperm.

V. WHEN FERTILIZATION IS COMPLETED
   A. At that moment there begins the long sequence of complex events which—
      if all goes well—will result nine months later in the birth of a baby.

References for Section 4

Eastman, Nicholson J., *Expectant Motherhood,* Little, Brown and Company, Boston, 1963.
Guttmacher, Alan F., *Pregnancy and Birth,* The New American Library of World Literature, New York, 1963.
Miller, John Seldon, *Childbirth,* Atheneum, New York, 1966.

Section 5. Prenatal Development
   I. EMBRYOLOGY OR FETOLOGY IS THE PERIOD FROM CONCEPTION TO BIRTH
      A. The study of growth during this period is today well documented.
      B. Scientists know:
         1. That multiplication of cells enlarges the organism.
         2. That the movement of groups of cells helps shape the organism.
         3. That differentiation alters the form and function of cells to prepare
            them for different duties.
         4. That chromosomes, through their genes, play the role of planners and
            supervisors in determining the order and timing of development.

  II. GROWTH IS AN EXTRAORDINARILY COMPLICATED BUSINESS
      A. In the realm of inanimate matter, it is relatively easy to understand.
         1. It consists of an increase in size—like in crystals, icicles, stalactites,
            and stalagmites.
         2. The inanimate object grows from the outside by simple accretion.
         3. It adds onto its surface more and more of the material of which it is
            composed.

B. The living organism, on the other hand, grows by metabolism, from within.

　　1. It takes in all kinds of substances, breaks them down into their chemical components to provide energy, and then reassembles them into new materials.

　　2. Living things, no matter what their specific natures, have to work to grow.

　　3. In addition to an *increase in size,* organic growth involves *differentiation* and *change in form.*

　　4. These three elements comprise *development*—the series of orderly and irreversible stages that every organism goes through from the beginning of life to its end.

　　5. The everyday words *growth* and *development* are used almost interchangeably.

　　6. To the scientist, however, growth is only one aspect of the larger process of development.

C. Without a favorable environment, normal growth cannot occur.

　　1. Of the many environmental factors that influence growth, that of an adequate supply of nutrients is of greatest importance.

　　2. After conception, nutrition is furnished by the egg cell prior to implantation in the uterus.

　　　　a. Then, the developing embryo obtains its nourishment from the body of the mother.

　　　　b. The mother's nutrition is of great importance in furnishing the nutrients demanded by the growing fetus.

　　3. After the child is born, nutrients must be supplied in the form of food.

　　4. The quantities of different nutrients needed are determined by the rate of growth and development.

　　　　a. In the first year of life when growth is rapid, these quantities are great in proportion to body size.

　　　　b. The quantities needed then decrease for the next few years and increase again markedly during the adolescent growth spurt.

III. IN MANY FORMS OF LIFE, INCREASES IN SIZE AND COMPLEXITY ARE ACCOMPANIED BY SPECTACULAR CHANGES IN FORM

A. Equally spectacular are the processes which transform a fertilized egg into a baby, the baby into a child, an adolescent, and finally an adult.

B. The changes that occur in the uterus are, of course, the most extraordinary, and the forces that lie behind them are still only partly understood.

C. It was not until 1944 that the Harvard University gynecologist, John Rock, actually witnessed the fertilization of a human egg in a small dish. Within forty hours, the single fertilized egg splits into two cells.

IV. GIVEN A FAVORABLE ENVIRONMENT, THE EMBRYO DEVELOPS RAPIDLY

A. By the start of the fourth week:

　　1. It has already acquired a primitive nervous system.

　　2. A U-shaped heart has formed.

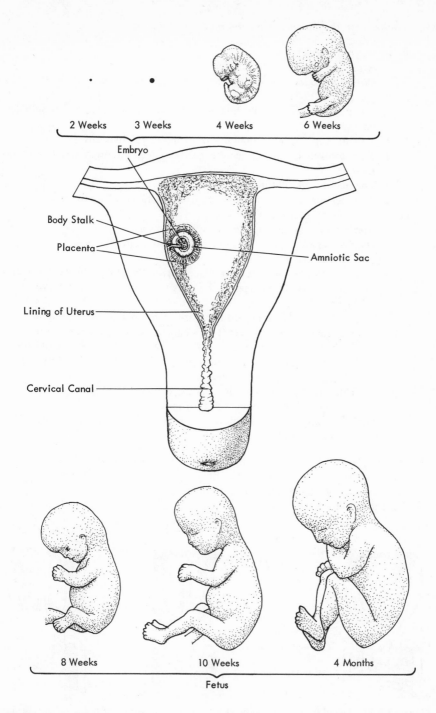

2 Weeks   3 Weeks   4 Weeks   6 Weeks

Embryo

Body Stalk

Placenta

Amniotic Sac

Lining of Uterus

Cervical Canal

8 Weeks   10 Weeks   4 Months

Fetus

Figure 14-10. Human embryo, showing change in size and structure from a few days to four months.

B. By the fifth week:
1. Arms and legs begin to develop.
2. Within three more weeks, the arms and legs will be clearly visible.
C. By the end of the seventh week:
1. The head is recognizably human—for eyes, ears, nose, and mouth are now present.
2. The brain has developed all five of its major subdivisions.
3. The stomach begins to secrete gastric juices although it contains no food.
4. The major musculature has also formed.
5. The skeleton has begun to change from elastic cartilage to bone.
D. By the beginning of the ninth week:
1. The baby is still incomplete but well on its way.
2. Its chances of being born alive have risen from 90 per cent to 95 per cent by surviving this long.
3. The structural changes taking place during the first eight weeks of embryonic life reflect changes in the cells that make up the embryo.
   a. Liver cells are now clearly distinguishable from the cells of the heart, and bone cells cannot do the work of brain cells, or vice versa.
   b. Yet, each of these different cells contains exactly the same genes.
   c. With the exception of the sperm and egg, each cell has a full set of hereditary material and is thus potentially capable of performing the functions of any kind of cell.
   d. The cells begin to specialize as the embryo develops, learning to act on only one of these many sets of instructions.
   e. Eventually, the cell achieves its permanent and, in most cases, irreversible character.

V. By the Ninth Week, the Developing Baby Has Moved So Far Along the Road to Birth That It Has Become a Fetus—an Offspring
A. The cartilage has begun to turn to bone.
B. The skeleton is emerging.

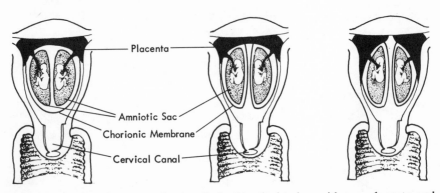

Figure 14-11. Development of twins. Left: Identical twins, with one placenta and one set of extraembryonic membranes. Center: Identical twins, with one placenta and separate extraembryonic membranes. Right: Fraternal twins, each with separate placenta and extraembryonic membranes.

C. All the vital organs have been outlined and formed.

D. By the fourth month, the fetus:

1. Can bend sharply from the hips and the waist.
2. Can twist its body.
3. Can shift from one side to the other.
4. Can roll over completely.
5. Can turn somersaults.
6. These practice movements make themselves known to mother as kicks and starts.

E. The baby's sex was determined at the time of conception, yet the reproductive system does not begin to develop until the second month.

1. Differences between the sexes are unmistakable by the time the embryo has become a fetus.
2. By the ninth week, the gonads have differentiated into testes and ovaries.

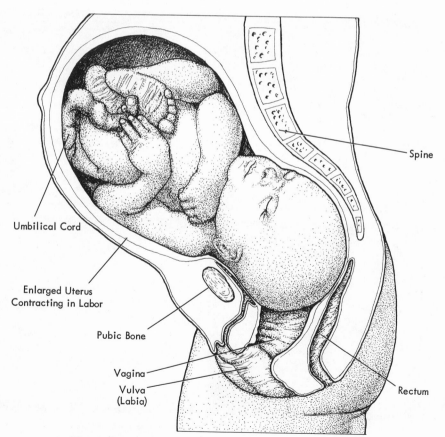

Figure 14-12. Position of baby at beginning of labor.

VI. FROM HERE TO BIRTH, THE DEVELOPMENT OF FUNCTION BECOMES THE MOST IMPORTANT PART OF GROWTH
   A. The remaining seven months are primarily months of practice.
   B. During this time, the baby's body learns to use all the equipment that it has been building.

VII. THE BABY IS READY FOR BIRTH AFTER FORTY WEEKS IN THE UTERUS
   A. The mother is also ready to give up the baby.
      1. The elastic walls of the uterus have been stretched to capacity.
      2. Contractions begin that will push the baby out.
      3. These labor pains have an enormous force behind them, for the uterus is the most powerful muscle in the human body.
      4. The cervix is forced open so that the baby can enter the birth canal.
   B. Until this moment of birth, the mother has done everything for the baby.
      1. She has supplied food, protection, warmth, a nest in which to grow, and has breathed for him.
      2. Then at birth, the baby takes its first breath.

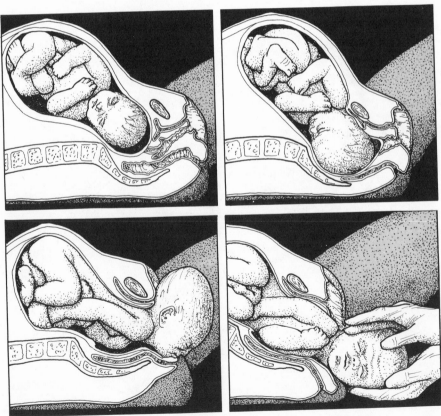

Figure 14-13. Stages in expulsion of baby from uterus.

3. This is the climax to nine months of growth in the uterus.
4. Not until the baby reaches puberty will comparably dramatic changes occur.

References for Section 5

Tanner, James M., Gordon R. Taylor, and the Editors of Time-Life Books, *Growth*, Life Science Library, Time-Life Books, New York, 1965, 200 pp.

CHAPTER

15

Puberty and Adolescence

Section 1

I. PUBERTY: THE PERIOD OF ENTERING MANHOOD AND WOMANHOOD
   A. Definitions of puberty are:
      1. The whole process of sexual maturation.
      2. Sexual maturity.
      3. The age at which one is able to produce live germ cells.
      4. The menarche, or start of menstruation, in girls.
   B. A number of physical changes occur prior to and concurrent with puberty.
   C. When the experts talk of pubescence, they are acknowledging such criteria as:
      1. Growth spurts in certain body dimensions.
      2. Genital growth.
      3. Ratings of the characteristics of pubic hair as to amount, color, distribution, texture, and the eventual development of the kink.
      4. Voice changes.
   D. At puberty, when the final stage of growth begins, the adrenals and gonads become active with dramatic suddenness.
      1. The pituitary begins to secrete large quantities of gonadotropins (hormones).
      2. Under their influence, the testes and ovaries produce the hormones that bring the secondary sex characteristics to maturity.

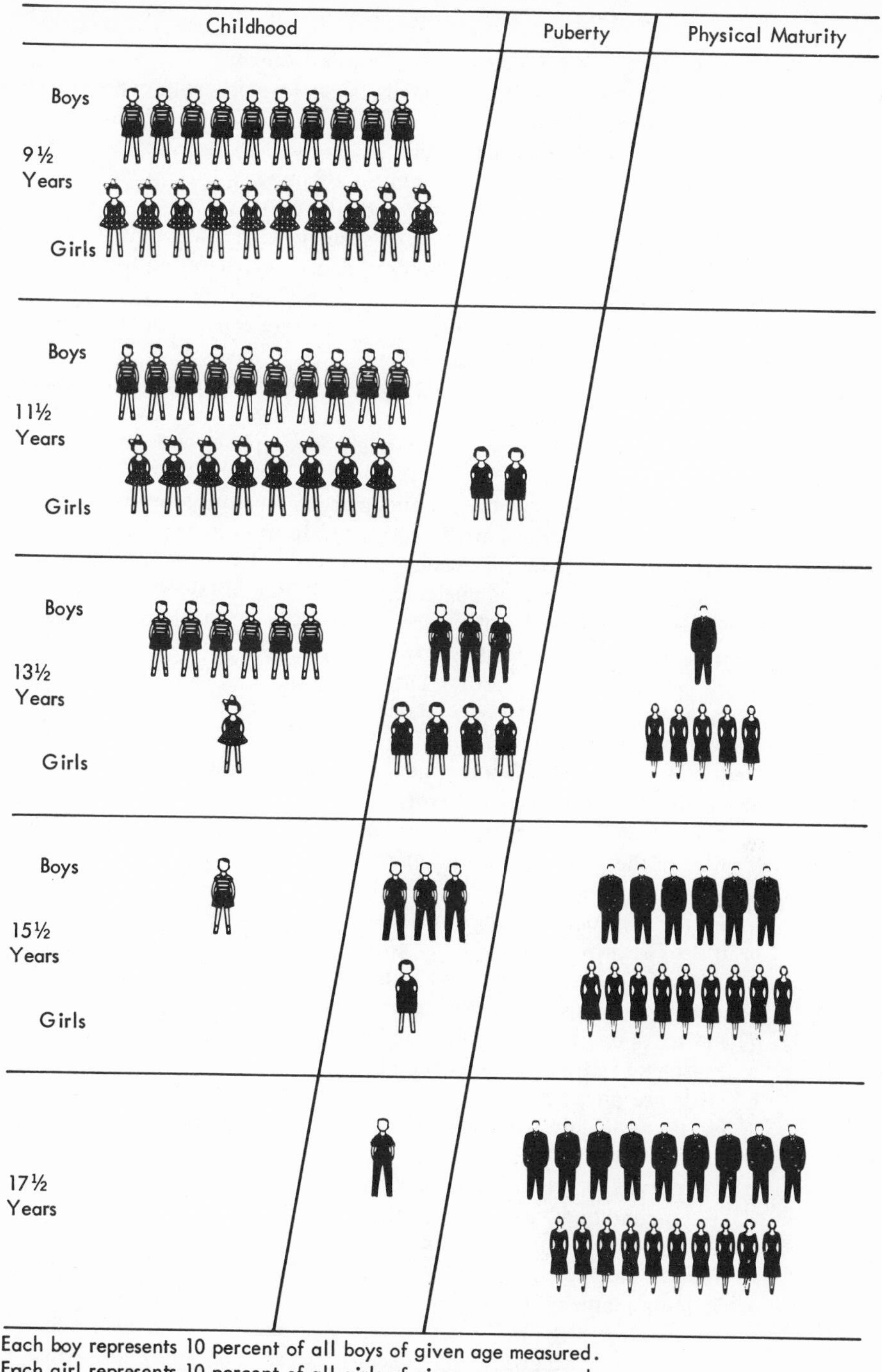

	Childhood	Puberty	Physical Maturity
Boys 9½ Years Girls			
Boys 11½ Years Girls			
Boys 13½ Years Girls			
Boys 15½ Years Girls			
17½ Years			

Each boy represents 10 percent of all boys of given age measured.
Each girl represents 10 percent of all girls of given age measured.

Figure 15-1. Age range of transition from childhood to physical maturity in boys and girls.

    3. The boy becomes a man; the girl becomes a woman.

    4. At the same time, the adrenal glands begin to work as growth glands through their hormones.

E. For the girl, there is the menstrual debut.

    1. The average girl reaches the menarche at about age thirteen.

    2. Some reach the period before the end of age ten, while a small percentage do not reach it until sixteen or even eighteen years.

    3. The menarche does not assure ability to conceive—there is a lag in time.

    4. Reproductive capability is far greater after the age of fifteen.

    5. Girls tend to reach menarche earlier in temperate zones than in northern polar regions or in southern tropics.

F. In ordinary children, all the changes associated with puberty occur during the adolescent growth spurt.

    1. These changes develop in a relatively coordinate and harmonious fashion.

    2. Usually, the outward evidences of emerging maturity begin to show themselves at about the same time that the spurt commences.

G. Puberty is marked in many cultures by traditional ceremonies.

    1. Among Jews it is the religious ceremony of Bar Mitzvah. On the Sabbath closest to his thirteenth birthday, the male reads the daily passage from the sacred Torah for the first time in his life.

II. Other Pubertal Changes

A. Hair growth accelerates.

    1. Hair in the arms and pubes change in amount and distribution.

    2. Sweat glands increase their activities.

      a. This occurs in the armpits especially.

      b. Also in the groin, and in the mammary, genital, and anal regions.

    3. Voice changes occur.

      a. This change does not occur at a fixed time.

      b. It does occur in both boys and girls.

      c. The voice can suddenly break and drop a whole octave.

B. The psychological effects of early and late maturation.

    1. The effect upon the girls is illustrated by the following:

      a. Early maturation is deemed an advantage for girls.

      b. Girls are physically advanced when boys are still childish; this also causes problems within their own sex as one youth matures and another awaits maturity.

      c. There is a lack of corresponding social and intellectual advances.

      d. These conditions may bring parental conflicts, too.

    2. The effect upon the boys is illustrated by the following:

      a. Early maturing boys are at a decided advantage through the years.

      b. Rapidly maturing boys have an earlier assurance of maleness.

      c. Late maturers are historically worried about their poor physique.

      d. Feelings of inadequacy and poor self-esteem may bring problems.

      e. Early maturers show good adjustment and fine parental relations.

III. The Role of the Endocrine Glands in Puberty and Adolescence
   A. The major changes of puberty and adolescence—sexual maturation and accelerated growth—are brought about by marked changes in hormone secretions.
   B. In both sexes, the process begins when the hypothalamus of the brain signals the pituitary gland to take up a new role.
      1. So the pituitary begins putting out two new hormones—which are the same in both sexes—that stimulate the gonads (testes and ovaries), which have been almost inactive since before birth.
      2. Although each sex has its own distinctive sex hormones, each sex also produces small amounts of the other sex's hormones.
      3. The process now diverges in the two sexes.
      4. Studies have consistently found a high correlation between hormone content and maturity of interests.
      5. Thus, there is a vital relationship between psychological and physiological phenomena within the individual adolescent.
   C. For most boys, the physical transition to manhood begins around the age of eleven.
      1. Three hormones released by the pituitary gland stimulate the testes and adrenal glands which results in the secretion of androgens.
      2. Testosterone, the androgen produced by the testes, induces sexual development and growth of body hair.
      3. Androgens from both glands contribute to the remarkable growth spurt occurring in adolescent boys.

Section 2

I. The Spurt in Physical Growth that Takes Place During Adolescence
   A. This spurt is the most obvious aspect of that transitional period but it is not the most important.
      1. The alterations in appearance that accompany adolescence are merely external evidences of internal processes that are producing greater changes in the body than it has experienced since birth.
      2. The adult is not simply bigger and stronger than the child—he is now a different person.
      3. Specifically, he is a person who has achieved sexual maturity, and he has fallen heir to all the possibilities and problems that this status implies.
      4. The physical modifications of adolescence—apart from those which are simply increases in size—are nearly all related in one way or another to this single central fact.
   B. So are also many of the psychological changes related to physical growth.
      1. Because the adolescent is physically a different person, he must behave differently.
      2. However, while the physical developments take place automatically, the changes in behavior do not.
         a. Most of them must be learned.

      b. And this learning process in Western countries is protracted, difficult, and often painful.

C. All these dramatic physical occurrences are bound to affect the adolescent's feelings about himself and others.

  1. A physician who specializes in the problems of adolescence lists some of the many questions that the adolescent asks himself:

    (a) What sort of person am I?

    (b) Are my thoughts and feelings similar to those of other people or am I quite different?

    (c) Am I better or worse than other people?

    (d) Would people want me if they knew what I was really like or would they reject me?

    (e) What sort of people are my parents?

    (f) How do they compare with other children's parents?

    (g) What do I think about my friends?

    (h) What sort of person do I wish to be?

  2. When comparing himself with his contemporaries, the adolescent often focuses on external matters such as good looks.

    a. Boys tend to fret because they are short or fat or do not have athletic builds or because they have bad skin.

    b. Girls worry because they are too tall or fat or generally homely or because their breasts are small or their figures unformed.

    c. The late maturers tend to be the most critical of themselves—particularly boys.

    d. The slow-growing boy's problems are added to those which affect the boys and girls of the early years of adolescence.

  3. Social custom in our society ignores an elementary fact, namely, that until quite late in the teens, girls outpace boys in development.

    a. They reach puberty at a younger age and they experience psychological changes before their male contemporaries.

    b. Junior high school girls are at least two years ahead of their male classmates in physical development.

    c. Consequently, girls and boys alike have little opportunity to learn to know members of the opposite sex who are at the same level of development as themselves.

    d. Many American parents encourage their preadolescent children to "go steady."

    e. The result is that teenagers do not get enough time to learn the meaning of friendship with members of the same sex.

D. Man, of all animals, is the slowest to reach physical maturity.

  1. This delayed maturity must be related to his intelligence, and so maturity is also related to learning.

  2. But learning is a time-consuming matter.

  3. Consequently, *man's protracted childhood is a necessity in order to give him time to learn all that is needed to survive as an adult.*

  4. In primitive societies, the years of childhood offer all the learning time needed to fit him into his culture.

5. Consequently, sexual maturity and social maturity are reached at approximately the same time.
6. In today's industrialized societies, the situation is very different, since our modern cultures demand complex skills and complex behavior patterns which require more than just a dozen years to acquire.
7. The time lapse between sexual and social maturity in the United States and other advanced countries is consequently long and drawn out.
E. The adolescent is no longer physically dependent, but is still dependent psychologically and economically.
1. He is increasingly being held responsible for his actions, but continues to be controlled and supported by his parents.
2. Generally, he is now physically ready for an adult sex relationship long before he is physically ready economically or psychologically for marriage.
3. In contrast with our society, primitive societies, such as the Samoans, are *simple* and *consistent,* and the adolescent absorbs their way of life without thinking.
4. By contrast, in our society the adolescent is presented with a confusing variety of options whether it be in religion, vocational possibilities, leisure-time pursuits, or in sex behavior.
5. For these reasons, his behavior is likely to swing from one extreme to another.
   a. He often rebels against orders from the adult world when what he wants is really to be protected by it.
   b. His parents prod him to grow up and be independent but cannot give him the economic means to achieve this goal.
   c. His parents may encourage him to "go steady" at an early age, but they caution him against sex.
F. American parents became increasingly permissive from the twenties to fifties of this century.
1. Lacking guidance from those who were older and more experienced, these children turn to each other and create their own distinctive subculture.
2. A measure of tension and anxiety while growing up seems to be the price exacted for civilization and freedom.
3. It appears that many people have recently been recognizing that over-permissiveness in child-rearing needs to be reversed.

II. THE SECONDARY SEXUAL CHARACTERISTICS
A. They are due to sex hormones.
1. Changes occur during adolescence.
2. For females from puberty (ages twelve to fourteen) to seventeen to twenty.
3. For males from puberty (ages fourteen to sixteen) to eighteen to twenty.
B. Physical characteristics—in addition to general body growth in weight and height—are these:

1. Male
   a. Vocal cords increase in length resulting in deepening of voice.
   b. Larynx increases in size so Adam's apple becomes more prominent.
   c. External genitals grow more rapidly.
   d. Muscles become firmer.
   e. Appearance of hair on face (beard), axillae, and pubes.
2. Female
   a. Pelvis widens.
   b. Hair develops on axillae and pubes.
   c. Menstruation begins.
   d. Breasts develop.
   e. Fat develops on hips.
   f. Increased physical attraction.
C. Mental and emotional characteristics include:
   1. Male
      a. Qualities of manliness, vigor, enterprise, and ambition gradually become those of the adult man.
      b. Impulses of adventure, combat, and sex develop.
      c. Awkwardness in early years of adolescence is the rule.
      d. Emotional interests in the other sex are developing.
   2. Female
      a. The female mind acquires traits of being more reserved, more emotional, more patient, less vigorous; also more conservative—less willing to take chances.
      b. Emotional interest in other sex is developing; this occurs earlier in girls.
      c. Maternal instinct is developing.
D. Results of loss or underfunctioning of sex glands are the following:
   1. When loss occurs before puberty, the sexes tend to become more alike both physically and temperamentally; if loss occurs after puberty, the effect is less marked.
   2. Castration is illustrated by these animals—oxen, steer, capon, eunuch.
   3. Menopause (climacteric): end of period during which follicles of ovaries develop.
      a. It is the end of menstruation and childbearing.
      b. Various physical and emotional changes occur during adjustment period.
      c. Disease or removal may induce early or artificial menopause and sterility.
   4. Artificial sex hormones are used to counteract individual's loss of own hormones.
E. The secondary sexual characteristics evolved over millions of years because they were useful.
   1. They have survived, it appears, partly because they are still useful in attracting the opposite sex.
   2. Though standards of beauty vary enormously from one people to another, a powerful, broad-shouldered man or a curved, feminine-looking woman will evoke interest almost anywhere in the world.

3. In man, as in other species, the secondary sex characteristics appear to act as automatic releasers of the mating impulse.
4. Individuals in whom they are well developed are more likely to be chosen as mates, and therefore are more likely to pass on the bodily traits that have proven advantageous to the human species.

III. THE SEX IMPULSE: ITS BIOLOGICAL PSYCHOLOGICAL AND SOCIAL ELEMENTS
   A. Definition and nature.
      1. Is impulse toward opposite sex. Also called instinct for race-preservation, the reproductive instinct, or the mating instinct. The term sex impulse is the more inclusive, has broader connotations, is therefore preferred.
      2. Terms of similar meaning: sex urge, sex drive, sex appetite, sex desire, passion, libido.
      3. The sex impulse is an emotion; therefore it seeks an outlet in action. It is similar to fear which prepares for running away or to anger which prepares for fighting.
      4. The normal and organic end of sex impulse is mating (insemination) for the biologic purpose of fertilization.
      5. It is a normal factor in life, that is, it is present normally in humans.
      6. It is the only physical function requiring another for fulfillment.
      7. The sex impulse is present early in life.
         a. It reaches a higher level of intensity following puberty.
         b. It tends to subside with old age.
   B. How the sex urge is influenced, stimulated, or aroused.
      1. The mere matter of sex difference is insufficient to stimulate sex impulse.
      2. By appealing to the senses, through:
         a. Touch.
         b. Sight.
         c. Hearing.
         d. Smell.
      3. The mind and body have become more sensitive to sex in man, with the result that the sex impulse is more readily stimulated through both physical and mental attraction.
      4. External anatomy must be recognized as a psychological stimulus of sex appeal.
      5. Sex appeal should be, and usually is, on bases of biological fitness:
         a. Health.
         b. Strength.
         c. Attractiveness.
         d. Intelligence.
         e. Ability to bear children.
      6. Sex impulse is capable of being aroused by internal and external bodily conditions.
         a. Health, with following tendencies:
            Good health, resulting in more normal desires. Poor health. resulting in abnormal desires, or lack of desire.

      b. Irritations are of two kinds:
         Internal: filled bladder, etc.
         External: tight clothing, etc.
      c. Narcotics: marijuana, opiates affect the sex impulse.
      d. Alcohol affects it adversely.
   7. Feelings based upon sex impulse are strengthened or awakened by memories and imagination.
      a. Desirable memories and imaginations; effects of such.
      b. Undesirable memories and imaginations; effects of such.
C. How sex urge is satisfied.
   1. Usually by physical, emotional, or mental means accompanied by mutual (generally) pleasure or satisfaction.
   2. Sex urge is capable of vicarious gratification by other means than purely sexual.
      a. Sublimation, such as work and recreation.
      b. Substitution, such as through recreation.
   3. Gratification can be delayed or deferred for a long period of time.
D. There are two main types of attraction based upon sex impulse.
   1. Infatuation is largely selfish, physical, and sensual; and is temporary.
   2. Love is a matter of mental as well as physical compatibility and unselfishness. It is more sustained and generalized.
E. The selfish vs. the altruistic in humans, as related to sex, is illustrated by:
   1. Self-preservation: hunger, anger, fight.
      a. It is personal, selfish, immediate.
      b. It concerns mainly the relation of the individual with his environment.
   2. Race-preservation: This is the ultimate purpose of the sex drive.
      a. Altruistic: It entails sacrifice, therefore is not selfish in its primary form.
      b. It is of social significance.
   3. The sex instinct serves both types of needs; it adds pleasure to an instinctive function which ultimately entails sacrifice.
F. Other more general considerations based upon the sex impulse.
   1. In primitive society, the normal outlets for the sex impulse are simple and basic, leading directly to attraction, possession, mating, rearing of family.
   2. In modern society, highly artificial in many ways, it has been necessary for society to hold in restraint the stronger emotional outlets, and to surround the sex urge with decency and dignity appropriate to human beings through:
      a. Codes of etiquette.
      b. Customs.
      c. Folkways.
      d. Mores.
      e. Laws.
      f. Traditions.
      g. Taboos.
      h. Conventions.

3. Society attempts to limit the outlets to those which are of value mutually to the individual and to society.
4. Man has a greater degree of control over his sex activities because:
    a. Sex in man is not seasonal.
    b. Man has intelligence.
5. As a consequence of Item 4, preceding, man has within himself the power to:
    a. Rise above the physical or animal plane in regard to sex expression; or
    b. Misuse his responsibility and fall below that of the animal plane.
6. Sex attraction (physical, mental, emotional, and spiritual) leads to longer bonds or ties between mates with values to them and to their offspring resulting in specific effects on:
    a. Father.
    b. Mother.
    c. Children.
    d. Society in general.
G. The normal, wholesome, desirable outcomes or results of sex and sexuality are:
    1. Interest in opposite sex.
    2. Emotional growth of adolescence.
    3. Attraction.
    4. Courtship.
    5. Love.
    6. Marriage.
    7. Parenthood: motherhood, fatherhood.
    8. Brotherhood and sisterhood.
    9. Family.
    10. Home with its ideals.
    11. Devotion, sacrifice, service, cooperation.
H. The abnormal, unwholesome consequences of sex and sexuality through its misuse or abuse and because of ignorance include:
    1. Emotional unbalance.
    2. Personal ill health.
    3. Masturbation.
    4. Homosexuality.
    5. Petting and excessive liberties.
    6. Sexual vulgarity, salaciousness.
    7. Sexual perversions.
    8. Premarital incontinence.
    9. Promiscuity.
    10. Illegitimacy.
    11. Abortion.
    12. Prostitution.
    13. Venereal disease.
    14. Broken homes.
    15. Unsuccessful marriage.
    16. Propagation of unfit.

IV. The Goals of the Adolescent Period
  A. General emotional maturity including:
    1. Habits of facing and solving conflicts.
    2. Objective interpretations of situations.
  B. The establishment of heterosexual interests.
    1. Normal interest in members of opposite sex.
    2. Experience with many possible mates.
    3. Eventual selection of one mate.
  C. General social maturity.
    1. Feelings of secure acceptance by peers.
    2. Social poise and tolerance.
    3. Freedom from slavish imitation of peers.
  D. Development of intellectual maturity.
    1. Demand for evidence before acceptance.
    2. Desire for explanation of facts.
  E. Emancipation from home control.
    1. Development from close parental control to self-control.
    2. Development from reliance upon parents for security to reliance upon self.
  F. Selection of an occupation.
    1. Reasonably accurate estimate of abilities.
    2. Reconciliation of interest and abilities.
  G. Development of a philosophy of life.
    1. Behavior guided by moral principles.
    2. Behavior based on conscience and duty.
  H. Identification of self.
    1. Accurate perception of self.
    2. Good idea of other people's perception of self.

V. Intellectual Development
  A. Mental growth occurs.
  B. Special intellectual abilities develop.
    1. Memory:
      a. The ability to memorize and recall increases with age.
      b. Imagination develops.
      c. Adolescents are suggestible, becoming less so as they grow older.
      d. Reasoning, thinking, judging, obtaining insights develops.
      e. Humor also develops.

VI. Emotional Development
  A. There are several basic human needs including:
    1. Physical security.
    2. Sexual satisfaction.
    3. Love and acceptance.
    4. Status and recognition.
    5. Intellectual life and creativity.
    6. Realization and improvement of self.

B. Personality development continues and eventually stabilizes.

VII. SOCIAL DEVELOPMENT
   A. Adolescent peer group involves the teenager with:
      1. Friendship.
      2. Leadership.
      3. Dating.
   B. Home life and the family are deeply involved as well through:
      1. Various types of parental behavior.
         a. Rejectant or indifferent.
         b. Indulgent.
         c. Autocratic.
         d. Democratic.
         e. Acceptant.
      2. Conflict between generations.
      3. Delinquency.

VIII. MORAL DEVELOPMENT IS ALSO OCCURRING THROUGH THE FOLLOWING:
   A. There occurs growth in attitudes, such as:
      1. Prejudice.
      2. Tolerance.
   B. Identifications are made such as:
      1. Hero worship.
   C. Forming are religious beliefs and moral behavior such as:
      1. A philosophy of life.
      2. An interest in or revolt against religion.

IX. THE PROBLEMS DURING ADOLESCENCE INCLUDE THE FOLLOWING:
   A. Problems of health and growth.
   B. Problems of personality.
   C. Problems of home and family.
   D. Problems of social status.
   E. Problems of sex and heterosexual relationships.
   F. Problems of religion and morals.
   G. Problems of school and study.
   H. Problems of choosing a vocation.

References

Blos, Peter, *On Adolescence,* The Free Press of Glencoe, Illinois, 1962, 269 pp.
Breckenridge, Marian, and Vincent Lee, *Child Development,* W. B. Saunders Co., Philadelphia, 1965, 485 pp.
Davis, Maxine, *Sex and the Adolescent,* Diablo Press, New York, 1960.
Landis, Paul, *Adolescence and Youth,* McGraw-Hill Book Company, New York, 1955, 470 pp.

Lerrigo, Marion, and Helen Southard, *Approaching Adulthood,* American Medical Association, Chicago, 1962, 47 pp.

Southard, Helen F., *Sex Before Twenty: New Answers for Youth,* Dutton and Company, New York, 1967, 116 pp.

Also, see books on child growth and development, child psychology, and adolescent psychology.

16

Special Physiological Functions

Section 1. Menstruation

I. INTRODUCTION

   A. There are two dramatic changes that take place in a woman's reproductive life: menstruation or the menarche, which commences usually in the early teens, and menopause—also called the climacteric or "change of life"—which occurs some thirty-five to fifty years later.

   B. Menstruation is a normal physiological process which signals the coming of puberty and is only one of the four steps in the menstrual cycle.

II. DEFINITIONS

   A. Menstruation is the discharge of blood from the uterus through the vagina that normally recurs at approximately four-week intervals in women between the ages of puberty and menopause. It may last from one to eight days.

   B. Menarche is the onset of menstruation in girls occurring in late puberty and ushering in the period of adolescence.

III. PURPOSE

   A. The purpose of menstruation is to prepare the body for the biological function of reproduction.

B. The cycle is the preparation and maintenance of the uterus for implantation of the fertilized egg.

C. Menstruation is only interrupted normally by pregnancy.

IV. THE FEMALE REPRODUCTIVE SYSTEM

A. Comprises both external and internal organs.

1. External organs: They are grouped under the name vulva or external genitalia.

   a. Labia majora: The elongated folds running downward and backward from the mons pubis. They are formed in the embryo from the same genital swellings which form the scrotum of the male.

   b. Labia minora: Small folds between the labia majora and the opening of the vagina.

   c. Clitoris: A small, elongated, erectile body, situated at the anterior part of the vulva capable of erection; analogous to the penis in the male.

   d. Vestibule: The space between the labia minora into which the urethra and vagina open.

2. Internal organs: All located within the pelvis.

   a. Vagina: A collapsible tube extending from the vulva to the cervix of the uterus.

   b. Uterus: The hollow, muscular organ in the female which is the place of nourishment of the fetus.

   c. Fallopian tubes: Also called oviducts and uterine tubes, extend from the upper lateral angle of the uterus to the region of the ovary on the same side. The motion of the cilia in the tubes actually moves the egg into the uterus.

   d. Ovaries: Produce both the eggs and the female hormones estrogen and progesterone. Also contain follicles (egg cells). Following puberty, the follicles release a mature sex cell or ovum each month.

   e. Pituitary gland: Situated at the base of the brain, it produces three gonadotropic hormones: FSH, LH, and LTH. These hormones are secreted at puberty to stimulate the ovaries and the testes.

V. THE MENSTRUAL CYCLE

A. The period of regularly recurring physiological changes in the lining of the uterus which culminate in its shedding (menstruation).

B. Duration and variation of the cycle.

1. The average menstrual cycle is twenty-eight days.

2. For some women, it may last twenty-one days, for others thirty-five or more.

3. However, a woman with a twenty-eight day cycle has a slightly greater chance for becoming pregnant than a woman with a thirty-five day cycle; the former ovulates thirteen times a year, to the latter's ten.

C. The menstrual cycle is composed of four phases:

1. The postmenstrual or the resting phase.

   a. The endometrium or uterine lining is thin after menstruation.

   b. At this point the pituitary gland sends out a hormone to the ovary, and one egg begins to ripen.
   c. This stage lasts five days.
2. The intermenstrual phase.
   a. Ovaries release another hormone which causes the endometrium to thicken.
   b. After the fifth day of this phase (and the fourteenth day in the cycle) a mature egg breaks out of the follicle, and ovulation occurs.
   c. This phase lasts about fourteen days.
3. The premenstrual phase.
   a. During this period the lining of the uterus becomes soft, thick, and velvety. The egg moving along the Fallopian tube, now reaches the uterus.
   b. If the egg is not fertilized, it degenerates and is absorbed. The upper layers of the uterine lining begin to shed.
   c. This phase lasts about five days.
4. The menstrual phase.
   a. Two ounces of thin, watery blood and tissue is discarded after the nonfertilization of an egg.
   b. This phase lasts about four days.
   c. The full cycle of approximately twenty-eight days is now completed, and a new one starts.

VI. MENOPAUSE
   The time of reproductive decline is known as the climacteric, menopause, or "change of life."
   A. The menstrual cycle usually ends in the mid-to-late forties.
   B. The ovaries become smaller; Graafian follicles disappear and are replaced by fibrous tissue.
   C. The hormonal pattern controlling the menstrual cycle is disrupted, and until an adjustment is made, the entire glandular system may be thrown slightly off balance.
   D. The nervous system may also be affected, and a woman may experience anxiety, "hot flashes," sweating, palpitation of the heart, and headaches.

VII. PROBLEMS RELATED TO MENSTRUATION
   A. Cramps and upset stomach.
   B. Sensitivity in certain parts of the body.
   C. Premenstrual tension.
   D. Excessive fatigue and perspiration.
   E. Pimples.

VIII. COMMON METHODS FOR MENSTRUAL HYGIENE
   A. *Grass bandages:* In some tribes of Africa, menstruating women, for centuries, have used bandages made out of grass or some kind of vegetable fiber. In Indonesia, balls of soft vegetable fibers have been used as tampons.

    B. *Cellulose pads:* During World War I, French nurses found that cellulose pads made excellent sanitary napkins.

    C. *Cloth bandages:* During the Roman Empire, women began to use cloth bandages which required soaking, washing, and drying during the period.

    D. *Disposable sanitary napkins:* Made of cotton or cellulose and wrapped in gauze for use with pins and belts.

    E. *Internal sanitary protection* (tampons): Cannot be used by teenagers. A tampon is a small roll of soft surgical cotton with an attached cord. This is enclosed in a smooth container-applicator, which is inserted into the vagina so that the top of the tampon comes in contact with the cervix. The container is then removed, leaving the tampon in place with its cord remaining outside.

References for Section 1

Bauer, W. W., and Florence A., *Way to Womanhood,* Doubleday and Company, Inc., New York, 1965.

Blos, Peter, *On Adolescence,* The Free Press of Glencoe, Inc., New York, 1965.

Bowman, Henry, *Marriage for Moderns,* McGraw-Hill Book Company, New York, 1962.

Breckenridge, Marian, and Lee E. Vincent, *Child Development,* W. B. Saunders Company, Inc., Philadelphia, 1965.

Corner, George, *Attaining Womanhood,* Doubleday and Company, Inc., New York, 1965.

Crawley, Lawrence Q., James Malfetti, and Ernest Stuart, *Reproduction, Sex, and Preparation for Marriage,* Prentice-Hall, Inc., Englewood Cliffs, N. J., 1964.

Duvall, Evelyn Millis, *Love and the Facts of Life,* Association Press, New York, 1963, 352 pp.

Fedder, Ruth, *A Girl Grows Up,* Whittlesey House, New York, 1948, 271 pp.

Hector, Robert, *What Shall I Tell My Child?* Crown Publishers Inc., New York, 1966, 177 pp.

Jenkins, Gladys, et al., *These Are Your Children,* Scott, Foresman and Company, Chicago, 1953.

Kilander, H. Frederick, *Health for Modern Living,* Prentice-Hall, Inc., Englewood Cliffs, N. J., 1965, 400 pp.

Naismith, Grace, *Private and Personal,* David McKay Company, Inc., New York, 1966, 189 pp.

Williams, Mary M., and Irene Kane, *On Becoming a Woman,* Dell Publishing Company, New York, 1959, 139 pp.

Section 2. Menopause

    I. INTRODUCTION

        A. As the onset of menstruation marks the beginning of a woman's reproductive years, so the cessation of menses or menopause signalizes the end of the child-bearing era.

        B. The interruption of cyclic flowing, however, is only one of the many changes that take place during this transitional phase of a woman's life. Therefore, the term *climacteric* more appropriately describes this epoch, though the term *menopause* is often employed interchangeably in common usage.

II. DEFINITIONS
   A. The menopause is a period during which ovaries cease to produce and liberate ova, and the uterus gradually abandons the monthly process of shedding and regenerating its lining.
      1. Its duration does not usually exceed two years.
      2. As long as any menstrual periods occur at all, however erratically, there is a possibility of ovulation, and hence a possibility of pregnancy.
      3. It is the end result of the climacteric.
   B. The cessation of menstruation is not the climacteric, as is commonly thought.
      1. The climacteric is that phase of life in the female when a decrease in estrogen activity occurs as a result of the failure of follicular secretion or maturation to take place.
      2. The initial diminution in follicular activity produces the classic symptoms of the climacteric, but despite this, the ovary still secretes small amounts of estrogens and other steroids during this time and may continue to do so for a number of years.

III. THERE ARE SEVERAL FACTORS INFLUENCING THE TIME OF MENOPAUSE
   A. Heredity.
   B. General state of health.
   C. Climate.

IV. THE AGE AT ONSET OF THE MENOPAUSE MAY VARY
   A. Generally speaking, the earlier the onset of puberty in both women and men, the later will be the onset of the climacteric.
   B. The usual interpretation is that early onset of puberty indicates a highly responsive and effective endocrine system.
   C. According to Kinsey and others, the median age for the onset of menopause has advanced from 46.6 years to 50.1, but a wide variation from this is perfectly normal.
      1. Kinsey's findings seem to indicate that 12 per cent of women reach the menopause between 36 and 40, 15 per cent between 51 and 55, and another 6 per cent earlier or later.
      2. According to the National Center for Health Statistics, 10 per cent of female population of the United States reach natural menopause by 38 years; 20 per cent by age 43; 50 per cent by age 49; 90 per cent by age 54; and 100 per cent by age 58. Their findings also indicate that 25 to 50 per cent of women in the United States experience menopause as a result of an operation.

V. CAUSES OF THE MENOPAUSE
   Cessation of menstruation may occur in many ways:
   A. Spontaneous: When the ovary fails to respond to gonadotropic stimula-

tion. Simultaneously, there may be both decreased estrogen secretion and enhanced estrogen output.

B. Hysterectomy: Although endometrial shedding is absent, the ovary will continue to function after hysterectomy. Lack of estrogen will not be evident until the woman attains her usual age of spontaneous menopause.

C. Bilateral oophorectomy: When the principal sources of estrogen and progesterone are removed, endometrial bleeding will not occur.

D. Ovarian radiation: Deep X-ray therapy applied to the ovary or application of radium in the vagina and the uterus.

VI. SYMPTOMS OF THE MENOPAUSE

A. In some women, menopausal symptoms may occur early, that is, before actual cessation of menses.

B. In others, these symptoms will coincide with cessation of menstruation, or or may not appear until years after the actual menopause.

C. In effect, there are wide individual differences in time of appearance as well as in severity and duration of symptoms.

D. According to Goldzieher and Goldzieher, estrogen is one of the most important metabolic regulators. Hence, its withdrawal must be associated with some sort of metabolic disorder, for the body is not likely to accept without protest the cessation of hormonal supply within the accustomed physiologic range.

E. On the whole, symptoms of the menopause appear to be related to disturbance of endocrine balance caused by declining ovarian function. Some of the more typical symptoms are:

1. Menstrual irregularities: Deviations from the normal bleeding pattern are usually the first objective signs of the onset of menopause. Periods become irregular, and in some cases there may be midcyclic bleeding as well as excessive flow.

2. Neurocirculatory symptoms:
   a. "Hot flushes" or "flashes" restricted to the head, neck, and upper chest.
   b. Profuse sweating.
   c. "Ringing" in the ears.
   d. Dizziness.

3. Nervous symptoms:
   a. Anxiety.
   b. Headaches of various types.
   c. Insomnia.
   d. Palpitations of the heart.

4. Psychic symptoms:
   a. Emotional instability.
   b. Mental depression.
   c. "Negative-state balance."

5. General symptoms:
   a. Miscellaneous disturbances: for example, gastrointestinal complaints, particularly constipation.

    b. Ailments may be more prevalent due to estrogen deprivation: for example, postmenopausal osteoporosis.

    c. Menopausal arthritis.

VII. UNUSUAL SYMPTOMS

    A. Abnormal vaginal discharge.

    B. Excessive or too frequent periods.

    C. Irritation or ulceration of the genitals.

    D. Urinary or bowel disturbances.

    E. Abdominal pain, distension, or swelling.

    F. Continued backache.

VIII. DIAGNOSIS

    A. Physical examination.

      1. Because the symptom-complex of the menopause often simulates the symptomatology of certain organic diseases, a thorough physical examination provides valuable assistance in ruling out complaints.

      2. A good health rule for a mature woman is to undergo a periodic examination for any signs of trouble in the genital region of the body.

    B. Vaginal smear ("Pap" test).

      1. Since the vaginal mucosa is a sensitive indicator of ovarian function, vaginal smears may provide a valuable index of ovarian function and guide to therapy.

      2. A Pap test is a simple test for cancer of the cervix.

      3. The atrophic changes which appear in the vaginal smears of women in the menopause vary depending upon the degree of estrogen deficiency.

IX. TREATMENT OR THERAPY

The aim of therapy is to facilitate the readjustment of the menopausal patient to her new physiologic environment.

    A. Hormone therapy:

      1. Based on medical history, physical examination, Pap test.

      2. It relieves unpleasant symptoms, but often has unpleasant side effects —ache in lower abdomen, sore full breasts, makes fibroid tumors hemorrhage quite often. Hence, the smallest dose of hormone that will relieve symptoms is the best dose.

      3. Hormones are to be used only under medical supervision and discontinued as early as possible and under the doctor's supervision.

      4. The purpose of estrogen therapy at the menopause is to provide remission of the distressing symptoms which are referrable to declining ovarian function.

      5. Hormones beautify aging feminine skin, relieve aches due to rarefied bone with little calcium deposits, make skin in vagina tougher, and reduces growth of cancer cells in male prostate gland.

    B. Psychotherapy:

Includes guidance, education, reassurance in channeling interest into rewarding enterprises.

    C. Mild sedatives or tranquilizers are presently made use of in the treatment of climacteric symptoms.

    D. Psychiatric care.

    E. Endocrine therapy for osteoporosis.

X. CLIMACTERIC IN MALES

Studies seem to show that only a few males reach a period in middle life that may be recognized as a climacteric, accompanied by:

    A. Reduction in the frequency of sexual activity. Kinsey and others indicate that almost half the men between the ages of 75 and 92 report that they engage in satisfactory sexual intercourse. They further reveal that the average frequency of coitus for the majority of men over 65 is approximately four times a month, and that masturbation is a recurrent practice among 25 per cent of them.

    B. Reduction in size and firmness of the testicles, and the tubules begin to degenerate and inhibit sperm production.

    C. Symptoms of depression or paranoia which sometimes accompany the physical changes of the climacteric can affect both men and women alike.

    D. Little or no evidence of a sharp decline in hormonal production, if the so-called climacteric occurs.

    E. The onset is usually after the age of 50 years, but may occur earlier. The transition takes about two years, or more.

    F. The decline in fertility and virility eventually occurs in all men after the climacteric.

XI. POSTMENOPAUSAL

    A. More stable in thought and action.

    B. No decline in sexual desires.

    C. Good health and renewed interests in social work.

    D. More knowledge and less "old wives' " tales about the process.

References for Section 2

Bauer, W. W., M.D., *Today's Health Guide,* American Medical Association, Chicago, 1965. 624 pp.

Cinberg, Bernard L., *For Women Only,* Dell Publishing Company Inc., New York, 1968. 188 pp.

DeCoursey, Russell M., *The Human Organism,* McGraw-Hill Book Co., Inc., New York, 1961. 661 pp.

Diehl, Harold S., M.D., *Healthful Living,* McGraw-Hill Book Co., Inc., New York, 1964. 691 pp.

Goldzieher, M. A., and J. W. Goldzieher, *Geriatrics,* Vol. 18, January 1963.

Gray, Madeline, *The Changing Years,* Doubleday Company, New York, 1967. 279 pp.

Kilander, H. Frederick, *Health For Modern Living,* Second Edition, Prentice-Hall Inc., Englewood Cliffs, N.J., 1965. 400 pp.

Lincoln, Mariam, M.D., *You'll Live Through It,* Harper & Row, New York, 1965. 221 pp.

Lloyd, Charles W., M.D., *Human Reproduction and Sexual Behavior,* Lea and Febiger, Philadelphia, 1964. 307 pp.

Masters, William H., and Virginia Johnson, *Human Sexual Response,* Little, Brown & Company, Boston, 1966. 366 pp.

National Center for Health Statistics, *Age at Menopause,* Vital Health Statistics, PHS Publication No. 1000-Series 11-No. 19, Washington, U.S. Government Printing Office, October 1966. 30 pp.

Wilson, Robert A., M.D., *Feminine Forever,* M. Evans & Company, Inc., New York, 1968. 224 pp.

17

Preventing Pregnancies

Section 1. Contraception

I. DEFINITION AND MYTHS

    A. Planning births—spacing children—to safeguard the health of both mother and child.

    B. Myths about birth control.

        1. Contraceptives will make you sterile.

        2. Contraceptives cut down sexual pleasure.

        3. Birth control will make us promiscuous.

        4. Contraceptives cause cancer.

        5. Breast feeding prevents pregnancy.

        6. Having a baby makes you healthy.

II. BIRTH CONTROL METHODS

    A. The Pill.

    B. Intrauterine devices.

    C. The diaphragm.

    D. The condom.

    E. Chemical methods.

    F. The rhythm method.

III. THE PILL
A. Definition.
   1. It consists of a combination of synthetic hormones similar to those produced by the female.
   2. It is available by prescription.
   3. The two common types are as follows:
      a. One pill uses a balanced combination of the hormones progestin and estrogen.
      b. The other is a combination pill—one kind being taken for fifteen or sixteen consecutive days; the other kind for five days.
      c. Of the two types, the combination pill is the more certain method of preventing unwanted pregnancies.
B. Means of preventing conception.
   1. It prevents the ovary from releasing an egg.
C. Reliability.
   1. It has the highest effectiveness; it rates higher than any other method if taken as prescribed.
   2. An error in beginning, or in omission for a day, may result in failure.
D. Methods of use.
   1. The pill is taken for twenty or twenty-one consecutive days each month beginning five days after the menstrual period.
E. Side effects.
   1. A majority of women experience few, if any, side effects.
F. Reversibility.
   1. Ovulation ordinarily occurs during the menstrual cycle immediately following termination of its use.

IV. INTRAUTERINE DEVICES (I.U.D.)
A. Definition.
   1. It is a small device (loop, spiral, ring, bow) made of plastic or stainless steel.
   2. It is used as a foreign body to discourage pregnancy.
B. Means of preventing conception.
   1. The device is inserted into the uterus by the doctor and left there indefinitely.
   2. It does not prevent the ovary from releasing eggs.
   3. How it works is not exactly known.
C. Reliability.
   1. In a majority of instances it will prevent pregnancy.
   2. However, it may be expelled unknowingly.
   3. It is not recommended for women who have not had children.
D. Methods of use.
   1. It is inserted by the doctor.
   2. A complete annual physical is a must.
   3. The device must be checked frequently to make sure that it has not been expelled.

E. Side effects.
   1. Many women have no problem.
   2. Some have cramps and bleeding between menstrual periods.
   3. If there is excessive discomfort, the doctor will remove the device.

V. THE DIAPHRAGM
   A. Definition.
      1. The diaphragm is a mechanical device inserted into the vagina.
      2. It is a flexible rubber cup-shaped device.
      3. It is inserted before coitus.
      4. It is used with vaginal cream or jelly.
   B. Means of preventing conception.
      1. It is placed in the vagina to cover the entrance to the uterus.
      2. It prevents sperm from passing into the uterus.
   C. Reliability.
      1. If used correctly there is a high degree of success.
      2. Two or three out of 100 women using the diaphragm become pregnant each year.
   D. Methods of use.
      1. It is fitted by a doctor and he shows the correct method of insertion.
      2. The woman must return to the doctor every two years and after each pregnancy to have the diaphragm checked for size.
   E. Side effects.
      1. There are none, if properly inserted.

VI. CONDOM
   A. Definition.
      1. It is a thin sheath of rubber or similar material.
      2. It is worn over the penis during sexual intercourse.
   B. Means of prevention.
      1. It catches and holds sperm so they do not enter the vagina.
   C. Reliability.
      1. It offers good protection.
      2. Failures may be due to tearing or slipping off during sexual intercourse.
   D. Methods of use.
      1. Husband places it on penis after erection.
      2. For extra protection wife should use contraceptive jelly, cream, or foam.
   E. Side effects.
      1. No physical side effects.

VII. CHEMICAL METHODS
   A. Definition.
      1. These chemical methods include vaginal foam, jelly, cream, suppository, or tablet.
      2. They serve as chemical barriers.

B. Means of prevention.
   1. Coats surface of vagina and entrance of the uterus.
   2. Destroys sperm cells.
C. Reliability.
   1. Vaginal foam more effective than other methods.
   2. Not as effective as the methods previously described.
D. Methods of use.
   1. Instructions must be followed.
   2. It should be used before each sexual act.
   3. It provides protection for about an hour.
E. Side effects.
   1. No physical side effects.

VIII. THE RHYTHM METHOD
   A. Definition.
      1. It is the avoiding of sexual intercourse during the wife's fertile period.
         a. This occurs just before or after the egg has been produced in her body.
   B. Means of preventing conception by the rhythm method.
      1. Women release egg about once a month.
         a. It occurs usually fourteen days before menstruation.
         b. This may vary from month to month.
         c. It is necessary to determine when the egg is produced.
      2. Calculating the safe period is essential.
         a. The three days during which intercourse can lead to pregnancy are:
            (1) The two and one-half days before ovulation.
            (2) And the half day after it.
         b. Ovulation causes a change in the body temperature.

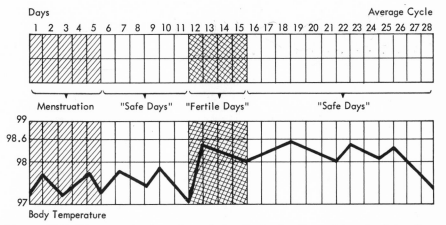

Figure 17-1. The menstrual cycle and the "safe days" as determined by fluctuations in body temperature.

      (1) Therefore the thermometer should inform the woman that ovulation is beginning.

      (2) Body temperature can vary due to many causes; hence the calculations could be incorrect.

  C. Not everyone can use this method.

    1. About 15 per cent of women menstruate irregularly and so an accurate calendar cannot be maintained.

    2. It is not recommended for women whose longest cycle is ten days longer than their shortest one.

    3. It is not recommended for the months immediately after childbirth.

  D. Reliability.

    1. This method is uncertain unless the menstrual cycle is regular so that the fertile period can be determined.

    2. The woman must not have relations for a specified time.

  E. Method of use.

    1. Consult the doctor for help in determining when the fertile period is likely to be each month.

    2. Records must be kept for previous menstrual periods for twelve months in order to determine the cycles.

  F. Side Effects.

    1. There are no physical side effects.

    2. Many couples are unwilling or unable to refrain for the time required to be safe.

  IX. SURGICAL STERILIZATION

    A. There are two types for the female:

      1. Hysterectomy, which is the removal of the uterus.

      2. The closing of the Fallopian tubes.

    B. There is one procedure for the male, namely, vasectomy, which is the severing of the sperm duct.

References for Section 1

Bowman, Henry, *Marriage for Moderns,* McGraw-Hill Book Company, New York, 1965.

Clark, Marguerite, *Medicine Today,* Funk and Wagnalls, New York, 1960.

The Consumers Union, *Family Planning,* Consumers Union of the U.S., New York, 1966, 186 pp. Part I: "Preventing Pregnancy."

Guttmacher, Alan F., M.D., *Planning Your Family,* The Macmillan Company, New York, 1964, 329 pp. Part I: "Birth Control."

Hall, Robert E., *Nine Months' Reading—A Guide for Pregnant Women,* Doubleday and Company, New York, 1963.

Lynch, William, *Marriage for Catholics,* Irident Press, New York, 1964.

Naismith, Grace, *Private and Personal,* David McKay Company, New York.

Section 2. Abortion

  I. DEFINITIONS

    A. There are a number of definitions for the term *abortion,* as follows:

      1. The interruption of pregnancy before the fetus has grown sufficiently to live outside the mother's body.

2. The termination of pregnancy at any time before the fetus has attained a stage of viability, i.e., before it is capable of extrauterine existence.
3. The premature expulsion of the products of conception, such as the fertilized egg, the embryo, or the nonviable fetus.

B. There are two related terms.
   1. The term *miscarriage* is one. It refers to an interruption of the fetus within the first six months of development; this is also called abortion.
   2. Another term is *premature birth* which refers to an interruption of the fetus beginning with the seventh month of development.

II. TYPES OF ABORTION
   A. There are a number of types of spontaneous abortions which occur naturally with no known specific cause and without outside intervention.
      1. Threatened: This type exists when the patient has uterine bleeding and/or pain.
      2. Inevitable: So defined when the bleeding is copious and pains are severe.
      3. Complete: Meaning that all the products of conception or gestation have been expelled.
      4. Incomplete: Applies when only a portion of the product of conception has been passed, with the remains—usually the placenta—in the uterus.
      5. Missed: Applies when the embryo or fetus dies in the uterus but fails to expel it within eight weeks thereafter.
      6. Habitual: Refers to the situation of three or more successive pregnancies being spontaneously aborted.
   B. Induced abortion is the type most commonly thought of by the lay public when the word *abortion* is used; it is brought about intentionally and is of two types:
      1. Therapeutic: Defined as instrumental termination of pregnancy by a physician because of some grave maternal disease which would make continuation of the pregnancy extremely hazardous to the mother.
      2. Criminal or illegal: Termination of pregnancy is done without medical or legal justification either by:
         a. Unskilled doctors or other persons, or
         b. Self-administration of various solutions to the problem.

III. CAUSES OF SPONTANEOUS ABORTIONS
   A. In the United States it is estimated that at least 10 per cent of all conceptions result in abortion.
   B. Of these, more than 50 per cent occur because of embryonic defects.
   C. Some of the specific causes of abortion include:
      1. Poor health of the mother, which may include:
         a. Severe malnutrition.
         b. Nephritis.
         c. Diabetes mellitus.
         d. Tuberculosis endometritis.
      2. Some complications of pregnancy.

3. Abnormal condition of the baby or its environment.
4. Intrinsic defects in the egg or the sperm.
5. Poorly prepared uterine lining for receiving the fertilized egg.

IV. ABORTION PROCEDURES
   A. Dilatation and curettage is the more common method.
      1. It is for pregnancies of less than three months' duration.
      2. No incision is required.
      3. The fetus is evacuated through the vagina.
      4. It consists of a simple surgical procedure done under anesthesia.
      5. Little blood loss occurs.
      6. Recuperation is rapid.
   B. Hysterotomy—miniature caesarean—is another method.
      1. This method is necessary to use after the twelfth week of pregnancy.
      2. An incision is required in the lower abdomen.
      3. It requires anesthesia and hospital recuperation of one week.
   C. Swedish method: injections into the fetus.
      1. This is a new method for pregnancies between the fourteenth and twenty-second week.
      2. A needle is inserted one inch below the navel; six ounces of amniotic fluid is removed and replaced with a salt solution.
      3. It is highly effective and safe.
   D. The risk involved in an induced abortion brought about by surgical means.
      1. There is little danger in the legal variety.
      2. In the dilatation and curettage method, the risk is infinitesimal; deaths are recorded at two per 1000.
      3. In hysterotomy, there is one death per 1000 performed.

V. INDICATIONS FOR THERAPEUTIC ABORTION
   A. Medical indications include the following:
      1. Cardiovascular disease which tends to increase the risk of maternal death during pregnancy.
      2. Gastrointestinal disease.
      3. Renal disease.
      4. Neurological disease such as multiple sclerosis.
      5. Pulmonary disease of which tuberculosis accounts for nearly all of the pulmonary conditions thought to indicate abortion.
   B. Fetal indications include these:
      1. Drugs: For example, the drug Thalidomide taken by the mother during pregnancy causes severe fetal abnormalities.
      2. Rubella (German measles) causes fetal abnormalities and defects in early pregnancy.
      3. Radiation may cause malformation or death of the fetus when given in therapeutic doses to the mother in the first few months of pregnancy.
      4. Genetic: Therapeutic abortion on genetic grounds is, at the present time, rarely done.
      5. Erythroblastosis fetalis: The fetus is likely to die in utero as a result of incompatibility of the Rh factor.

C. Psychiatric indications include, for example, cases where the patient is emotionally disturbed and threatens suicide.

VI. THE PROBLEM OF INDUCED ABORTION
A. It is of enormous magnitude in terms of both incidence and resultant mortality.
1. It is estimated that one out of every five pregnancies in the United States terminates in illegal induced abortion.
2. The total is more than one million annually.
3. More than five thousand deaths possibly result from these abortions.
B. Who have abortions?
1. It is the young (between twenty-one and twenty-five years) married woman who is most likely to undergo an abortion in the United States today.
2. Although two out of three abortions in America involve married women, the case of the unmarried girl is more tragic.
3. The shocking problem of unwanted pregnancy and abortion is now spreading among teenagers.
4. Mrs. Katherine Brownell Oettinger, chief of the U.S. Children's Bureau, has stated: "We are so concerned about the younger girls—both those who become illegitimate mothers and those who have abortions. Forty per cent of all illegitimate babies are born to girls under twenty. This is the group that gives us the double whammy—illegitimacy and abortion." (*Newsweek,* August 15, 1960.)
5. The choices open to a pregnant high school girl today are abortion, disgrace, or reluctant and often disastrous marriage.
C. Illegal abortions in addition to being expensive are dangerous because:
1. Inadequate equipment is often used.
2. The operation often takes place in unsanitary surroundings.
3. The woman is likely to be without proper postoperative care.
D. Some highlights concerning abortion from the Kinsey group's study are these:
1. One out of every three or four women having live births had one or more abortions.
2. The higher the educational level, the greater the tendency was to seek abortion.
3. Illegal abortion is more a problem of married women who have several children—which is contrary to the popular notion that the problem mostly involves illegitimate pregnancy.
E. American women favor abortion according to a poll conducted by the National Institute of Child Health and Human Development. It obtained the following statistics, as reported in 1967.
1. Of U.S. wives, 91 per cent favor abortion under certain conditions.
2. Of those who were polled, 87 per cent favored abortion "if the pregnancy seriously endangered the woman's health."
3. In cases of rape, abortion was favored by 52 per cent.
4. In case the woman had reason to believe that the child would be born deformed, abortion was favored by 50 per cent.

    5. Approval of abortion for unmarried women or for those who were poor or had large families was considered less popular.

VII. ABORTION REFORM GAINS
  A. As of 1968, thirty-nine states permit abortion only to save the mother's life.
  B. California, Colorado, and North Carolina have recently modified their statutes on the subject and many other states are studying the matter.
  C. A new policy statement of the American Medical Association follows the model code of the American Law Institute. It would approve therapeutic abortions to:
    1. Safeguard the life or health of the mother.
    2. To prevent the birth of a child with a physical or mental defect.
    3. To terminate a pregnancy resulting from rape or incest.

VIII. THE CURRENT TREND IS TO GET ABORTION LEGALIZED
  A. This presents a moral, ethical, and religious dilemma for all involved.
    1. Many people contend that no one has the right to interfere with the life of a fetus.
    2. Other people contend that parents should be the sole judge of whether they want an abortion.
    3. Some say that present laws give the fetus more rights than the mother who might be injured if she went through with the pregnancy.
    4. Some religions maintain that abortion is murder (infanticide).
  B. Important questions arise.
    1. One question asked is "When does human life begin?" A poll of the world's scientists say that life begins at conception.
    2. Another question asked is "When is the embryo or the fetus a personality?" The answer to this question seems to depend upon definitions.
  C. Attitudes of major religions toward abortion.
    1. Roman Catholic: Abortion is not permitted unless the termination of pregnancy is the natural by-product of a necessary operation.
    2. Protestant: Sanctioned by many denominations in order to save the life of the mother.
    3. Jewish: Sanctioned to save the life of the mother.
  D. We need to address ourselves to those deeper conditions which cause abortion to flourish.

IX. PREVENTION AND COUNSELING
  A. Adequate sex education may contribute to the prevention of the problems that may lead to abortions—both the spontaneous and the induced types.
  B. Through conception control, the problem can be reduced.
  C. Consultation centers are available where women with unwanted pregnancies may go for counseling by competent professionals. With experienced counseling:
    1. Many women find that they can and want to go to term.
    2. Others find that they may qualify for a therapeutic abortion.

3. Still others can have the possibilities of adoption explored.
4. Those who are still intent on an illegal abortion can be educated about its dangers and the necessity for early treatment afterward.

References for Section 2

American Medical Association, *Today's Health Guide,* Chicago, 1965.

Consumers Union, *Report on Family Planning,* Consumers Union Publication, New York, 1966, 187 pp.

Crossen, R. J., *Synopsis of Gynecology,* C. V. Mosby Company, St. Louis, 1959.

Fitzpatrick, Elise, and Nicholson J. Eastman, *Obstetrics for Nurses,* J. B. Lippincott Company, Philadelphia, 1960, 572 pp.

Guttmacher, Alan E., M.D., *Planning Your Family,* The Macmillan Company, 1964, 329 pp., Part II, Ch. 16, "Abortion."

Lader, Lawrence, *Abortion,* Beacon Press, Boston, 1966, 206 pp.

Shafer, Sawyer, McCluskey, and Beck, *Medical-Surgical Nursing,* C. V. Mosby Company, St. Louis, 1961, 876 pp.

Wilson, R. A., *Feminine Forever,* M. Evans Company, New York, 1966.

18

Health Aspects
of Family Living

Section 1. Health Aspects in Planning to Have Children

I. INTRODUCTION

    A. It is well to bear in mind that becoming a parent is one of the most important things you will do in your life.

    B. Therefore, young people should start thinking like parents the minute they get engaged.

    C. During the engagement, or at the very latest immediately after their marriage, is the time to visit a doctor who will take complete medical histories.

    D. The doctor may recommend a genetic counselor if he feels that a study in depth is indicated.

        1. Genetic counseling is based on medical studies and family histories concerning heredity—particularly the risks of hereditary abnormalities.

        2. Today when a genetic counselor is given certain facts, he can often tell parents, or prospective parents, what the chances are that certain inherited defects or disorders will, or will not, appear in their children.

II. SOME STATISTICS ABOUT BABIES

    A. To the prospective parent one could ask the question: "What kind of a human being will you bring into the world?"

        1. The chances are good that your children will be born healthy.

        2. However, we do have 700 babies born *every* day with birth defects significant enough to affect their daily lives.

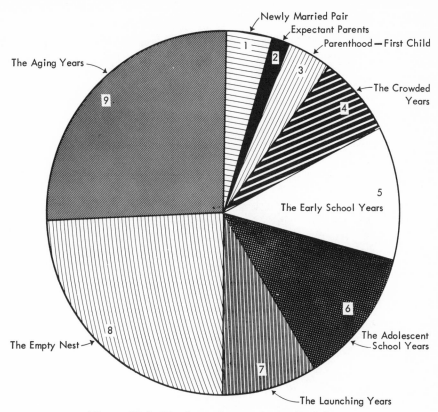

Figure 18-1. Pie chart of stages in family living.

   a. This means more than a quarter of a million such babies a year.

   b. Also, on the average, it happens to one out of every ten families.

   c. Parents in general think that this kind of a problem can never happen to them—but it does.

   d. Fortunately, the aforementioned statistics can be changed if we put to use some of the new medical knowledge made available in recent years.

  B. Each day babies are born with many different types of defects.

    1. Some may be obvious, such as cleft lip or congenitally dislocated hip.

    2. Others may be hidden, like a hearing impairment or a heart defect.

    3. Some types of defects are detectable soon after birth.

    4. Others do not show up for months or even years, such as diabetes.

    5. Many are structural defects, such as a club foot.

    6. Some are chemical imbalance or chromosomal abnormalities which might cause mental deficiency, as in Down's syndrome (mongolism).

III. WHY DO THESE ABNORMALITIES OCCUR?

  A. It used to be believed that it could be the result of:

    1. A punishment for some past deed.

  2. Or an accident of fate.

  3. Or any number of other reasons that have been handed down in the form of myths from generation to generation.

 B. We now know that the problem might be due to a number of factors such as:

  1. The union of defective genes from both parents.

  2. Accidents in cell division.

  3. Environmental influences on the fetus.

  4. A combination of hereditary and environmental influences.

  5. And the situation of far too many mothers and fathers not taking seriously enough the matter of having a baby. *They simply do not know all that can go wrong, especially during the early weeks of pregnancy.*

IV. LET US NOW CONSIDER THE WIFE WHO MAY BE PREGNANT

 A. She will not know whether or not she is pregnant for a week or so:

  1. Not until she misses her menstrual period.

  2. Or it maybe will be another full month before she is really sure.

 B. All the following is happening in the first forty days—perhaps even before she knows for sure that she is pregnant:

  1. The fetus is less than an inch long, but:

  2. All its organs are being formed.

  3. It has a heart that is beating.

  4. It has a human face including eyes, ears, a nose, and little bumps that are its milk teeth.

  5. It has tiny arms and legs and hands and feet.

  6. Its liver and kidneys work; and its nervous system is beginning to function.

 C. *These first forty days are the period of most rapid growth in the whole life of a human being.*

 D. All the growing that is done in the next twenty-five years is simply a refinement of things that happen in these first forty days.

 E. *And now is the time when the greatest damage can be done to those fragile organs and limbs.*

 F. Now is the time, therefore, for the pregnant woman to be careful.

  1. She should avoid sick people.

  2. She should avoid exposure to any contagious disease, particularly German measles.

  3. In the instance of syphilis, it is important to remember that a mother with an untreated case has only one chance in six of having a normal baby.

  4. Attempts at self-induced abortion usually fail and, furthermore, may cause damage to the developing fetus.

  5. It is important that any woman who is in an accident or is sick should tell any doctor that she is, or may be, pregnant; knowing this, he can use his judgment about prescribing abdominal X-ray.

  6. The pregnant woman should stop taking aspirin, nosedrops, and laxatives; for, in fact, any kind of medicine—even the regular prescription that she takes all the time—might cause damage during these first forty days.

7. The pregnant woman must avoid even the most innocent kind of self-medication which means:
   a. No baking soda for an upset stomach.
   b. No vitamin pills.
   c. No reducing pills.
   d. No tranquilizers.
   e. No pep pills.
   f. *No medicine.*
8. Instead she should see a doctor immediately; it might be her own doctor or one at the maternity clinic or at the health department clinic.
9. It is only a doctor who can set up a special program that is tailored to the needs of the individual patient.
   a. He will make tests.
   b. He will outline a diet.
   c. He may prescribe supplements—iron, vitamins, and other medication *if* she needs them.
   d. He will discuss with her the question of exercise and rest.
   e. If she is a smoker, he may tell her to stop smoking. It is known that excessive smoking is associated with a lower birth weight which in turn can be a complicating factor for a small baby.

V. WHEN THE DAY OF BIRTH ARRIVES, THE DOCTOR PLAYS A DECISIVE ROLE
   A. The Apgar test is given within one minute after the birth of a baby.
      1. This test is for the purpose of determining the health of a baby at the moment of birth.
      2. The test comprises five steps, namely, the recording of heart rate, respiration, muscle tone, reflexes, and color.
   B. A test for phenylketonuria, known as PKU, may be given in a few days.
      1. PKU is an error in body chemistry that causes a build-up of phenylalanine which, if untreated, results in gross mental retardation.
      2. Early discovery and prompt dietary treatment can help prevent brain damage.
   C. Whether or not a birth defect is visible or hidden, doctors today can often perform miracles.

VI. HAZARDS AFTER BIRTH
   A. Here are some statistics concerning the hazards to babies:
      1. An American baby with significant birth defects comes into the world every two minutes. Of these, at least 18,000 die in the first year of life.
      2. Annually, 500,000 babies die before they are born.
      3. From the thirty-sixth week of pregnancy to the fourth week of life is an eight-week span during which 3.5 per cent of our population dies.
      4. An equal percentage is found to be defective.
   B. Part of the problem is that many women do not seek prenatal care.
      1. Such women not only have a variety of health problems that affect their babies, but they also have two or three times as many premature babies as women who have prenatal care.

2. Premature babies have many more problems with physical and mental development than do full-term babies.
3. Unfortunately, many of these untreated mothers are teenagers, and they need extra help during pregnancy.
4. Girls as young as fifteen or thirteen, or even twelve years of age, may be physically able to become pregnant, but they and many other young mothers still have not completed their adolescent growth.

C. Most parents have healthy babies, but the odds are against a mother with:
   1. Hepatitis.
   2. Untreated syphilis.
   3. An unhealthy thyroid.
   4. A history of miscarriages.
   5. Age over forty years.
   6. Age under eighteen years.

D. The important questions is, therefore, "Will you be fit to have children when you want to have them?"

Section 2. Medical Examinations

I. CONSIDERATION WILL BE GIVEN TO THREE KINDS OF MEDICAL EXAMINATIONS IN THE CONTEXT OF PREPARATION FOR MARRIAGE AND PARENTHOOD, NAMELY, THE GENERAL EXAMINATION, THE PREMARITAL EXAMINATION, AND THE PRENATAL EXAMINATIONS

II. THE GENERAL PHYSICAL EXAMINATION IS THE MOST IMPORTANT OF THE EXAMINATIONS
   A. The reason is that it involves a person's health at every point in his life.
   B. A general physical is made up of many parts to check one's general health and usually includes a check on the following:
      1. Blood pressure.
      2. Heart beat.
      3. Eyes, ears, nose, and throat.
      4. Intestines.
      5. Lungs.
      6. Weight and height.
      7. Reflexes and muscle tone.
      8. Urinalysis.
      9. Other aspects as needed.
   C. One should have a check-up annually.

III. THE PREMARITAL EXAMINATION IS IMPORTANT IF THE MARRIAGE IS TO BE HAPPY BY AVOIDING PHYSICAL COMPLICATIONS
   A. The purposes of the premedical examination include the following:
      1. To ascertain the state of general health and to point out any symptoms that might affect the couple's choice or their future conjugal relationships.
      2. To discover details of the anatomy that might affect the couple's sexual adjustment.
      3. To discover any anatomical characteristics that would make it inadvisable to become pregnant.

4. To test for the presence or absence of the Rh factor in the couple's blood.
5. To give the couple an opportunity to talk over with the physician their contemplated marriage and their initiation into it and have questions answered.
6. To permit the couple to get advice, if they so desire, on some method of controlling conception that would be acceptable to them.[1]

B. The premarital examination is similar to the general physical examination with certain important additions.
1. Blood tests for syphilis and the possibility of an Rh factor.
2. The male and the female may each have separate tests of the genital area.

C. The female is tested for the following:
1. Size and general build, the amount and distribution of fat, and the pattern and extent of hair—both on the body as a whole and particularly in the pubic area.
2. The size and formation of the clitoris and the vulva which indicate sexual development.
3. The structure and appearance of the urethra and vagina—significant in case of inflammation.
4. Ascertaining whether the hymen is intact and noting its rigidity and thickness.
5. A check of glandular behavior.

C. The male is tested for the following:
1. The size, position, and firmness of the testicles.
2. The thickness of the vas deferens.
3. The position of the external openings at the tip of the penis. If displaced to either upper or lower side of shaft, it must be corrected.
4. The presence or absence of the foreskin to see whether it is too tight.
5. The condition of the prostate gland and the seminal vesicles to see whether their size and consistency are normal; may check secretion for bacteria or other potentially harmful organisms.

D. Counseling is considered necessary. It is also part of the physical examination and may consist of:
1. A discussion of birth control methods.
2. Advice on methods of coitus.
3. Answers to questions of personal hygiene.

E. Premarital blood tests are required in all except six states.
1. The number of days before marriage for such tests ranges from seven to forty days.
2. Louisiana tests males only.

IV. The Prenatal Examinations Occur Several Times During a Pregnancy.
A. The first examination is general in nature.
1. The blood pressure is taken.
2. The heart is examined for rate, function, and rhythm.
3. The breasts are examined to note the pattern of the nipples and their

[1] Henry A. Bowman, *Marriage for Moderns,* McGraw-Hill Book Company, 1960, p. 197.

suitability for nursing and to determine whether cysts or tumors are present.

4. A urinalysis is made.

5. The amount of red blood cells in the blood is checked.

6. Blood tests for syphilis and the Rh factor are made.

7. Dentists should examine the teeth during the first three months of pregnancy.

8. A pelvic examination is made comprising:

    a. A check of neck of the uterus.

    b. Taking a smear as a check on cancer of the uterus.

    c. Taking the pelvic measurements to be sure that there is enough room for the baby to be born normally.

9. Pregnancy is confirmed and the date of arrival is determined.

B. The later examinations include a discussion as to the woman's state of health, and a check on:

1. Blood pressure.

2. Weight and diet.

3. The position of the fetus.

C. Weekly visits need to be made.

1. The doctor rectally checks the position of the baby.

2. Weight and blood pressure are taken.

3. The necessary arrangements with the hospital are made.

D. Counseling is available for both parents-to-be.

V. DIAGNOSIS OF PREGNANCY IS POSSIBLE BY MEANS OF THE FOLLOWING TESTS OR EXAMINATIONS:

A. One means is the bimanual examination which consists of:

1. Palpation with a finger of one hand in the vagina and the application of pressure over the lower abdomen with the fingers of the other hand.

2. The uterus, Fallopian tubes, and ovaries are carefully felt and checked for size, position, contour, consistency, and mobility.

3. This examination is not useful in determining pregnancy in the early weeks.

B. There are two tests that are used to diagnose pregnancy.

1. The Aschheim-Zondek test.

    a. It is based on the fact that there is surplus hormone in the urine of a pregnant woman.

    b. Urine of a pregnant woman, when introduced into an immature female mouse, causes ovulation.

    c. The test is 98 per cent accurate.

    d. It can be used in the first month of pregnancy.

2. The Friedman test.

    a. This test is similar to the Aschheim-Zondek test except that it is performed on a female rabbit that has been isolated from males for thirty days.

    b. If the woman is pregnant, the urine will cause the rabbit to ovulate or have follicle formation.

    c. The test is 100 per cent accurate when carefully administered.

C. Diagnosis in the last half of the pregnancy is determined by:

    1. The fetal heart.

    2. The palpation of the fetal outline.

    3. The perception of active and passive fetal movements.

    4. X-ray—after the fourth month.

References for Sections 1 and 2

Bowman, Henry A., *Marriage for Moderns,* McGraw-Hill Book Co., Inc., New York, 1960.

Cooley, Donald G., ed., *Family Medical Guide,* Meredith Press, New York, 1966.

Duvall, Evelyn M., and Reuben Hill, *Being Married,* Association Press, New York, 1960.

Kavinoky, Nadina, "Premarital Medical Examination," *J. Am. Med. Ass.,* October 1954, p. 693.

Mace, David R., *Marriage: The Art of Lasting Love,* Doubleday & Company, Inc., New York, 1952.

Skidmore, Rex A., and Anthon S. Cannon, *Building Your Marriage,* Harper & Brothers Publishers, New York, 1951.

Stone, Hannah, and Abraham Stone, *A Marriage Manual,* Simon and Schuster, New York, 1952.

Warner, Marie Pichel, *The Couple Who Want a Baby,* Funk & Wagnalls Company, New York, 1961.

Womble, Dale L., *Foundations for Marriage and Family Relations,* The Macmillan Company, New York, 1966.

Section 3. Impotence and Frigidity

I. IMPOTENCE APPLIES TO THE MALE.

    A. It varies from the inability to attain or maintain full erection to total loss of erection prowess.

    B. It can be further defined as:

        1. Primary impotence—the difficulty has existed from the onset of sexual activities.

        2. Secondary impotence—the difficulty arises later in life, following a history of effective sexual functioning.

    C. The factors causing impotence include the following:

        1. Psychological factors: Impotence is practically always of psychic origin, such as:

            a. Negative attitudes toward sex and women.

            b. Homosexuality.

            c. Mental blocks.

        2. Physiological factors include:

            a. Gonadal deficiency.

            b. Prostatitis.

      c. Urethritis.
      d. Diabetes.
      e. Drugs—tranquilizers, anticholinergic drugs.
      f. Fatigue.
  D. Treatment consists of the following methods:
    1. Hormone treatment—androgen administration.
    2. Psychotherapy.
    3. Sexual counseling.

II. FRIGIDITY OCCURS IN THE FEMALE.
  A. There are four types of frigidity.
    1. Persistence of clitoral orgasm.
    2. Failure to attain orgasm.
    3. Failure of sexual arousal and gratification.
    4. Negative reactions to sexual situations.
  B. The factors causing frigidity.
    1. The physiological factors include:
      a. Endocrinopathies.
      b. Endometriosis.
      c. Cystitis.
      d. Stenosis of the vagina.
      e. Vulvovaginitis.
      f. Fatigue.
    2. The psychological factors include:
      a. Negative attitudes toward sex and men.
      b. Trauma in childhood.
      c. Fear of pregnancy.
      d. Preoccupation.
  C. Treatment comprises the following methods:
    1. Psychotherapy.
    2. Tranquilizers.
    3. Sexual counseling.
    4. Oral contraceptives.

References for Section 3

Bartone, Francis, "Recognition and Management of Impotence," *Medical Aspects of Human Sexuality,* Vol. I, No. 2, October 1967, pp. 76–87.

Hutton, Laura, *The Single Woman,* Roy Publishers, New York, 1960, 132 pp.

Klemer, Richard H., *Counseling in Marital and Sexual Problems,* The Williams and Wilkins Company, Baltimore, 1965, 294 pp.

Masters, William H., and Virginia Johnson, *Human Sexual Response,* Little, Brown and Company, Boston, 1966.

Rubin, Isador, *Sexual Life after Sixty,* Basic Books, New York, 1965, 235 pp.

19

Special Topics

Section 1. Sex-Linked Traits and Other Influences of Sex on Inheritance
I. THE SEX CHROMOSOMES
    A. The human body contains two chromosomes—an X and a Y.
        1. The X chromosome is three times larger than the Y chromosome.
        2. The X chromosome has 4 per cent more DNA at its disposal than the Y.
        3. The X chromosome contains a full complement of genes; the Y does not.
           a. To date (1968) there are no proven genes in the Y chromosome.
    B. The female cell contains two X chromosomes and the male one.
        1. The X chromosome carries at least some female determining factors; others may be in autosomes (name used to refer to all other chromosomes).
        2. The double X of the female protects her against the development of deficiency disorders even though she has inherited a defective gene.
    C. The male contains one Y chromosome; the female none.
        1. The Y is the bearer of the male-determining factors.
        2. The Y is a weaker chromosome than the X because of its size and its lack of genes.
           a. Because of occurrences in incomplete sex-linkage it is thought that there must be some genes in the Y chromosome.
        3. The lack of corresponding genes in the Y chromosome to those in the X chromosome leaves the male open to deficiencies of defective genes.

D. In some occurrences, there is an XO or an XXY chromosome count present in a human.
   1. This is result of nondisjunction at either mitosis or meiosis.
   2. The individual either becomes intersexual or a female.

II. SEX-LINKED TRAITS

A. When a trait is conditioned by a gene lying in the X chromosome, it is said to be sex-linked.
   1. This means such characteristics will be linked with sex in heredity.
   2. It does not mean that such characteristics are linked to a particular sex, but that such characteristics will follow distribution of the X chromosome in both sexes.
   3. All sex-linked mutant genes are recessive.
B. There are sixty deficiency traits which have been proven to be sex-linked, and twenty deficiency traits that are due to sex-linked genes and their influences.
   1. The proven sex-linked genes include:
      Partial color blindness, deutan series and protan series.
      Total color blindness.
      Glucose-6-phosphate dehydrogenase deficiency.
      Xg blood-group system.
      Muscular dystrophy, Duchenne type and Becker type.
      Hemophilia A and B.
      Agammaglobulinemia.
      Hurler syndrome.
      Late spondylo-epiphyseal dysplasia.
      Aldrich syndrome.
      Hypophosphatemia.
      Hypoparathyroidism.
      Nephrogenic diabetes insipidus.
      Neurohypophyseal diabetes insipidus.
      Oculocerebrorenal syndrome of Lowe.
      Hypochromic anemia.
      Angiokeratoma diffusum corporis universale.
      Dyskeratosis congenita.
      Dystrophia bullosa hereditaria, maculatus.
      Keratosis follicularis spinulosa cum ophiasi.
      Ichthyosis vulgaris.
      Anhidrotic ectodermal dysplasia.
      Amelogenesis imperfecta, hypomaturation type.
      Absence of central incisors.
      Congenital deafness and progressive deafness.
      Mental deficiency.
      Borjesson syndrome.
      Spinal ataxia.
      Cerebellar ataxia with extrapyramidal involvement.

Spastic paraplegia.
Progressive bulbar paralysis.
Charcot-Marie-Tooth peroneal muscular atrophy.
Diffuse cerebral sclerosis.
Parkinsonism.
Ocular albinism.
External ophthalmoplegia and myopia.
Microphthalmia.
Nystagmus.
Megalocornea.
Hypoplasia of iris with glaucoma.
Congenital cataract (total and with microcornea).
Stationary night blindness with myopia.
Choroideremia.
Retinitis pigmentosa.
Macular dystrophy.
Retinoschisis.
Pseudogliomia.
Van den Bosch syndrome.
2. Conditions for which the evidence for sex-linkage is considered inconclusive range from the inability to smell cyanide and the testicular feminization syndrome, to familial obstructive jaundice.
C. There are some traits which are considered to be incompletely sex-linked.
1. The manner in which these conditions behave in inheritance leads to the conclusion that the human Y chromosome must possess some genes.
2. All other chromosomes are called autosomes and these would not react to the presence of either of the sex chromosomes.
3. The factor that makes them similar is that the traits are passed to a male or a female depending on which chromosome it was connected to.
4. These genes can cross from the X to the Y in a male.
5. Examples of these incomplete sex-linked genes are:
a. Xeroderma pigmentosum (childhood skin disease, often fatal).
b. Cerebral sclerosis (mental defect).
c. Recessive form epidermolpis bullosa (malignant skin blisters).

III. SEX-INFLUENCED TRAITS
A. Influenced genes are conditioned by the genes carried in autosomes and are inherited by both sexes.
1. Sex controls dominance.
2. The gene which is dominant in one sex is recessive in the other.
3. Examples of these traits are:
a. White forelock.
b. Absence of upper lateral incisor teeth.
c. Simple ichthyosis (scaling skin).
d. Heberden's nodes (enlargement of terminal joints of fingers).

IV. SEX-LIMITED TRAITS
  A. These traits are expressed in one sex and not in the other.
    1. They can be in either the autosomes or the sex chromosomes.
    2. Expression depends on the presence or absence of one or more sex hormones.
      a. The amount of such hormones present within an organism will determine how much of the trait will show.
    3. Complete development in one sex and no presence in the other sex is very rare.
    4. Examples of these traits are:
      a. Milk production and menstruation in females (complete in one).
      b. Appearance of coarse hairs on the external ear of white men during the process of aging (again one sex).
      c. Beard of mustache hair is present in both sexes but normally expressed only in one.
      d. Baldness can be passed to daughter and son, but again it becomes recessive in the female and dominant in the male.
    5. A sex-limited trait is fully expressed in only one sex, while previously mentioned sex-influenced traits can be fully expressed in both sexes.

References for Section 1

Asimov, Isaac, *The Genetic Code,* The Orion Press, New York, 1962.

Auerbach, Charlotte, *The Science of Genetics,* Harper & Brothers, Publishers, New York, 1961.

Bonner, David M., *Heredity,* Prentice-Hall, Englewood Cliffs, N. J., 1961.

Goldstein, Philip, *Genetics Is Easy,* Lantern Press, New York, 1967.

Montagu, Ashley, *Human Heredity,* The World Publishing Company, New York, 1963.

Reed, Sheldon C., *Counseling in Medical Genetics,* W. B. Saunders Company, London, 1955.

Scheinfeld, Amram, *Your Heredity and Environment,* J. B. Lippincott Company, New York, 1965.

Singleton, W. Ralph, *Elementary Genetics,* D. Van Nostrand Company, Princeton, N. J., 1967.

Section 2. Blood Types
  I. DEFINITION OF BLOOD
    A. Comprises a mixture of cells and plasma.
      1. Cells.
        a. Red, white, platelets.
        b. 45 per cent of volume of blood.
      2. Plasma.
        a. Amber-colored liquid.
        b. 55 per cent of volume of blood.
    B. Average adult body contains twelve to thirteen pints of blood.
      1. Ten pints is in circulation.
      2. Two to three pints is in storage in the liver and spleen.

C. Blood is pumped by the heart through the blood vessels.
   1. Arteries and capillaries carry nutrients for life to each cell.
      a. Oxygen from the lungs.
      b. Food from the intestines.
      c. Water.
   2. Veins and more capillaries carry wastes from each cell to be expelled.
      a. Carbon dioxide through the lungs.
      b. Other wastes through kidneys.
      c. Some wastes through the skin in perspiration.

II. BLOOD CELLS AND PLASMA
   A. Red cells.
      1. Produced in bone marrow.
      2. Contain hemoglobin.
      3. Carry oxygen.
      4. If destroyed, some components are salvaged and reused.
   B. White cells (leukocytes).
      1. One white cell for every 600 red cells.
      2. The functions of the white cells are to:
         a. Fight bacteria.
         b. Absorb dead cells and foreign bodies.
   C. Platelets.
      1. Are colorless cells in the bone marrow.
      2. Assist in clotting of blood after injury to a blood vessel.
   D. Plasma.
      1. Is nine-tenths water.
      2. And one-tenth proteins, vitamins, and some fats.
         a. Proteins: hormones, enzymes, gamma globulin, albumin, fibrinogen.
      3. Useful in combating shock.
      4. Given to all regardless of blood group.

III. BLOOD GROUPS
   A. Blood group systems.
      1. ABO group.
      2. MNS group.
      3. P group.
      4. Rhesus group.
      5. Lutheran group.
      6. Kell group.
      7. Lewis group.
      8. Duffy group.
      9. Kidd group.
      10. Diego group.
      11. Sutter group.
   B. The main groups are:
      1. ABO group.
      2. Rhesus group.

C. ABO group.
  1. Possibilities in group:
     a. Red cells: AB, A, B, O.
     b. Plasma: anti-A, anti-B.
  2. Group A contains substance A and anti-B.
  3. Group B contains substance B and anti-A.
  4. Group AB contains substances A and B but neither anti-A nor anti-B.
  5. Group O contains neither A nor B but both anti-A and anti-B.
     a. It is called the universal donor.
     b. Group O may be given to other people of the ABO group in an emergency.
D. Rhesus factor (Rh).
  1. It is a hereditary blood constituent.
  2. There are two possibilities:
     a. Rh positive (dominant).
     b. Rh negative.
  3. The Rh factor is inherited from one or both parents.
  4. Both men and women have Rh positive and Rh negative in same proportion.

References for Section 2

Bowman, Henry, *Marriage for Moderns,* McGraw-Hill Book Company, New York, 1965.

Clark, Marguerite, *Medicine Today,* Funk and Wagnalls Company, New York, 1960.

Cross, Martin L., *The Doctors,* Random House, New York, 1966.

Hall, Robert E., *Nine Months' Reading—A Guide for Pregnant Women,* Doubleday and Company, New York, 1963.

Vroman, Leo, *Blood,* Natural History Press, New York, 1967, 174 pp.

Section 3. Cousin Marriages

I. HISTORICAL PERSPECTIVE
  A. Contrary to popular opinion, there are very few legal bars which prevent the recognition of cousin marriages.
  B. Some twenty-nine states prohibit marriages between first cousins.
     1. Six states prevent second cousins from marrying (Indiana, Minnesota, Nevada, Ohio, Washington, Wisconsin).
     2. However, most of these states do recognize the marriages of first cousins who go to another state to marry and then return to their home to live.
  C. Cousin marriages are considered by many to be both acceptable and favorable.
  D. At one time, European royalty preferred and arranged marriages between cousins.
  E. Today one marriage in 100 is likely to be between cousins.

II. THE POSITIVE ASPECTS AND ADVANTAGES OF COUSIN MARRIAGES
  A. They strengthen the kinship tie.
  B. They keep related families together.
  C. They prevent dispersion of the family property.

D. A monetary advantage is that they very often incur less marriage expenses.
E. In cases where cousins have no undesirable hereditary traits, their offspring will usually be of a superior quality—of a finer quality than nonrelatives would produce.

III. ADVERSE FACTORS RELATED TO COUSIN MARRIAGES
A. The main objection to marriages between cousins is the incest taboo.
B. A popular belief is that in-breeding is generally a producer of evil effects.
C. There are biological reasons for opposition to consanguineous marriages.
1. They give recessive genes a chance to show themselves.
2. If, as often happens, these genes are bad ones, the child is penalized.
D. Cousin marriages have a tendency to produce children with:
1. Idiocy.
2. Deaf mutism.
3. An eye disease known as retinitis pigmentosa.

IV. FACTS AND CONSIDERATIONS TO BE EXAMINED BY THOSE CONTEMPLATING A MARRIAGE WITH A COUSIN
A. If first cousins were of the best hereditary stock from a biological point of view, their marriage would be desirable.
B. Cousin marriages, when both individuals show the same abnormality, should be regarded with much suspicion.
C. Some families owe a part of their greatness to inbreeding.

References for Section 3

Kilander, H. Frederick, *Health for Modern Living,* Prentice-Hall, Englewood Cliffs, N. J., 1965.
Landis, Judson, and Mary Landis, *Building a Successful Marriage,* Prentice-Hall, Englewood Cliffs, N. J., 1958.
Popenoe, Paul, *The Child's Heredity,* The Williams & Wilkins Company, Baltimore, 1930.
Westermarch, Edward, *The History of Human Marriage,* Allerton Book Company, New York, 1922.
Westermarch, Edward, *A Short History of Marriage,* The Macmillan Company, New York, 1926.

Section 4. Artificial Insemination
I. THERE ARE SOME ADVANTAGES OF ARTIFICIAL INSEMINATION OVER ADOPTION
A. The genetic background of adopted babies is generally bad.
B. The A.I. child is biologically 50 per cent the couple's own.
C. Adoption involves complicated legal machinery.
1. It involves social workers, doctors, and lawyers.
2. In A.I., the process is a secret between the couple and the doctor.
D. The husband's infertility is a secret in A.I.
E. In A.I., the child is never told.
F. The husband and wife are part of the conception, prenatal period, and delivery.
G. In A.I., the child's physical appearance matches the family.
H. In A.I., the craving for "carry-with-child" is satisfied.

II. PSYCHOLOGICAL PROBLEMS INVOLVED
   A. Must avoid masculine-aggressive women with guilt feelings toward the husband.
   B. Must avoid men who look upon A.I. as a procedure akin to adultery.

III. LEGAL CONSIDERATIONS
   A. No court in the United States, Great Britain, or Canada has any statutory law aimed at defining whether A.I. is illegal.
   B. Illegality is therefore considered from two aspects:
      1. Whether the action of the wife is adulterous.
      2. Whether the child is not legitimate.
   C. The A.I. program.
      1. In Sweden may not be performed until an official permission is given.
      2. But an infant born out of wedlock would not be considered illegitimate if the child was the product of donor spermatozoa.
   D. In New York State, the Bureau of Health sets controls on donor samples.
   E. There is split opinion on whether legal sanctions are necessary or really wanted.

IV. RELIGIOUS CONSIDERATIONS
   A. The Catholic view.
      1. Donor insemination is specifically condemned as an adulterous and unnatural act.
      2. Husband insemination where husband's sperm is obtained other than by natural intercourse is strictly forbidden.
   B. The Jewish view.
      1. The Orthodox view is one of disapproval based on:
         a. The concept of wasting of the seed (masturbation).
         b. And the possibility of consanguinity.
         c. However, it is generally admitted that it is not an adulterous act.
      2. The Reform view is not set but seems to permit A.I. on the recommendation of physicians.
   C. The Protestant view.
      1. It is divided among the various denominations.
      2. They generally see masturbation for purpose of insemination as not being evil.

References for Section 4

Finegold, Wilfred J., *Artificial Insemination,* Charles C Thomas Publishers, Springfield, Ill., 1964.

McFadden, C. F., *Medical Ethics,* The David Press, Philadelphia, 1953.

Section 5. Masturbation
   I. DEFINITIONS
      A. Sexual self-stimulation that leads to climax or orgasm.
      B. The common fondling of the genitals by the young and the retarded.
      C. There are several related terms:
         1. Autoeroticism.

2. Self-abuse.
3. Playing with oneself.
4. Onanism (misnomer).

II. How Is Masturbation Practiced?
A. It is commonly practiced by stimulation of the genitals by the individual's own hand.
B. By rubbing thighs together.
C. By pressure or friction against an object.
D. It is accompanied by (1) erotic reading, (2) erotic pictures, and (3) day-dreaming.

III. Sociological Background
A. The most indulgent practices may be illustrated by the Alorese of Indonesia where sex experiences during the early period of childhood seemed confined to masturbation, which goes on freely in public.
B. The least indulgent of primitive societies studied seems to be the Manus of New Guinea, who masturbate in solitude.
C. Many other societies practice a smiling toleration of the act.
D. Kinsey study shows that over 80 per cent of unmarried males and about 50 per cent of unmarried females have at some time engaged in this form of sexual activity. Since there is no physical harm from such a practice, these percentages may suggest that it is not abnormal.
E. It is a frequent type of sexual activity for a large number of persons, being more common at upper social levels than at lower social levels and more common with males than with females.

IV. Incidence and Frequency of Masturbation
A. Males.
1. On the average, adolescent boys masturbate about two-and-a-half times a week, although 17 per cent masturbate from four to seven or more times a week.
2. The incidence of masturbation in men progressively declines in post-adolescent years, although it frequently continues on a sporadic basis throughout adult life.
3. The incidence of masturbation to the point of orgasm among men is fixed at about 95 per cent of the total male population. The college group has the highest—96 per cent of incidence; those who have attended high school, second highest—95 per cent; and those who attended grade school, the lowest—89 per cent.
4. Over two-thirds of all boys experience their first ejaculation through masturbation; about three-fourths learn how to masturbate from verbal or printed sources.
B. Females.
1. Of all types of sexual activity among women, masturbation ranks first as the most successful method of reaching orgasm. Furthermore, women reach orgasm more quickly through masturbation than through any other sexual techniques (75 per cent in under four minutes).

2. The Kinsey group reported that 34 per cent of the women who never went past grade school, 59 per cent of the women who had attended high school but not college; and 63 per cent of the female college graduates masturbate. Their range of frequency is from once or twice a lifetime to 100 orgasms an hour.

V. RELATION TO PSYCHOSEXUAL DEVELOPMENT
  A. Young accept body as pleasurable.
  B. Parents can cause negative reaction.
  C. Releases adolescent sexual tension:
    1. Sense of identity through fantasy.
    2. Sense of sexual self-image.
    3. Understanding of sex sensations.
  D. Can be negative:
    1. Boredom; frustration; loneliness; parental conflicts.

VI. ATTITUDES TOWARD MASTURBATION
  A. Some societies accept it.
  B. Ours condemns it:
    1. Judeo-Christian tradition is against it.
    2. Medical opinion used to be against it.
  C. No laws against it, but Wyoming ruled that inducing another individual to masturbate is illegal.
  D. Attitudes now are in flux.
  E. Some hold it beneficial as aid to mature psychosexual growth.

VII. ARGUMENTS AGAINST MASTURBATION
  A. It is physically harmful. (No foundation for this view.)
  B. It is harmful in a marriage relationship; true only in a very limited number of cases due to psychological reasons.
  C. It is psychologically harmful because of the guilt and worry over it.
    1. True in majority of the cases, as shame and guilt may cause mental conflict.
    2. Prolonged conflict may cause damage.
    3. May cause more withdrawal on the part of an already withdrawn individual.
  D. It is immoral, because the only normal sexual behavior is intercourse in marriage. Basic facts about masturbation will aid in solving the problem.
  E. Every normal person has a feeling of inferiority, but certain practices can tend to accentuate the feeling instead of reducing it, as is essential to effective and happy adjustment.

VIII. FANTASY AND MASTURBATION
  A. Males: Three-fourths have fantasies.
  B. Females: One-half have fantasies.
  C. Hypotheses:
    1. Masturbation without fantasies becomes a mechanical act.
    2. Heterosexual fantasies are healthy.

3. Homosexual or sadomasochistic fantasies are unhealthy.
4. Act of fantasy may serve as substitute for violence.

IX. PREVENTION OR ERADICATION OF PRACTICE OF MASTURBATION
  A. Sublimation, that is, the replacement or deflection of drives into nonsexual and useful social directions.
  B. Wholesome association with the opposite sex in everyday contacts. These associations tend to emphasize reality rather than promote fantasy.
  C. Keeping occupied at all times.
  D. Resolving tensions as quickly as possible.
    1. Younger children tend to resort to genital play under stress or tense situation.
    2. Actually, frustration in adults leads to autoerotic tendencies, as well as excessive heterosexual practices.
  E. Avoiding solitude—being with others tends to project one's interest to others rather than to himself.
  F. Cleanliness, and an effort to stimulate self-regard and self-reverence.

X. MENTAL RETARDATION AND MASTURBATION
  A. Both have tended to upset people badly because of ignorance; misunderstanding; superstition.
  B. Masturbation is as harmless for the retarded as for anyone else.
  C. Contribute to maturity.
  D. If the retarded child is inclined to masturbate publicly, it can be minimized by:
    1. Providing simple games.
    2. Periodic exercise.
    3. Giving individual food.
  E. Publicity should be given about humane treatment for the retarded, and the normality of sexual expression.

XI. CONCLUSIONS
  A. Masturbation is normal.
  B. Parents and adults ought not to try to prevent private masturbation, but ought to indicate what is acceptable in public.
  C. Anxiety causes increase in frequency, but if *compulsive* masturbation is found along with other disorders, psychiatric help might be needed.
  D. Masturbation may be very beneficial when the overlay of anxiety disappears.

References for Section 5

Cory, D. W., and J. P. LeRoy, *The Homosexual and His Society: A View from Within,* Citadel Press, New York, 1963.

Duvall, Evelyn Millis, *Facts of Life and Love for Teen-agers,* Association Press, New York, 1963.

Garre, W., *Basic Anxiety: A New Psycho-biological Concept,* Philosophical Library, Inc., New York, 1962.

Johnson, Warren E., *Masturbation,* SIECUS Study Guide No. 3, New York, 1967, 20 pp.

Johnson, Warren E., *Mental Retardation and Masturbation,* SIECUS Publication Office, New York, 1967, 4 pp.

Lerrigo, Marion O., and Helen Southard, *Parents' Privilege,* American Medical Association, Chicago, Illinois, 1965.

Whitting and Child, *Child Training,* Yale University Press, New York, 1953.

Section 6. Homosexuality

I. INTRODUCTION

    A. It must be understood that there is no simple dichotomy of the homosexual and the heterosexual.

    B. These terms represent extreme poles on a continuum.

    C. Notable figures in history have been homosexuals.

II. DEFINITIONS

    A. *Homosexuality,* in its generic meaning, refers to sexual attraction to a person of the same sex as oneself, and this includes relations between females as well as those between males, although the term *lesbian* is more commonly applied to females.

    B. These relationships may vary from homosexual fantasies through kissing and mutual masturbation, to fellatio, cunnilingus, and pederasty.

III. CLASSIFICATION

    A. Heterosexual—sexual attraction to, or sexual activity with, members of the opposite sex.

    B. Homosexual—a person who prefers a member of the same sex as the sexual companion.

    C. Bisexual—literally, having sex organs of both sexes, as in hermaphrodites; having a sexual interest in both sexes.

    D. Latent homosexuality—a possibility, a tendency, but not openly expressed.

IV. INCIDENCE AND FREQUENCY

    A. Males.

        1. It is generally accepted by sexologists that about 4 per cent of all white men are exclusively homosexual all their lives, 8 per cent for at least three years between the ages of sixteen and fifty-five, and 37 per cent have experienced some form of overt homosexuality to the point of orgasm. The percentages are equally pertinent to the American Negro.

        2. The strength of an individual's religious convictions influences both the incidence and frequency of homosexual contacts.

            a. The more intense the commitment to religion, the less homosexual activity there is.

            b. The incidence is slightly higher among Catholic men than among the other two religious groups, the incidence among Jewish men being slightly lower than the Protestants.

B. Females.

    1. Kinsey's findings reveal that 28 per cent of women (compared with 50 per cent of males) have experienced some sort of homosexual response.

        a. Only about 1 per cent to 3 per cent of the female population between the ages of twenty and thirty-five are exclusively homosexual.

        b. Compared with 37 per cent of all men, only 13 per cent of all women have had homosexual contact to the point of orgasm.

        c. Thus, in homosexual relationships, twice as many men as women experience sexual response short of orgasm, while three times as many men as women respond to orgasm.

    2. The incidence of lesbianism at various educational levels differs from those pertaining to male homosexuality. The percentages of women who by age thirty have experienced homosexual contact to the point of orgasm are:

        a. Those educated to the level of elementary school, 6 per cent.

        b. Those educated to the level of high school, 5 per cent.

        c. Those educated to the level of college, 10 per cent.

    3. Here follow data for all three main religious groups.

        a. Of those nominally affiliated with the Roman Catholic Church, 25 per cent have experienced homosexual contact to orgasm, while 5 per cent of devout Catholic women have had this experience.

        b. Among Protestants and Jews, a similar correlation exists between serious religious affiliation and homosexual experience.

V. TYPES OF HOMOSEXUALS

A. Transient: Describes one who utilizes homosexual outlets for a limited period in his sexual life.

    1. Another type may engage in heterosexual outlets as well.

    2. He may even be married, but occasionally seeks relations with his own sex.

B. Permanent: Prefers sexual experiences with his or her own sex to the exclusion of the other.

    1. He creates a distinct social dilemma because he or she does not fit into the family pattern.

    2. He frequently gets involved in temporary relationships which dissolve in emotional and social chaos.

VI. THEORIES OF CAUSATION

A. There is no specific cause of homosexual behavior.

    1. Many factors are involved.

    2. Their relative importance varies a great deal.

B. Inborn genetic disorder: Some assume homosexuality is passed on by the vehicle of recessive genes.

    1. Many families show a high incidence over two or more generations.

    2. Kinsey reports that some persons do change over their life span from exclusively heterosexual to exclusively homosexual patterns.

    C. A constitutional factor: Relative balance, rather than presence or absence, is the contributing factor to the degree of masculinity or femininity of the individual.

        1. Studies show that in some cases hormonal imbalance does exist, but its significance as a causality has not been established.

    D. Glandular disorder: Some investigators have found a high percentage of female hormones in the male homosexual's blood stream, and vice versa.

        1. These men prove that such an abnormal androgen-estrogen upset in ratio is a sign of homosexuality.

        2. It is extremely doubtful that hormonal factors are related, except in a very indirect way.

    E. Result of arrested or distorted psychosexual development such as:

        1. Hostility to mother.

        2. Hostility to father.

        3. Affection for mother is excessive.

        4. Affection for father is excessive, especially when the father is not sufficiently masculine.

    F. A learned pattern of behavior, in which cultural pressures and opportunities are the determining influences.

VII. LEGAL ASPECTS

    A. Origin of laws.

    B. State laws vary from state to state, but, in most, homosexual acts are felonies punishable by imprisonment for periods from one year to life.

    C. American Law Institute: May 1955—recommended that sodomy between consenting adults "be removed from the list of crimes against the peace and dignity of the State."

VIII. PSYCHOLOGICAL FACTORS

    A. Normal psychological development is dependent upon a lifelong pattern of effective emotional relationships, primarily obtained within the family but also extending beyond it.

    B. The following are major conditioning emotional experiences associated with the personality disorder of homosexuality:

        1. Early homosexual experience.

            a. This may have been pleasurable either as a result of seduction by an experienced person or as a voluntary exploration.

            b. Under such stresses a child who is experiencing emotional deprivation is susceptible.

        2. Rearing a child as a member of the opposite sex: parents who did very much want a daughter and got a son may bring him up in a girlish manner with long hair, female clothing, etc.

        3. Prolonged heterosexual frustration:

            a. This refers to prisons and the sort of institutions that afford long-term segregation.

        4. Castration anxiety may be a factor.

5. Cross-identfiication:
   a. Here, the child closely identifies with the interests and emotional attitudes of the opposite parent whom he strives to emulate.
   b. He may show homosexual tendencies which may crystallize in overt homosexual experiences.

IX. SYMPTOMS

A. Overt expression of homosexuality may take the following form:
   1. Mutual masturbation.
   2. Sodomy (anal coitus).
   3. Fellatio (oral contact with male organ).
   4. Interfemoral coitus.

X. PREVENTION

A. Create a climate of opinion in which homosexuality can be openly and intelligently discussed—by parents, educators, and counselors.
B. Provide for a healthy sex education.
C. Increasing efforts to provide family counseling and child guidance services which will not only promote psychologically healthy family life but will also provide assistance to children with early symptoms of developmental difficulties.

XI. TREATMENT

A. Psychotherapy can be effective only if the individual is:
   1. Strongly motivated to overcome his problem. It seems that many homosexuals have not developed a personality or character structure and, hence, are less responsive to treatment.
   2. If the motivation for treament is strong, a skilled therapist can do much to restore the individual to a more fulfilling way of life.
B. Other forms of treatment include the following:
   1. Shock therapy.
   2. Psychosurgical procedures.
   3. Endocrine therapy.
C. Homosexuals themselves cling tenaciously to their deviant practices— trying to adjust to two societies, seeking to belong to both, and naturally falling short of this goal.

References for Section 6

Berg, L., and R. Pennington, *An Introduction to Clinical Psychology,* Ronald Press, New York, 1966.
Crawley, Lawrence, James Malfetti, and Ernest Stewart, *Reproduction, Sex and Preparation for Marriage,* Prentice-Hall, Englewood Cliffs, N. J., 1964, 231 pp.
Duvall, Evelyn M., *Sex Ways in Fact and Faith,* Association Press, New York, 1961, 253 pp.
Gide, Andre, *Corydon,* Noonday Press, New York, 1950.
Greenspan, Herbert, and John Campbell, "The Homosexual as a Personality Type," *Am. J. Psychiat.,* Vol. 101, 1945, pp. 682–89.

Kilander, H. Frederick, *Health for Modern Living,* Prentice-Hall, Englewood Cliffs, N. J., 1965, 400 pp.

Kisker, John, *The Disorganized Personality,* McGraw-Hill Book Company, New York, 1964.

McCary, James L., *Human Sexuality,* Van Nostrand Company, Princeton, N. J., 1967, 374 pp.

Marmor, Judd, *Sexual Inversion,* Basic Books, New York, 1965.

20

Venereal Disease
and Prostitution

Section 1. The Venereal Diseases
I. GENERAL INFORMATION
  A. Venereal diseases are those communicable diseases which are usually contracted through sexual relations and which affect the genital organs.
   1. The term is derived from Venus, the Roman goddess of love.
   2. Syphilis and gonorrhea are the two most common venereal diseases in the United States.
   3. Others, which are relatively rare in the United States, include *chancroid, lymphogranuloma,* and *granuloma inguinale.*
  B. Some additional general information about venereal diseases follows.
   1. They rank among the major social problems in the world today.
   2. Both are responsible for a great deal of suffering, and syphilis is the direct cause of many deaths.
   3. Although syphilis and gonorrhea are different diseases, they may be contracted at the same time and from the same source.
   4. The source of venereal infection is always another infected person.
   5. Excluding the cases of congenital syphilis, it is estimated that approximately 99 per cent of the cases of syphilis in the United States are contracted through sexual intercourse—illicit and marital—and about 1 per cent from other methods such as kissing.
   6. The incidence of syphilis and gonorrhea together is greater than any other communicable disease.

C. Four methods are used in discovering new cases of venereal disease.
  1. Most important is contact investigation—examining individuals with whom an infected person has had sexual relations.
  2. Selective mass blood testing is used extensively.
  3. Nearly all states use legal measures as a means of finding infected persons, such as compulsory prenatal and premarital blood tests.
  4. Essential is education of the public about venereal disease through the schools, colleges, and health departments—particularly about the availability and use of case-finding services.
D. Concerning frequency of VD, it is not known exactly how many cases of venereal disease there are in the United States.
  1. One reason for this lack of information is that physicians are often reluctant to report cases to their health departments.
  2. Also, many people have venereal disease without realizing it.
  3. Many individuals who have or think they have VD are reluctant to visit the doctor or clinic.
E. Vaccines and treatment
  1. At present the development of a vaccine for either syphilis or gonorrhea is remote.
  2. The syphilis-causing organism stimulates the body of an infected person to produce antibodies, but these antibodies do not provide lasting immunity.
  3. Consequently, reinfection is possible.
  4. Gonorrhea does not activate the body to produce antibodies.
  5. Penicillin is used in the treatment of both diseases.

II. VD AND HISTORY
A. There is evidence that syphilis is a very old disease.
  1. That syphilis was present in early Egyptian days is the conclusion drawn from the examination of mummies.
  2. Hippocrates, in 460 B.C., described syphilis-like sores which appeared on the sexual organs after mating.
  3. Celsus, a Roman physician, described in 25 A.D. what seemed to have been syphilis in ancient Rome.
  4. The Old Testament of the Bible has several passages which suggest that this disease was present in ancient times.
  5. Archeological findings indicate that syphilis may have existed in the Old World before Columbus' voyage to America.
  6. Plagues of syphilis have been the cause of millions of the world's crippled, blind, insane, and dead.
  7. Throughout history it has infected young and old, rich and poor, prince and pauper.
B. Syphilis appeared quite suddenly at the beginning of the sixteenth century.
  1. After Columbus' return to Spain in 1493, syphilis began to attract much attention.
  2. His crew members, on their return to Spain, infected a number of women who in turn infected other men.

3. There is also little doubt that Columbus himself died from the disease fourteen years later.
4. There was a serious outbreak of this disease between February and May of 1495.
5. By June, 1495, it had reached France, Switzerland, and Germany, and in 1497, it was in England, Scotland, and Greece.
6. Vasco da Gama carried it to India in 1498, and by 1501 it was in China.

C. Syphilis has played an important part in shaping the course of history.

1. Venereal disease traveled with armies throughout history, being spread mainly by prostitutes and camp followers.
2. In February, 1495, Charles VIII of France laid seige to Naples. His mercenary army included men from Spain. Following the fall of Naples, an epidemic of syphilis began to rage. Charles was the last of his dynasty to rule France because all his heirs to the throne were born dead of syphilis.
3. Other kings and emperors acquired syphilis which affected their minds and consequently their actions.

D. In the United States:

1. VD became a very serious problem in the War of 1812.
2. When the Staten Island (New York) Hospital was opened in 1831, 26 of the first 100 patients were suffering from syphilis.
3. More than 77,000 Union soldiers contracted syphilis during the Civil War.
4. In World War I, about 3 million cases of syphilis, to say nothing of gonorrhea, were contracted by the soldiers of all armies.
5. One million men in the U.S. Armed Services were found to have syphilis between 1940 and 1945.

E. Some medical discoveries related to VD.

1. Mercury was used in treating syphilis for centuries.
2. In 1870, Neisser discovered the organism causing gonorrhea.
3. In 1906, Schaudin and Hoffman discovered the microbe which caused syphilis.
4. In 1906, Wassermann and others developed a blood test for syphilis.
5. In 1909, Ehrlich announced the discovery of a cure for syphilis called salvarsan, and also known as 606. Treatment with this drug unfortunately took 72 weeks.
6. In 1943, Dr. John Mahoney found a new cure—penicillin—for treating both syphilis and gonorrhea.
7. By 1953, the treatment for VD was reduced to two weeks and eventually to a single but powerful injection.

F. Changes in VD rates following use of penicillin.

1. New cases of primary and secondary syphilis began to drop sharply. In 1947, 106,539 newly acquired cases were reported, and by 1957 the number had dropped to 6,251.
2. Almost everybody thought the end of syphilis was in sight, and programs for its control began to be curtailed.
3. Then, in 1958, the incidence started to rise, and by 1967 it was 21,090.

    4. For gonorrhea, the lowest number of new cases was in 1958 with 220,191; but by 1967 the number had grown to 375,606.

    5. For total infectious VD (primary and secondary syphilis and gonorrhea), the lowest rate of 133.2 per 100,000 population was reached in 1958. By 1967, the rate had climbed to 203.9.

    6. Actually, as estimated by experts, the true figure is *three and one-half times the reported figure.*

III. SYPHILIS

  A. Syphilis is caused by a spirochete called *Treponema pallidum.*

    1. It is corkscrew-shaped, as seen under the microscope.

    2. Once it is outside the human body, it dies quickly when exposed to heat, drying, sunlight, or soap and water.

    3. The usual measures of sanitation and personal cleanliness are, therefore, adequate protection against the transmission of syphilis by *indirect* means, such as toilet seats and towels.

    4. The spirochete enters the anogenital, oral, or other mucous or moist skin surfaces, usually during sexual contact.

  B. Incubation period.

    1. There is an incubation period, following the time when the germ enters the body, which averages about 20 days but may range up to 90 days.

    2. During this period, there are no signs or symptoms of disease.

    3. The germs, however, are being carried deep into the body through the blood and lymph systems.

  C. Primary syphilis.

    1. Signs of the disease can usually be seen for the first time between 10 to 90 days after inoculation.

    2. The first sign is usually a single lesion, or sore, called a "chancre" (shanker).

    3. It usually appears at the place where the germ first entered the body— usually the genital area.

    4. Chancres may also appear on lip, breast, finger, anus, cervix, and on the abdominal and genital areas of the body.

    5. The sore is almost always painless, its surface is loaded with spirochetes, and it is highly infectious.

    6. Since the chancre may look like any other sore, it can be identified as syphilitic only through microscopic analysis.

    7. It usually disappears after awhile, even though the patient receives no treatment.

    8. The infected woman seldom is aware of the earliest sign of her disease since the chancre occurs most commonly in the vagina or on the cervix where it is not visible.

  D. Secondary syphilis.

    1. As the lesion disappears, the organisms leave to enter the circulatory and lymphatic systems.

    2. Syphilis is no longer a local disease, but becomes systemic with the entire body now infected.

3. The manifestations of secondary syphilis begin to appear—a rash, fever, malaise, loss of hair, and secondary lesions in the moist areas of the body such as the genitals, anus, and mouth.

4. These secondary skin and mucous membrane lesions, as in primary syphilis, will be loaded with syphilitic germs.

5. The duration of secondary syphilis varies, but the symptoms commonly vanish spontaneously in less than a month.

6. From this point. syphilis loses its communicability and is said to be latent.

E. Late symptomatic syphilis.

1. The latent phase may appear dormant for 5 to 25 years before the body damage becomes apparent.

2. During this time the microorganism is quietly at work in the body where it is capable of invading all tissues of the body.

3. Late syphilis causes two kinds of damage:

   a. Chronic and destructive but localized as related to the skin, bone, and viscera.

   b. General damage to the heart or to the central nervous system.

4. Late lesions of the skin cause a lot of destruction; and the lesions look bad but they are not infectious.

5. Central nervous system syphilis, or neurosyphilis, results from inflammation of the central nervous system. This may result in syphilitic insanity (paresis), severe crippling or paralysis, or blindness.

6. Syphilis of the heart, or cardiovascular syphilis, may become increasingly serious 5 or 6 years following infection, often resulting in death.

F. Congenital syphilis.

1. Although syphilis cannot be inherited, it can be transmitted from a syphilitic mother to an unborn child unless adequate treatment is given.

2. This prenatal infection is known as *congenital syphilis*. It can result in stillbirths, infant deaths, deformity, insanity, and blindness.

3. The baby has one chance in two of escaping infection if the mother's syphilis is more than 4 years' duration.

4. Syphilitic infection of the unborn child will never occur if the mother receives treatment during the first 18 weeks of pregnancy.

5. After that period, treatment of the mother through the remaining months of pregnancy almost always cures the baby *in utero,* except in the few cases in which the treatment comes so late that the fetus is already near death.

6. Early congenital syphilis—in children under two years of age—is similar to secondary syphilis but often more severe.

7. To prevent congenital syphilis, most states have laws requiring that prenatal blood tests for syphilis be done on all pregnant women.

8. Congenital syphilis is really inexcusable today.

G. Blood tests for syphilis.

1. The Wassermann test was the first one for syphilis.

2. Today, many other kinds of blood tests for syphilis are being used.

3. No blood test can tell absolutely whether the patient has syphilis.

    4. Some tests, when they are positive, can tell reasonably accurately whether the patient probably *had* syphilis; but it will not tell whether he has been cured since the cured patient may have a positive Wassermann for the rest of his life.

    5. Today at least 9 million living Americans have such a positive blood, but only about 1 million of that number need treatment; the other 8 million do not have *active* syphilis.

H. Diagnosing syphilis.

    1. If there is evidence in any way suggesting syphilis, the possibility of an active infection must be considered.

    2. To diagnose syphilis accurately and to determine whether the patient needs treatment, the physician must do the following:

        a. Take a history; has the patient been exposed to the disease, or has he had any treatment?

        b. Do a physical examination and look for signs.

        c. Examine material from the surface of lesions under a darkfield microscope looking for syphilis germs.

        d. Make blood tests.

        e. Probably also make a similar test of the fluid inside the spinal column.

I. Treatment of syphilis.

    1. Syphilis can be cured with the correct amount of penicillin.

    2. Since some persons will be allergic to penicillin, the physician may have to substitute some other kind of antibiotic.

    3. Since the disease may be hidden for the first months following exposure, all persons known to have been exposed to infectious syphilis should be treated immediately for their own protection and that of others.

IV. Outbreaks of Venereal Disease

A. The spread of venereal disease by sexually promiscuous persons is illustrated by charts of "outbreaks," defined as chains of infection involving 10 or more persons.

B. The chains are discovered by the consecutive tracing of all sex contacts of each person involved.

C. They are broken by bringing every contact to examination and treatment as needed.

D. Exposed persons showing no clinical or serological evidence of syphilis on first examination are given epidemiological (preventive) treatment anyway.

E. "Cluster testing" is a means of catching a missing contact, particularly where there is a prevalence of VD.

    1. An infected person will be asked not only who his sex contacts are, but who among his friends or in his place of employment is likely to have similar experience.

    2. This procedure has helped in the tracing down of infected people who might otherwise have been overlooked.

F. The description of an outbreak in a West Virginia community, reported by the health department of that state, gives a picture of what is involved.

1. This outbreak evolved from a patient diagnosed and reported by a private physician as having primary syphilis.
2. Application of the epidemiologic process by venereal disease fieldworkers from the state health department resulted in 142 persons being examined in this outbreak.
3. Epidemiologic (preventive) treatment was administered to all contacts *not* infected but who had been exposed within the critical period prior to the treatment of the patient, thereby greatly curtailing the potential spread of the disease.
4. Individuals involved in this chain of infection ranged in age from 15 to 44 with an average age of 23; 49 per cent were married; and approximately one of every two, or 42 per cent, was a teenager.
5. To break this chain of infectious syphilis, it was necessary to initiate investigations in 12 cities, 7 states, and 5 foreign countries.
6. Figure 20-1 presents the West Virginia outbreak in a way that illustrates the "chain" of individuals involved.

J. Premarital blood tests.
   1. All except six states require couples to take a blood test for syphilis prior to being issued a marriage license, or before the marriage ceremony is performed.
   2. This requirement helps to prevent the spread of infection from one marriage partner to the other.
   3. It also helps to prevent the infection of subsequent offspring.
   4. Premarital examinations also help to prevent serious consequences to the marriage relationship.
   5. Premarital blood tests indicated that one out of every 90 persons preparing for marriage in 1966 was alerted to the possibility of being infected with syphilis.

K. Prenatal blood tests.
   1. The prenatal blood test is for the purpose of preventing newborn babies from being infected with congenital syphilis.
   2. State laws requiring a prenatal test have helped reduce the number of babies born with syphilis.
   3. However, six states still have no premarital examination laws.
   4. A woman treated with penicillin for syphilis will not require further treatment in the event of pregnancy, assuming that there has been no relapse or reinfection.
   5. Prenatal blood tests, in 1966, showed that one out of every 113 pregnant women was alerted to the possibility of syphilitic infection.

V. GONORRHEA
   A. Gonorrhea is called the great sterilizer.
      1. Gonorrhea is the most common of the venereal diseases.
      2. It is caused by a bacterium known as the gonococcus of Neisser.
      3. The gonococcus can penetrate only columnar or transitional epithelial cells such as those found in the urethra, cervix, and rectum.

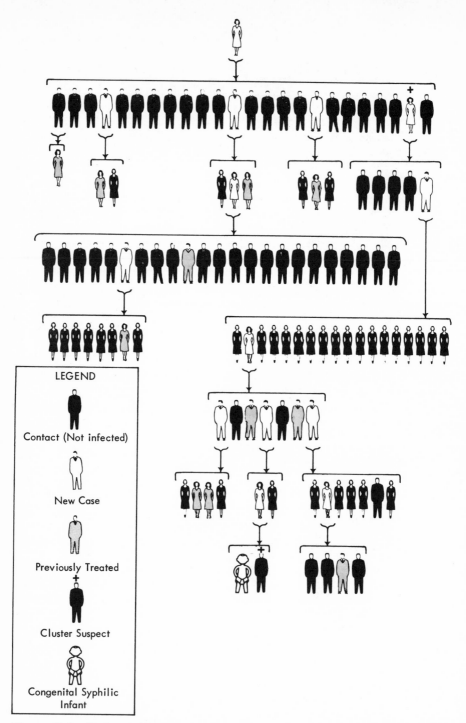

Figure 20-1. Chain of infection in an outbreak of venereal disease in a West Virginia community.

4. Consequently, this disease is usually transmitted from an infected to an uninfected person through sexual intercourse.
5. Since similar cells are found inside the eyelids and in the vaginal linings of girls prior to the age of puberty, the disease may be transmitted non-sexually from mother to offspring, either during birth or later.
6. *Ophthalmia neonatorum* is often caused by gonorrheal infection contracted from an infected mother during delivery.
    a. This disease is an inflammation of the lining of the eyelid of newborn infants.
    b. To prevent blindness, drops of silver nitrate are put in the eyes at birth.
    c. This procedure is now required by 47 of the 50 states.
7. Infection of young girls may occasionally occur accidentally from articles containing pus from an infected person, such as towels and clothing and from toilet seats.
8. Accidental infection of the conjunctiva of the eyelids can also occur in adults and children from, for example, the indiscriminate use of common towels.
9. The gonococcal bacteria is killed quite easily by drying, heat, and weak disinfectants.
    a. The bacteria in pus outside the body may live an hour.
    b. However, it may live for years in the moisture of the human body.
B. Historical points about gonorrhea.
    1. That gonorrhea existed thirty centuries ago is revealed in Chinese writings.
    2. It is referred to in the Bible (Lev. XV).
    3. Boston had a serious epidemic in 1646.
    4. Gonorrhea was first distinguished from syphilis in 1790.
C. Incubation period and symptoms.
    1. The incubation period may range from one day upward.
    2. In the majority of men, symptoms appear sometime between the third and eighth day. It is difficult to determine in women.
    3. Pain and a burning sensation develop in the sex organ upon urinating, especially in the male.
    4. A yellowish discharge issues from the genital organs.
    5. Although this discharge stops after several weeks, even without treatment, the bacteria continue to live in the deeper parts of the reproductive system.
    6. An abscess may eventually develop in the prostate gland of the male, and active germs may be discharged during sexual intercourse.
D. Effects of gonorrhea.
    1. Although gonorrhea is seldom fatal, it is always a serious menace to health.
    2. Untreated gonorrhea *in the male* may lead to the following:
        a. There may be painful and incapacitating lesions in the urethral tract.
        b. The disease may cause sterility due to blockage of the seminal duct by scar tissue, thereby making the emission of sperm impossible.

      c. Blood stream invasion may sometimes result in heart disease.

      d. A gonococcal arthritic condition may also develop.

   3. Untreated gonorrhea *in the female* may lead to the following:

      a. There may be complete or partial blockage of the Fallopian tubes, by scar tissue.

      b. When the blockage is complete, the sperm will be unable to make its way to the egg to fertilize it and the egg will not be able to pass into the uterus.

      c. Partial blockage may allow the smaller sperm to make its way up the Fallopian tube to the egg, but the fertilized egg may not be able to pass down to the uterus.

      d. In such a case, the egg may develop in the tube (ectopic pregnancy) until the tube ruptures, causing peritonitis and sometimes death. Gonorrhea, however, is not the only cause of tubal pregnancy.

      e. The untreated female may, like the male, develop heart disease and gonorrheal arthritis.

  E. Diagnosis of gonorrhea.

   1. There has been no practical blood test developed for gonorrhea; the disease does not activate the body to produce antibodies.

   2. In the male, diagnosis of gonorrhea is relatively simple, being determined by:

      a. A history of sexual activity.

      b. A microscopic demonstration of the gonococci either directly from urethral discharge or from cultures of prostatic fluid.

   3. In the female, diagnosis may be difficult, being usually established through:

      a. A history of exposure to infection.

      b. Demonstration of the gonococcus from cultures of urethral and cervical discharges.

  F. Treatment of gonorrhea.

   1. Modern treatment with penicillin is swift, certain, and relatively inexpensive.

   2. Other antibiotics have proved effective for patients who cannot tolerate penicillin.

   3. The disease can be treated at any stage.

   4. However, treatment must be given early in order to prevent damage.

  G. Casefinding.

   1. Detection in a man is not a problem, once he goes to a doctor.

   2. Because so many women with gonorrhea do not have symptoms, casefinding depends largely on identifying symptomatic males and bringing their contacts to treatment.

VI. OTHER VENEREAL DISEASES

  A. In addition to syphilis and gonorrhea, there are three other venereal diseases in the United States of lower incidence, as described here.

  B. Chancroid.

   1. Chancroid is caused by infection with the bacillus *Hemophilus ducreyi.*

2. Its incubation period is usually about 3 to 5 days.
3. One or more lesions will develop on the genital organs; the initial lesion usually vanishes spontaneously.
4. The lymphatic glands in the inguinal area become enlarged in about 50 per cent of those infected.
5. The bacillus can be identified on smear or culture of exudate.
6. Treatment with tetracycline is effective.
7. The organism is easily destroyed by temperature change and weak disinfectants.

C. Lymphogranuloma venereum.
1. This disease is caused by a virus.
2. The incubation period is from 5 to 21 days.
3. The initial symptom is usually an insignificant small papule.
4. The disease also produces enlargement of lymphatic glands as well as drainage through fistulous openings.
5. A complement fixation test exists for its diagnosis and a skin test is also available.
6. The disease is treated by the use of tetracycline.

D. Granuloma inguinale.
1. This venereal disease is caused by the organism *Donovania granulomatis*.
2. The incubation period may be from 8 to 12 weeks or more.
3. An initial lesion appears, usually in the genital areas.
4. The lesions heal and produce scars while spreading continues.
5. There is a characteristic sour and pungent odor.
6. The organism may be demonstrated on smear or biopsy from a lesion.
7. Tetracycline is also used for treatment.

References for Section 1

American Association for Health, Physical Education, and Recreation, *Facts About Syphilis and Gonorrhea* (student's manual), National Education Association, Washington, D.C., 1965, 154 pp.

American Social Health Association, *Today's VD Control Problem,* New York, 1968.

New York City Board of Education, *A Resource Guide on Venereal Disease Control,* Curriculum Bulletin 1967–1968, New York, 1967.

Webster, Bruce, *What You Should Know About VD—and Why,* Scholastic Book Services, New York, 1967, 64 pp.

Section 2. Prostitution

I. PROSTITUTION IS DEFINED AS SELLING SEXUAL FAVORS

II. THERE ARE VARIOUS TYPES OF PROSTITUTES
A. The party girl.
1. She is one who goes out on no more than one date per evening and where the question of fee is not made explicit.
2. They occasionally refuse their favors as a means of denying that they are engaged in prostitution.

B. The call girl.
1. She is also called a "hustler" or "hooker."
2. This type operates on an appointment basis, maintaining her own residence, which may or may not serve as a place for entertaining clients.
3. The call girl is considered the aristocrat of the prostitution profession because of her fees and because she caters to a high socioeconomic clientele.
4. She herself usually comes from a middle or upper class background.

C. The streetwalker.
1. She is referred to as a "common prostitute."
2. Business is solicited by walking the streets.
3. She is inexpensive and caters to a low socioeconomic clientele.

D. The house girl.
1. She operates within a house of prostitution.

E. The kept woman.
1. She gives her sexual favors to only one man at a time in return for financial security during the time the arrangement is in effect.

III. PSYCHOLOGICAL AND SOCIAL FACTORS INFLUENCING THE CHOICE OF THE PROFESSION (REGARDING THE CALL GIRL)

A. Family background is an important factor.
1. It usually consists of divorced parents or unhappy homes where parents frequently quarreled.
2. The prostitute, as a child, may have seen one of her parents performing the sex act with a person other than the legal spouse.
3. Parental attitude was one of complete rejection (usually by both parents) which lead to a feeling of worthlessness that was characteristic of all call girls who participated in a psychoanalytic study.
4. Discipline or control was uneven.
   a. There was little consistency in their early life.
   b. Girls went from family to family, foster home to foster home, boarding school to boarding school.
5. Girls report experiences of early rewarded sex—engaging in some form of sexual activity (as a young child) with an adult for which they were rewarded.

B. Behavioral symptoms (of the call girl).
1. Anxiety and depression.
2. Vagueness of self-image.
3. Because the girls have a poor sense of self, they have difficulty forming satisfactory relationships with other people.
4. Because they rejected the group norms of society, they attempted to disguise the rejection by donning the mask of conformity. For example, they cherished the external symbols of middle class conformity, such as the mink coat and the expensive car.
5. They exhibited lack of controls, behaving impulsively in a manner that made them social outcasts.

IV. SOCIAL CHANGE THAT AFFECTS PROSTITUTION
   A. During the present century, a rise in feminine sex freedom has occurred.
   B. Available evidence seems to show that, with the greater availability of ordinary women, we should expect the role of the prostitution to decline in both volume and status.

References for Section 2

Greenwald, *The Call Girl,* Ballantine Books, New York, 1958.

Merton and Nesbit, *Contemporary Social Problems,* Harcourt, Brace and World, New York, 1961.

21

Myths About Sex

Despite this age of scientific knowledge, many people still harbor superstitions about sex and childbirth.

Section 1. Myths About Pregnancy
  I. MYTH: That it is the woman who determines the sex of the child.
   A. Each of the sex cells of both the father and the mother contains 23 pairs of chromosomes. The twenty-third pair is called the X pair. In the female, the X pair is similar to the other 22 pairs, whereas in the male one chromosome in the twenty-third pair is of normal size and the other, called the Y chromosome, is shorter. Thus the twenty-third pair in the male has an X and a Y chromosome.
   B. When a sperm containing an X chromosome fertilizes an egg, it gives rise to a new cell with two X chromosomes—and the baby will be a female. But when a sperm with a Y chromosome fertilizes an egg, it produces an XY combination—and the baby will be male.
   C. Clearly, then, the sex of a child is determined by the father.

 II. MYTH: That the fetus sleeps all day and picks the night to start kicking.
   A. Pregnant women believe that the fetus takes a malicious delight in keeping them from sleeping.
   B. On the contrary, the fetus lives completely in the dark and cannot tell the time.

C. If it seems to move more at night, it is possible that the woman is more likely to feel its movement in the stillness of the night with nothing to distract her.

III. MYTH: That, as some women believe, a bad tooth should not be pulled during pregnancy.
   A. Why some women have this belief is not clear. There is an old German superstition that if a pregnant woman has a tooth pulled, her child will be born with a malformed back.
   B. But there is no scientific basis for this belief.

IV. MYTH: That every child costs a tooth.
   A. Maybe this was true before we knew anything about diet.
   B. Now, of course, any woman can find out by asking a physician about her diet and supply of calcium and vitamins, so that the child does not deprive her of her own normal quota.

V. MYTH: That a pregnant woman must eat for two.
   A. During pregnancy a woman must supply all of the proteins, minerals, and vitamins for herself and for the developing fetus.
   B. Her requirements for most nutrients increase about 30 per cent for the fourth, fifth, and sixth months, and about 50 per cent for the remaining months.
   C. Her need for calories increases only about 10 per cent in the second three months and another 10 per cent in the last three months.
   D. Obviously, then, it is not necessary for her to sit at the table and eat for two.

VI. MYTH: That gonorrhea and syphilis are inherited.
   A. Many false beliefs have sprung up about the subject of heredity.
   B. Venereal disease may indeed be acquired at birth, but not through heredity.

Section 2. Myths About Menstruation

I. INTRODUCTION (STATEMENT OF FACTS)
   A. Despite the fact that menstruation is a normal and desirable physiological process, some women suffer from it in part because of the superstitions and misconceptions surrounding it.
   B. Mothers, out of their own lack of knowledge, pass on age-old folklore to their daughters. So it is that many of our young girls come to class with immature attitudes especially toward menstruation. These attitudes must first be brought out into the open, so that they can recognize them for what they are.

II. MYTH: Flowers will wilt if you touch them while menstruating.
   A. Primitive people could not understand that even if a flower did die after a menstruating woman touched it, the flower was wilting in the absence of water, or because of other factors.
   B. Students should bear in mind that menstruation is a normal, natural part of life.

III. MYTH: That menstruation is bad blood coming out.
   A. Blood is always associated with wounds, accidents, and illness. Even today, many less informed women ascribe to it the work of demons.
   B. Actually menstrual blood is perfectly harmless in content and the source of the flow is uterine rather than vaginal.

IV. MYTH: That girls should not bathe during menstruation.
   A. It is true that sharp changes in temperature during bathing may temporarily stop the bleeding, and so a female should take precautions against any abrupt temperature changes.
   B. Otherwise there is no reason why bathing, as well as other normal everyday activity, should not be carried on.

V. MYTH: That the ebb and flow of menstruation are controlled by the moon, just as tides are.
   A. A German writer constructed an ingenious theory to explain the connection between the moon and menstruation. Primitive people liked to hunt for their women on moonlit nights.
   B. The only trouble with this moon theory is that the lunar month, during which the moon goes through all its phases, is about 29½ days long, whereas the menstrual cycle averages from about 28 to 32 days, with variations from month to month in most women.
   C. In fact, irregularity in menstruation is more the rule than the exception in contrast to the habits of the moon.
   D. One is forced to conclude that phases of the moon have no effect on women whatsoever.

VI. MYTH: There are educators, parents, and recreational leaders who feel that swimming during menstruation is harmful, unhealthy, or unesthetic.
   A. Attitudes of high school and college girls and their physical education teachers toward exercising during menstruation all too often do not reflect current scientific knowledge about the subject.
   B. This may be because habits and reactions toward the menstrual process passed along from generation to generation are hard to alter, or it may be that physical educators themselves are not well informed and do nothing to alter their attitudes.
   C. Such ill-founded restraints can help to create a contagious atmosphere conducive to cyclic teenage disability.
   D. Studies have proved that swimming or exercise of any form does not have a harmful influence on the menstrual process. On the contrary, girls who exercise consistently throughout the month have less discomfort than do less active girls. (See Appendix, pp. 402–409.)
   E. The objection to swimming during this period was based on the suspicion that water would enter the vagina and cause infection. This has been proven to be false.
   F. The United States governmental agency which regulates civil aviation advises that it is dangerous for women to pilot airplanes three days before, during, and three days following their menstrual period.

VII. MYTH: That the mere presence of a menstruating woman will cause new wine to become sour.
  A. In Germany, they believed that the presence of a menstruating woman near the fermentation vessels would speed up fermentation and spoil the wine.
  B. This myth could be eliminated with just a little of education.

Section 3. Myths About Menopause
  I. INTRODUCTION (STATEMENT OF FACTS)
  A. "Change of life" or menopause, as it is medically known, is the process of the ending of ovulation and menstruation that signifies the end of the child-bearing period of life.
  B. Broadly speaking, the term is used to indicate complex bodily changes—mainly glandular, sometimes mental and emotional—that may accompany this process.

  II. MYTH: That many women become insane during the menopause period.
  A. The type of insanity popularly associated with the menopause is called involutional melancholia, or menopausal depression.
  B. According to Metropolitan Life Insurance Company, only about 1 in every 25,000 women in the total female population committed to state hospitals suffers from melancholia. This includes all age groups.
  C. A fair statistical guess is that the chance of a menopause causing mental illness is about 1 in 50,000.

  III. MYTH: That menopause or hysterectomy terminates a woman's sex life.
  A. It is now known that women's sex drive often does not diminish even when the ovaries are surgically removed.
  B. Hormones are only one of many factors affecting the capacity for sexual response; more crucial factors are her emotional stability and attitude toward sex.
  C. Kinsey's study indicates that ordinarily no physical reasons exist for her sex life to end because of menopause.
  D. In total hysterectomy, there would not even be the reason of hormonal imbalance to account for the loss of the sex drive. If any change does occur, it might be in the direction of increased sex drive, since fear of pregnancy is now removed.
  E. Considering all factors, a woman can expect to maintain her sex drive at approximately the same level between the ages of 30 and 60 years despite the menopause.

Section 4. Myths About Premarital Sex
  I. INTRODUCTION (STATEMENT OF FACTS)
  A. The urge to engage in sexual intercourse is a biological impulse.
  B. It produces tensions which impel the individual to overt sexual expression.
  C. Since the urge, although normal, may be in conflict with social mores, a number of superstitions and misconceptions have arisen to rationalize breaking the social code.

II. MYTH: It is a sign of manhood to engage in premarital sexual relations.
   A. This is one of those half-truths upon which people who rationalize their behavior so often rely.
   B. The ability to engage in sexual acts marks the passage from biological childhood to manhood; this part of the statement is true.
   C. But manhood actually denotes maturity of thought, appraisal of consequences, fulfillment of social responsibilities, and effort to realize ideals.
   D. If these as well as biological conditions are met then, indeed, the boy has become a man.

III. MYTH: Premarital sexual relations are necessary for health.
   A. This is an outcome of the notion that "self-expression" is healthful, and that "suppression" is injurious to health. But this is not true.
   B. Expression of self that results in serious disease or hurts another person or increases the depth of self-centered attitudes is not healthful, and suppression of personal desires can occur without injury to one's personality.
   C. In fact, in daily routine, desire has been brought under self-control so that people can obey traffic regulations; observe the social amenities at a party; and confine his sexual behavior to expression that will be constant with increased maturity.

IV. MYTH: Premarital sexual relations are a personal decision and social standards have nothing to do with this.
   A. Self is pluralistic, in addition to the biological self.
   B. Social standards are a part of the individual, low or high, mean or noble, depending upon the groups of which he is a member.
   C. Life is dynamic, and standards of some kind always exist. For example, an adolescent who rebels against parental control can adopt in its stead the more rigid code of his gang.

Section 5. Myths About Homosexuality
   I. INTRODUCTION (STATEMENT OF FACTS)
   A. Homosexuality involves sexual contact between members of the same sex.
   B. The choice of a partner of the same rather than of the opposite sex is the determinant in homosexuality, not the technique used in sexual activity.

   II. MYTH: That man is bisexual.
   A. The myth of latent homosexuality and a homosexual stage of development in all individuals still persists.
   B. This is tied up with the notion that man is bisexual.
   C. However, the concept of bisexuality is strongly disputed, and its application to man is highly doubtful.

   III. MYTH: That a person gets his homosexual tendencies as a result of the balance of male and female hormones in his body.
   A. A homosexual tendency means that a person's sex interest is directed toward persons of the same sex, rather than toward persons of the opposite sex.

B. The male sex hormones bring about the development of secondary sex characteristics—deepening of the voice, growth of bodily hair, masculinization of the body. Also it sensitizes the nervous system to making them receptive to sexual stimulation. It makes the person more easily aroused by erotic stimuli. Example: when homosexuals have been given male hormone, they do not become heterosexuals.

C. If female hormone were given to a male, it would not make him homosexual; but it would feminize him—enlarge his breasts and destroy all or most of his sex desire.

D. Thus a person does not receive his homosexual tendencies as a result of the balance of male and female hormones in his body.

E. Actually, a person becomes homosexual as a result of some factors in his psychological development. Exactly what these factors are we do not know.

IV. MYTH: That the age at which a man is most likely to molest children is after sixty-five.

A. A number of studies have clearly shown that child molesting is most likely to take place at three different periods of life: adolescence; in the mid-to-late thirties; and in the late fifties.

B. As Dr. Mohr has noted in cases of child molesting, "contrary to common assumption, the old age group is the relatively smallest one."

C. Any case of child molesting involving an older man would reinforce the popular prejudice and have a tendency to stand out more than molesting by a younger person.

D. There is no difficulty in proving this to be false.

Appendixes

A

Suggested References in Sex Education

Bibliography No. 1
Books and Pamphlets for Small Children (Grades 1–3)

Appell, Clara, and Morey Appell, *We Are Six: The Story of a Family,* Golden Press, New York, 1959, 61 pp.

Bauer, William W., M.D., et al., *Just Like Me,* Scott, Foresman and Company, New York, 1963.

Beck, Lester F., *Human Growth,* Harcourt Brace and Company, New York, 1949, 124 pp.

Beyer, Evelyn, *All Babies Have Mummies and Daddies Just Like You,* William R. Scott Company, New York, 1946.

Brèckenridge, M. E., and M. M. Murphy, *Growth and Development of the Young Child,* W. B. Saunders and Company, Philadelphia, 1963.

Buck, Pearl S., *Johnny Jack and His Beginnings,* Day, Inc., New York, 1954.

Child Study Association of America, *What to Tell Your Children About Sex,* Permabooks, New York, 1958.

Clarksen, E. Margaret, *Susie's Babies,* W. B. Eordmans Publishing Company, Grand Rapids, Michigan, 1960, 73 pp.

Cockefair, Edgar, and Ada Cockefair, *The Story of You,* Monona Publications, Madison, Wisconsin, 1955, 34 pp.

DeSchwienitz, Karl, *Growing Up,* Fourth Edition, The Macmillan Company, New York, 1965, 95 pp.

Ets, Marie Hall, *The Story of a Baby,* The Viking Press, New York, 1948.

Gesell, A., and F. E. Ilg, *The Child From Five to Ten,* Harper Brothers, New York, 1946.

Gruenberg, Sidonie M., *The Wonderful Story of How You Were Born,* Doubleday and Company, Garden City, New York, 1952, 39 pp.

Hector, Robert, *What Shall I Tell My Child?* Crown Company, New York, 1966.

Hofstein, Sade, *The Human Story—Facts on Birth, Growth and Reproduction,* Scott, Foresman and Company, New York, 1967.

Irwin, Leslie, et al., *Growing Every Day,* Lyons and Carnahan, Chicago, 1965.

Lerrigo, Marion, and Helen Southard, *A Story About You,* American Medical Association, Chicago, 1964.

Levine, Milton, and Jean Seligmann, *A Baby Is Born,* Golden Press, New York, 1962, 53 pp.

Orenstein, Irving, *Where Do Babies Come From?* Pyramid Books, New York, 1962.

Power, Jules, *How Life Begins,* Simon and Schuster, New York, 1968, 95 pp.

Selsam, Ludwig, *All About Eggs and How They Change into Animals,* Young, Scott Books, New York, 1952, 70 pp.

Shane, Ruth, and Harold Shane, *The New Baby,* Golden Press, New York, 1957, 24 pp.

Whiting, Ellis, *The Story of Life,* Hammond Publishing Company, Milwaukee, 1957, 48 pp.

Wolcott, Carolyn, *God Made Me to Grow,* Abingdon Press, New York, 1960, 24 pp.

Zim, Herbert S., *What's Inside of Me?* William Morrow and Company, New York, 1952.

Bibliography No. 2

Books for Preadolescents (Grades 4–6)

Bell, Evelyn, and Faragoh, Elizabeth, *The New Baby,* J. B. Lippincott Company, Philadelphia, 1938.

Bibby, Cyril, *How Life Is Handed On,* Emerson Books, New York, 1947, 159 pp.

Clarkson, E. Margaret, *Chats with Young People on Growing Up,* Wm. Eordmans Publishing Company, Grand Rapids, Michigan, 1962, 93 pp.

Dickerson, Roy E., *Growing Into Manhood,* Association Press, New York, 1954.

Gramet, Charles, *Reproduction and Sex in Animal Life,* Abelard-Schuman, New York, 1962, 140 pp.

Hayes, M. V., *A Boy Today—A Man Tomorrow,* Optimist International, St. Louis, 1961.

Ingelman-Sundberg, Axel, and Claes Wirsen, *A Child Is Born, The Drama of Life Before Birth,* Delacorte Press, New York, 1965.

Irwin, Leslie, et al., *Choosing Your Goals,* Lyons and Carnahan, Chicago, 1965.

———, *Finding Your Way,* Lyons and Carnahan, Chicago, 1965.

————, *Understanding Your Needs,* Lyons and Carnahan, Chicago, 1965.

Kimberly Clark Corporation, *You're a Young Lady Now,* Neenah, Wisconsin.

Lerner, Marguerite, *Who Do You Think You Are?* Prentice-Hall, Englewood Cliffs, New Jersey, 1963.

Lerrigo, Marion, and Michael Cassidy, *A Doctor Talks to 9–12 Year Olds,* Budlong Press, Chicago, 1964.

————, and Helen Southard, *Parents' Responsibility,* American Medical Association, Chicago, 1964, 47 pp.

Levine, Milton, and Jean Seligmann, *The Wonder of Life: How We Are Born, and How We Grow Up,* Golden Press, New York, 1952, 116 pp.

Randall, Judith, *All About Heredity,* Random House, New York, 1963.

Scheinfeld, Amram, *Why You Are You,* Abelard-Schuman, New York, 1959, 171 pp.

Scott Paper Company, Home Service Center, *World of a Girl,* International Airport, Philadelphia, 1964.

Strain, Frances, *Being Born,* Appleton-Century-Crofts, New York, 1954, 144 pp.

Wilson, Charles, and Elizabeth Wilson, *Growing Up,* Bobbs-Merrill Company, Indiana, 1966.

Bibliography No. 3
Books for Teenagers (Grades 7–12)

Amstutz, H. Clair, M.D., *Growing Up to Love: A Guide to Sex Education,* Harold Press, Scottsdale, Pennsylvania, 1966.

Anderson, Carl L., *Physical and Emotional Aspects of Marriage,* The C. V. Mosby Company, St. Louis, 1953, 234 pp.

Armstrong, David W., *Questions Boys Ask,* E. P. Dutton and Co., New York, 1963, 1960 pp.

Baruch, Dorothy, *New Ways in Sex Education,* Bantam Books, New York, 1962, 256 pp.

Bauer, William W., *Moving into Manhood,* Doubleday and Company, New York, 1964, 107 pp.

Beach, Frank A., *Sex and Behavior,* John Wiley & Sons, New York, 1965, 592 pp.

Beck, Lester, *Human Growth,* Harcourt, Brace and World, New York, 1949, 128 pp.

Behlmer, Reuben B., *From Teens to Marriage,* Concordia Publishing House, St. Louis, 1959, 112 pp.

Bell, Robert, and Ezra Vogel, *A Modern Introduction to the Family,* Free Press of Glencoe, New York, 1960, 691 pp.

————, *Marriage & Family Interaction,* Dorsey Press, New York, 1963.

Berg, L., and R. Street, *Sex Methods and Manners,* McBridge, New York, 1953.

Bibby, Cyril, *How Life Is Handed On,* Emerson Books, New York, 1955, 159 pp.

Blos, Peter, *On Adolescence,* The Free Press of Glencoe, New York, 1962, 269 pp.

Blum, Sam, *What Every Nice Boy Knew About Sex,* Bernard Geis Associates, New York, 1967, 95 pp.

Bonaparte, Marie, *Female Sexuality,* Grove Press, New York, 1962.

Boone, Pat, *Between You and the Gate Post,* Prentice-Hall, Englewood Cliffs, New Jersey, 1960.

Boyer, Donald Allen, *For Youth to Know,* Laidlaw Brothers, New York, 1966, 56 pp.

Boyer-Brandt, *Human Growth and Reproduction,* Laidlaw Brothers, New York, 1967.

Breckenridge, Mariam, and Vincent Lee, *Child Development,* W. B. Saunders Co., Philadelphia, 1965, 485 pp.

Brenner, Ralph, and Shirley Brenner, *Sex and the Teenager,* Macfadden-Bartell Publishers, New York, 1964.

Bundensen, Herman, M.D., *Toward Manhood,* J. B. Lippincott Company, Philadelphia, 1951, 175 pp.

Cain, Arthur, *Young People and Sex,* Stein and Day Publishers, New York, 1967.

Call, *Toward Adulthood,* J. B. Lippincott Publishers, Philadelphia, 1964.

Caprio, Frank, *Sexual Behavior—Psychological Aspects,* Citadel Press, New York, 1961.

Casson, F. R., *It Is Healthy to Be Human,* Stein & Day Publishers, New York, 1968, 224 pp.

Catholic Center, *This Is a Great Sacrament,* University of Ottawa, 1962, 457 pp.

Child Study Association of America, *What to Tell Your Children About Sex,* Duell, Sloan & Pearce, New York, 1964.

———, *Sex Education and the New Morality,* Columbia University Press, New York, 1967, 90 pp.

———, *Sex Education Of America,* Columbia University Press, New York, 1967.

Clark, LeMon, *Intimate Sexual Problems Answered,* New American Library, New York, 1967, 191 pp.

Conover, Charles, *Moral Education in Family, School and Church,* Westminister Press, Philadelphia, 1962.

Corner, George W., *The Hormones in Human Reproduction,* Princeton University Press, Princeton, N. J., 1947, 281 pp.

———, *Attaining Manhood,* Harper & Row, New York, 1962, 112 pp.

———, *Attaining Womanhood,* Harper & Row, New York, 1952, 111 pp.

Davis, Maxine, *Every Woman's Book of Health,* McGraw-Hill Book Co., Inc., New York, 1961, 296 pp.

———, *Sex and the Adolescent,* Dialbo Press, New York, 1960.

Dickerson, Roy, *So Youth May Know,* Association Press, New York, 1948, 259 pp.

Diehl, Harold, and Anita Laton, *Families and Children,* McGraw-Hill Book Co., Inc., New York, 1955.

Douvan, Elizabeth, and J. Adelson, *The Adolescent Experience,* John Wiley & Sons, New York, 1966.

Duffy, Clinton T., and Al Hirshberg, *Sex and Crime,* Doubleday Publishers, New York, 1965, 203 pp.

Duvall, Evelyn, *Keeping up with Teen-agers,* Public Affairs, New York, 1947.

———, *Love and the Facts of Life,* Association Press, New York, 1963, 352 pp.

———, and Sylvanus Duvall, *Sense and Nonsense About Sex,* Association Press, New York, 1962, 124 pp.

————, and Sylvanus Duvall, *Sex Ways in Fact and Faith: Basis for Christian Family Policy,* Association Press, New York, 1961.

Duvall, Sylvanus M., *Men, Women and Morals,* Association Press, New York, 1952, 336 pp.

Eckert, Ralph C., *Sex Attitudes in the Home,* Association Press, New York, 1956.

Ellis, Albert, *Sex and the Single Man,* Lyle Stuart, New York, 1961.

————, *The Folklore of Sex,* Grove Press, New York, 1961.

————, *The American Sexual Tragedy,* Lyle Stuart, New York, 1962.

————, *Sex Without Guilt,* Lyle Stuart, New York, 1958.

————, and Albert Abarbanel, *The Encyclopedia of Sexual Behavior,* Hawthorn Books, New York, 1961, Vols. I and II.

English, O. Spurgeon, and Gerald H. Pearson, *Emotional Problems of Living,* W. W. Norton & Co., New York, 1955, 438 pp.

Farber, Seymour M., M.D., and Roger H. Wilson, M.D., *Teen-age Marriage And Divorce,* Diablo Press, Berkeley, California, 1968.

Fedder, Ruth, *A Girl Grows Up,* Whittlesey House, New York, 1948, 258 pp.

Fishbein, Morris, *Children for the Childless,* Doubleday & Company, Inc., New York, 1954, 223 pp.

Flanagan, Geraldine Lux, *The First Nine Months of Life,* Simon and Schuster, Inc., New York, 1962, 95 pp.

Flanders, Dunbar, M.D., *Your Preteenager's Mind and Body,* Laidlaw Brothers, New York, 1963, 226 pp.

Fletcher, Peter, *Understanding Your Emotional Problems,* Harper & Row Publishers, New York, 1966, 213 pp.

Ford, Clellan S., and Frank A. Beach, *Patterns of Sexual Behavior,* Harper & Row Publishers, New York, 1951, 307 pp.

Fraiberg, Selma, *The Magic Years: Understanding and Handling the Problems of Early Childhood,* Charles Scribner's Sons, New York, 1959, 305 pp.

Frazer, S., *The New Golden Bough,* Criterion Books, New York, 1959, 92 pp.

Freud, Sigmund, *Jokes and Their Relation to the Unconscious,* W. W. Norton & Company, New York, 1960.

————, *Three Essays on the Theory of Sexuality,* W. W. Norton & Company, New York, 1964, 75 pp.

Fromm, Erich, *The Art of Loving,* Harper & Row Publishers, New York, 1956, 133 pp.

Genne, Elizabeth, and William Genne, *Christians and the Crisis in Sex Morality,* Association Press, New York, 1962, 123 pp.

Gottlieb, Bernard, *What a Boy Should Know About Sex,* Bobbs-Merrill Company, New York, 1960.

————, *What a Girl Should Know About Sex,* Bobbs-Merrill Company, New York, 1961.

Gould, Joan, *Will My Baby Be Born Normal?* The Public Affairs Committee, Inc., New York, 1958, 20 pp.

Gray, Henry, *Anatomy of the Human Body,* Lea & Febiger, Philadelphia, 1959, 1,458 pp.

Greene, Thayer A., *Modern Man in Search of Manhood,* Association Press, New York, 1967, 128 pp.

Griffith, Jeannette, *Dearest Kate,* Doubleday & Company, Inc., New York, 1967, 160 pp.

Group for the Advancement of Psychiatry, *Sex and the College Student,* Atheneum Publishers, New York, 1966, 178 pp.

Gruenberg, Benjamin, *The Wonderful Story of How You Were Born,* Doubleday & Company, Inc., New York, 1960, 171 pp.

Guttmacher, Alan F., *Babies by Choice or by Chance,* Doubleday & Company, Inc., New York, 1959, 289 pp.

Hackett, C. G., and H. H. Remmers, *Let's Listen to Youth,* Science Research Associates, Inc., Chicago, 1960.

Hall, Robert E., *Nine Months' Reading—A Guide for Pregnant Women,* Doubleday & Company, New York, 1963, 169 pp.

Hartogs, Renatus, M.D., and Hans Fantel, *Four-Letter Word Games* (The Psychology of Obscenity), M. Evans & Company, Inc., New York, 1967, 186 pp.

Head, Gay, *Boy Dates Girl,* Scholastic Publishers, New York, 1955.

Hettlinger, Richard, *Living with Sex: The Student's Dilemma,* The Seabury Press, New York, 1966, 160 pp.

Hulme, William E., *Youth Considers Sex,* Thomas Nelson & Sons, New York, 1965, 95 pp.

Hume, William, *God, Sex and Youth,* Prentice-Hall, Inc., Englewood Cliffs, New Jersey, 1959, 179 pp.

Hummel, Ruth, *Wonderfully Made,* Concordia Publishing House, St. Louis, 1967, 46 pp.

Hutton, Laura, M.D., *The Single Woman,* Roy Publishers, New York, 1960, 132 pp.

Jenkins, Gladys, Helen Schacter, and William Bauer, *These Are Your Children,* Scott, Foresman & Company, Chicago, 1953, 371 pp.

Johnson, Charlene, *Altogether Lovely: A Book for Teen-age Girls,* Fortress Press, Philadelphia, 1960, 112 pp.

Johnson, Eric, *Love and Sex in Plain Language,* J. B. Lippincott Company, Philadelphia, 1967, 68 pp.

Jones, C. Curtis, *Youth Deserves to Know,* The Macmillan Company, New York, 1958, 134 pp.

Julian, J. Cloyd, and Elizabeth N. Jackson, *Modern Sex Education,* Holt, Rinehart and Winston, Inc., New York, 1967, 94 pp.

Kirkendall, Lester, *Understanding Sex,* Science Research Associates, Chicago, 1957, 48 pp.

——, *Sex Education As Human Relations,* Inor Publishing Co., A Division of Roxbury Press, Sweet Springs, Missouri, 1950, 351 pp.

Knopf, Olga, *The Art of Being a Woman,* Little, Brown Company, Boston, 1932, 295 pp.

Landis, Paul, *Adolescence and Youth,* McGraw-Hill Book Company, New York, 1955, 470 pp.

Lerrigo, Marion, and Helen Southard, *A Story About You,* American Medical Association, Chicago, 1965, 43 pp.

——, *Finding Yourself,* American Medical Association, Chicago, 1965, 50 pp.

————, *Approaching Adulthood,* American Medical Association, Chicago, 1962, 47 pp.

Levisohn, F., and G. Kelly, *What Teen-agers Want To Know,* American Medical Association, Chicago, 1962.

Liley, Margaret, *Modern Motherhood,* Random House, New York, 1968, 239 pp.

Linner, Birgitta, *Sex and Society in Sweden,* Pantheon Books, 1967.

Malinowski, Bronislaw, *Sex, Culture and Myth,* Harcourt, Brace & World, Inc., 1962, 336 pp.

Mead, Margaret, *Male and Female,* William Morrow and Company, Inc., New York, 1949, 477 pp.

Menninger, William C., M.D., Lester A. Kirkendall, and Clifford R. Adams, *How to Understand the Opposite Sex,* Sterling Publishing Company, Inc., New York, 1960, 192 pp.

————, et al., *How to Be a Successful Teen-Ager,* Sterling Publishing Company, Inc., New York, 1960, 256 pp.

Mozes, Eugene, *Plain Facts About Sex,* Lancer Books, New York, 1957, 117 pp.

Osborne, Ernest G., *Understanding Your Parents,* Association Press, New York, 1962, 122 pp.

Pemberton, Lois, *The Stork Didn't Bring You,* Hermitage Press, New York, 1948.

Pike, James A., *Teen-agers and Sex,* Prentice-Hall, Englewood Cliffs, N. J., 1965, 146 pp.

Potter, Edith L., *Fundamentals of Human Reproduction,* McGraw-Hill Book Company, New York, 1948, 231 pp.

Reiss, Walter, *For You Teen-agers in Love,* Concordia Publishing House, St. Louis, 1960, 78 pp.

Rubin, Isadore, and Lester Kirkendall, *Sex in the Adolescent Years,* Association Press, New York, 1968, 223 pp.

Rutgers, J., M.D., *How to Attain and Practice the Ideal Sex Life,* Cadillac Publications, New York, 1950, 313 pp.

Southard, Helen F., *Sex Before Twenty, New Answers for Youth,* E. P. Dutton & Company, New York, 1967, 116 pp.

Strain, Frances, *Love at the Threshold,* Appleton-Century-Crofts, New York, 1952, 349 pp.

Strain, Frances, *New Patterns in Sex Teaching,* Appleton-Century-Crofts, New York, 1952.

Strang, Ruth, *The Adolescent Views Himself,* McGraw-Hill Book Company, New York, 1957, 579 pp.

U.S. Department of Health, Education, and Welfare, *Pre-Natal Care,* Children's Bureau, Publication No. 4, U.S. Government Printing Office, Washington, D.C., 1949, 76 pp.

Vetter, Marjorie, and Laura Vitray, *The Questions Girls Ask,* E. P. Dutton & Company, New York, 1959, 156 pp.

Villee, Claude, *Biology,* W. B. Saunders Co., Philadelphia, 1962, 625 pp.

Williams, Mary McGee, and Irene Kane, *On Becoming a Woman,* Dell Publishing Company, New York, 1959, 159 pp.

Young, Leontine, *Out of Wedlock,* McGraw-Hill Book Company, Inc., New York, 1954, 261 pp.

Bibliography No. 4
Professional Books for Teachers
(Curriculum Methods, Materials, and Evaluation)

American Association for Health, Physical Education, and Recreation, *Sex Education Units for Grades 5, 6, and 7,* Washington, D.C., 1967.

American Home Economics Association, *Educating the Teen-Ager in Human Relations and Management of Resources,* New York, 1967.

American School Health Association, Committee on Health Guidance in Sex Education, *Growth Patterns and Sex Education, Kindergarten Through Grade Twelve,* Kent, Ohio, 1967.

American Social Health Association, *Problems of Sexual Behavior,* New York, 1958.

Atkinson, Donald, *Sexual Morality,* Harcourt, Brace and Company, New York, 1965.

Baker, John, *Sex Education in High School,* Emerson Books, Inc., New York, 1943, 154 pp.

Barr, Donald, *Sex, Love and Modern Education,* Emerson Books, New York, 1967.

Baruch, Dorothy, *New Ways in Sex Education: A Guide for Teachers and Parents,* McGraw-Hill Book Company, New York, 1959, 256 pp.

————, *One Little Boy,* Julian Press, New York, 1952.

Becker, Howard, and Reuben Hill, *Family Marriage and Parenthood,* D. C. Heath & Company, Boston, 1948.

Berg, L., and R. Street, *Sex Methods and Manners,* McBride, New York, 1953.

Bernard, Jessie, *Marriage and Family Among Negroes,* Prentice-Hall, Englewood Cliffs, New Jersey, 1966.

Bibby, Cyril, *Sex Education,* Emerson Books, New York, 1946, 311 pp.

Biester, Lillian, and William Griffiths, *Units in Personal Health and Human Relations,* University of Minnesota Press, Minneapolis, 1947, 267 pp.

Board of Education of the City of New York, *Pre-Kindergarten Curriculum Guide,* Board of Education Curriculum Bulletin, New York, 1965–66 Series No. 11, 149 pp.

Bowman, Henry A., *Marriage for Moderns,* McGraw-Hill Book Company, New York, 1965.

Brecher, Edward, and Ruth Brecher, *An Analysis of Human Sexual Response,* New American Library, New York, 1966.

Brenner, Ralph, and Shirley, *Sex and the Teenager,* Macfadden-Bartell, New York, 1964.

Butcher, R., and M. Robinson, *Unmarried Mother,* Public Affairs Committee, New York, 1959.

Butterfield, Oliver M., *Love Problems of Adolescence,* Emerson Books, New York, 1960.

————, *Marriage and Sexual Harmony,* Emerson Books, New York, 1960.

Casson, F. R., M.D., *It Is Healthy to Be Human,* Stein & Day Publishers, New York, 1968, 224 pp.

Chanter, Albert G., *Sex Education in the Primary School,* Macmillan Company, New York, 1966.

Chesser, Eustace, *Live and Let Live,* Philosophical Life, New York, 1958.

————, and Zoe Dawe, *The Practice of Sex Education,* Roy Publishers, New York, 1956, 227 pp.

Child Study Association of America, *Facts of Life for Children,* Bobbs-Merrill, New York, 1954, 286 pp.

————, *Sex Education and the New Morality,* Columbia University Press, New York, 1967.

Coffin, Tristram, *Sex Kick,* The Macmillan Company, New York, 1966.

Conover, Charles, *Moral Education in Family, School and Church,* Westminister Press, Philadelphia, 1962.

Corner, George W., *Attaining Manhood,* Harper & Row Publishers, New York, 1952.

————, *Attaining Womanhood,* Harper & Row Publishers, New York, 1953.

Cosgrove, Margaret, *Eggs,* Dodd, Mead Publishers, New York, 1966.

Crawley, Lawrence, James Malfetti, and Ernest Stuart, *Reproduction, Sex and Preparation for Marriage,* Prentice-Hall, Englewood Cliffs, New Jersey, 1964, 231 pp.

Crow, Lester and Alice, *Sex Education for the Growing Family,* Christopher Publishers, New York, 1959.

Davis, Maxine, *Sex and the Adolescent,* Dial Press, New York, 1958.

————, *Every Woman's Book for Health,* McGraw-Hill Book Company, New York, 1961, 296 pp.

Demant, V. A., *Christian Sex Ethics,* Harper & Row, New York, 1963, 127 pp.

Deutsch, Albert, *Sex Habits of American Men,* Prentice-Hall, Englewood Cliffs, New Jersey, 1948.

Eckert, Ralph, *Sex Attitudes in the Home,* Association Press, New York, 1956, 242 pp.

Ellis, Albert, *Psychology of Sex,* Emerson Books, New York, 1953.

————, *Sex and the Single Man,* Lyle Stuart, New York, 1963.

English, O. S., and Pearson Gerald, *Emotional Problems of Living,* W. W. Norton & Company, New York, 1945.

Farber, Seymour, and Roger Wilson, *Sex Education and the Teenager,* Diablo Press, Berkeley, California, 1967, 151 pp.

————, *Teenage Marriage and Divorce,* Diablo Press, Berkeley, California, 1967, 154 pp.

Filas, Francis, *Sex Education in the Family,* Prentice-Hall, Englewood Cliffs, New Jersey, 1966.

Fishbein, Morris, M.D., and Burgess Ernest, M.D., *Successful Marriage,* Doubleday and Company, Garden City, New York, 1957.

Fletcher, Joseph, *Situation Ethics—The New Morality,* Westminister Press, Philadelphia, 1966, 176 pp.

Force, Elizabeth, *Teaching Family Life Education—the Toms River Program,* Bureau of Publications, Teachers College, Columbia University, New York, 1962.

Gibson, Dorothy W., *Social Perspectives on Education,* John Wiley & Sons, Inc., New York, 1965, 481 pp.

Glassberg, B. Y., M.D., *Teenage Sex Counselor,* Barron's Educational Series, New York, 1965, 138 pp.

Gottlieb, Bernard, *What a Girl Should Know About Sex,* Bobbs-Merrill, New York, 1961.

————, *What a Boy Should Know About Sex,* Bobbs-Merrill, New York, 1960.

Gregor, Arthur S., *Time Out for Youth,* The Macmillan Company, New York, 1951, 235 pp.

Grunwald, Henry A., *Sex in America,* Bantam Books, New York, 1964.

Havighurst, Robert, and Hilda Taeba, *Adolescent Character and Personality,* John Wiley & Sons, Inc., New York, 1949.

Heath, Clark W., *What People Are—A Study of Normal Young People,* Harvard University Press, Boston, 1946.

Hilu, Virginia, *Sex Education and the Schools,* Harper & Row Publishers, New York, 1967, 153 pp.

Hodgson, Leonard, *Sex and the Christian Freedom,* S. C. M. Press, Illinois, 1967, 127 pp.

Hoeflin, Ruth M., *Essentials of Family Living,* John Wiley & Sons, Inc., New York, 1960.

Hollingshead, A., *Elmstown's Youth: The Impact of Social Classes on Adolescents,* John Wiley & Sons, New York, 1949.

Jenkins, Gladys G., et al., *These Are Your Children,* Scott, Foresman & Company, Chicago, 1953, 371 pp.

Johnson, Eric A., *Love and Sex in Plain Language,* J. B. Lippincott Company, Philadelphia, 1965.

Johnson, Warren, *Human Sex and Sex Education,* Lea and Febiger, Philadelphia, 1963, 200 pp.

Josselyn, Irene, *Adolescent and His World,* Family Service, New York, 1952.

Julian, Cloyd, and Elizabeth Jackson, *Modern Sex Education,* Holt, Rinehart & Winston, Inc., New York, 1967, 95 pp.

Kelly, George, *A Catholic Parent's Guide to Sex Education,* Hawthorn Books, Inc., New York, 1962, 158 pp.

Kinsey, A. C., et al., *Sexual Behavior in the Human Male,* W. B. Saunders Company, Philadelphia, 1952.

————, *Sexual Behavior in the Human Female,* W. B. Saunders Company, Philadelphia, 1953.

Kirkendall, Lester A., *Sex Education as Human Relations,* Roxbury Press, Sweet Springs, Missouri, 1950, 351 pp.

————, *Understanding* Sex, Science Research Associates, Chicago, 1957.

————, and Elizabeth Ogg, *Sex and Our Society,* Public Affairs, New York, 1966.

Krich, Aron, *Facts of Love and Marriage for Young People,* Dell Publishers, New York, 1962.

Landis, Judson, and Mary Landis, *Building Your Life,* Prentice-Hall, Englewood Cliffs, New Jersey, 1954, 331 pp.

————, *Your Marriage and Family Living,* McGraw-Hill Book Company, New York, 1954, 388 pp.

Lerrigo, Marion O., *Facts Aren't Enough,* American Medical Association, Chicago, 1962, 43 pp.

———, *A Story About You,* American Medical Association, Chicago, 1966, 43 pp.

———, and M. Cassidy, *Doctor Talks to 9–12 Year Olds,* Budlong, New York, 1965.

———, and Helen Southard, *Approaching Adulthood,* American Medical Association, Chicago, Illinois, 1966, 47 pp.

Manley, Helen, *A Curriculum Guide in Sex Education,* State Publishing Company, St. Louis, 1967, 65 pp.

Mead, Margaret, *Male And Female,* William Morrow and Company, New York, 1949, 477 pp.

Menninger, William C., *Blueprint for Teenage Living,* Sterling Publishers, New York, 1960.

Narramere, Clyde, *How to Tell Your Children About Sex,* Zendervan Publishing House, Michigan, 1958, 97 pp.

Schmieding, Alfred, *Sex in Childhood and Youth: A Guide for Christian Parents, Teachers and Counselors,* Concordia Publishing House, St. Louis, 1957, 149 pp.

Southard, Helen F., *Sex Before Twenty: New Answers for Youth,* Dutton and Company, New York, 1967, 116 pp.

Strain, Frances Bruce, *New Patterns in Sex Teaching,* Appleton-Century-Crofts, New York, 1951, 261 pp.

Swedish Board of Education, *Sex Instruction in Swedish Schools,* Board of Education Series, Stockholm, Sweden, 1964.

Swift, Edith Hale, *Step by Step in Sex Education,* The Macmillan Company, New York, 1958, 207 pp.

Vahanian, Paul, *Teaching Family Life Education,* Columbia University, New York, 1962, 38 pp.

Wessler, Martin, *Christian View of Sex Education,* Concordia Publishing House, St. Louis, Missouri, 1967, 87 pp.

Wilson, Charles, and Elizabeth Wilson, *Human Growth and Reproduction,* Bobbs-Merrill Company, Indianapolis, 1966.

Young, Leontine, *Out of Wedlock,* McGraw-Hill Book Company, New York, 1954.

Bibliography No. 5
Books for Parents

Adams, James, *Understanding Adolescence,* Allyn and Bacon Company, Boston, 1968, 395 pp.

Amstutz, H. Clair, *Growing Up to Love,* Herald Press, Pennsylvania, 1956, 107 pp.

Armstrong, David, *Questions Boys Ask,* E. P. Dutton and Company, New York, 1955.

Arnstein, Helene S., *What to Tell Your Child,* Pocket Books, New York, 1964.

Ashen, J., *The Family and Its Function,* Harper & Row, New York, 1949.

Bacmeister, Rhoda, *All in the Family,* Appleton-Century-Crofts, New York, 1951, 294 pp.

Baruch, Dorothy, *Parents Can Be People,* Appleton-Century-Crofts, New York, 1944, 262 pp.

————, *One Little Boy,* Julian Press, New York, 1952.

————, *New Ways in Sex Education: A Guide for Parents and Teachers,* McGraw-Hill Book Company, New York, 1959, 256 pp.

Bauer, William W., *Moving into Manhood,* Doubleday and Company, New York, 1963.

Beck, Lester, *Human Growth,* Harcourt, Brace and Company, New York, 1949, 124 pp.

Bibby, Cyril, *How Life Is Handed On,* Emerson Books, Inc., New York, 1955, 159 pp.

Bossard, James, *Parent and Child,* University of Pennsylvania Press, Philadelphia, 1953, 308 pp.

Brenner, Ralph and Shirley, *Sex and the Teenager,* Macfadden-Bartell, New York, 1964.

Bruckner, P. J., *How to Give Sex Instruction,* The Queen's Work, St. Louis, Mo., 1947, 64 pp.

Cain, Arthur, *Young People and Sex,* Doubleday and Company, Inc., New York, 1967.

Calderwood, Deryck, *Family Life Education for Adolescent Youth and Their Parents,* Emerson Books, New York, 1963.

Child Study Association of America, *What to Tell Your Children About Sex,* Duell, Sloan and Pearce, New York, 1964.

————, *Facts of Life for Children,* Bobbs-Merrill, New York, 1954, 286 pp.

Cosgrove, Margaret, *Eggs,* Dodd, Mead Publishers, New York, 1966.

Cox, Charles, *The Upbeat Generation,* Prentice-Hall, Englewood Cliffs, New Jersey, 1959.

Crow, Lester and Alice, *Being a Good Parent,* Christopher Publishers, New York, 1966.

Curman, Hans, M.D., *What Shall I Tell My Child?* Crown Publishers, Inc., New York, 1966, 170 pp.

De Kok, Winifred, *You and Your Child,* Philosophical Library, New York, 1955.

Diehl, Henry, and Anita Laton, *Families and Children,* McGraw-Hill Book Company, New York, 1955.

Driver, Helen, *Sex Guidance for Your Child: a Parent Handbook,* Monona Publications, Madison, Wisconsin, 1960, 192 pp.

Dunbar, Flanders, *Your Teenager's Mind and Body,* Hawthorn Publishers, New York, 1962.

Duvall, Evelyn, *Keeping up with Teenagers,* Public Affairs Committee, New York, 1963.

————, and Sylvanus Duvall, *Saving Your Marriage,* Public Affairs Committee, New York, 1967.

Eckert, Ralph, *Sex Attitudes in the Home,* Association Press, New York, 1956.

Ellzey, W. C., *Preparing Your Children for Marriage,* Association Press, New York, 1964, 159 pp.

English, O. S., and S. Finch, *Emotional Problems of Growing up,* Science Research Association, New York, 1951.

Faegre, Marion L., *Your Own Story,* University of Minnesota Press, Minneapolis, 1943, 52 pp.

———, *The Adolescent in Your Family,* Children's Bureau Publication No. 347, U.S. Department of Health, Education and Welfare, Washington, D.C., 1954, 110 pp.

Fedder, Ruth, *A Girl Grows Up,* Whittlesey House, New York, 1948, 258 pp.

Federal Security Agency, *Your Child from 6 to 12,* Children's Bureau Publication No. 324, U.S. Gov. Printing Office, Washington, D.C., 1963, 141 pp.

Fields, Morey R., Jacob Goldberg, and H. Frederick Kilander, *Youth Grows into Adulthood,* Chartwell House, Inc., New York, 1954, 236 pp.

Filas, Francis, *Sex Education in the Family,* Prentice-Hall, Inc., Englewood Cliffs, New Jersey, 1966, 107 pp.

Frank, Lawrence, *Your Adolescent at Home and in School,* New American Library, New York, 1956.

Gavin, Arthur, *The Circle of Sex,* University Books, Inc., New Hyde Park, New York, 1966, 150 pp.

Gittelsohn, R., *Consecrated unto Me: A Jewish View of Love, and Marriage,* Union of American Hebrew Congregations, 1965, 232 pp.

Glover, Leland, *How to Help Your Teenager Grow Up,* Crowell-Collier,ʼ New York, 1962.

Greenberg, S. M., *Everyday Problems of Girls and Boys,* Random House, New York, 1958.

Gruenberg, Sidonie, *Wonderful Story of How You Were Born,* Doubleday, New York, 1959.

Hector, Robert, *What Shall I Tell My Child?* Crown Publishers, New York, 1966, 177 pp.

Hymes, James, *Being a Good Parent,* Teachers College, Columbia University Press, New York, 1949.

———, *Understanding Your Child,* Prentice-Hall, Inc., Englewood Cliffs, New Jersey, 1952.

———, *How to Tell Your Child About Sex,* Public Affairs, New York, 1949, 28 pp.

Ingelman-Sundberg, Axel, M.D., *A Child Is Born,* Delacorte Press, New York, 1967. (Excellent Photographs by Lennant Nilsson.)

Johnson, Eric, *Love and Sex in Plain Language,* J. B. Lippincott and Company, Philadelphia, 1967.

Kelly, George, *Your Child and Sex: A Guide for Catholic Parents,* Random House, New York, 1964, 158 pp.

Kirkendall, Lester A., *Helping Children Understand Sex,* Science Research Associates, New York, 1952.

———, *Sex and Our Society,* Public Affairs Committee, New York, 1964.

Landis, Paul, *Coming of Age,* Public Affairs Committee, New York, 1956.

Lerrigo, Marion, and Milton Senn, *Parents' Responsibility,* American Medical Association, Chicago, Illinois, 1862, 47 pp.

Levine, Milton, *Facts of Life for Children,* Simon and Schuster, New York, 1954, 82 pp.

———, *A Baby Is Born,* Simon and Schuster, New York, 1949, 51 pp.

———, and Seligmann, *Helping Boys and Girls Understand Their Sex Roles,* Science Research Associates, New York, 1953.

Lord, Daniel A., *The Guidance of Youth,* The Queen's Work, St. Louis, Missouri, 1948, 74 pp.

Milt, Harry, *Young Adults and Their Parents,* Public Affairs Committee, New York, 1964.

Mooney, Belle S., *How Shall I Tell My Child?* Doubleday, New York, 1947, 171 pp.

Museum of Science and Industry, *Miracle of Growth,* University of Illinois, Chicago, 1950.

Neisser, Edith, *When Children Start Dating,* Science Research Associates, New York, 1960.

O'Connor, J., *Sex Character Education,* The Macmillan Company, New York, 1952, 212 pp.

Ogg, Elizabeth, *When a Family Faces Stress,* Public Affairs Committee, New York, 1963.

Pemberton, Lois, *The Stork Didn't Bring You,* Hermitage Press, New York, 1948, 213 pp.

Sattler, Henry V., *Parents, Children and the Facts of Life,* St. Anthony Guild Press, New Jersey, 1952, 265 pp.

Sands, Sydney, *Growing Up to Love, Sex and Marriage,* Christopher Press, New York, 1960.

Shultz, Gladys D., *It's Time You Knew,* J. B. Lippincott Company, Philadelphia, 1955.

Spock, Benjamin, *Problems of Parents,* Houghton-Mifflin, New York, 1962.

Strain, Frances B., *The Normal Sex Interests of Children,* Appleton-Century-Crofts, New York, 1948, 210 pp.

Strecker, E., and W. Lathbury, *Their Mother's Daughters,* J. B. Lippincott, Philadelphia, 1956.

Thurber, James, and E. White, *Is Sex Necessary?* Dell Publishing Company, New York, 1959, 199 pp.

Washburn, Ruth V., *Children Have Their Reasons,* Appleton-Century-Crofts, New York, 1943, 257 pp.

Whitman, Howard, *Let's Tell the Truth About Sex,* Grosset and Dunlop, New York, 1951, 242 pp.

Wolf, Anna, *Your Child's Emotional Health,* Public Affairs Committee, New York, 1958, 28 pp.

———, *The Parent Manual,* Simon and Schuster, New York, 1951, 348 pp.

Bibliography No. 6
Books on Preparation for Marriage and Family Life

Adams, Clifford R., and Vance O. Packard, *How to Pick a Mate,* E. P. Dutton & Company, New York, 1946.

——, *Looking Ahead to Marriage,* Science Research Associate Press, New York, 1960, 48 pp.

Alsop, G. F., and Mary McBride, *She's Off to Marriage,* The Vanguard Press, New York, 1942.

Anderson, Carl L., *Physical and Emotional Aspects of Marriage,* The C. V. Mosby Company, St. Louis, Mo., 1953, 234 pp.

Anderson, Wayne J., *Design for Family Living,* T. E. Denison and Company, New York, 1966.

Applehof, Gilbert, Jr., *You Can Be Happily Married,* The Macmillan Company, New York, 1941.

Avery, Curtis, *Toward Understanding the Problems of Early Marriage,* E. C. Brown Company, New York, 1960.

Baker, Ray, *Marriage and the Family,* McGraw-Hill Book Co., New York, 1957, 529 pp.

Baruch, Dorothy W., *Sex in Marriage: New Understandings,* Harper & Row Publishers, New York, 1963, 286 pp.

Bell, Robert R., *Premarital Sex in a Changing Society,* Prentice-Hall, Inc., Englewood Cliffs, New Jersey, 1966, 182 pp.

——, *Marriage and Family Interaction,* Dorsey Press, Inc., Homewood, Ill., 1963.

Bernard, Jessie, and Helen Buchanan, *Dating, Mating and Marriage Today,* Arco Publishing Company, New York, 1959.

Bertocci, Peter, A., *The Human Venture in Sex, Love, and Marriage,* Association Press, New York, 1963, 143 pp.

Black, D., *If I Marry Outside My Religion,* Public Affairs, New York, 1954, 98 pp.

Blood, Robert O., Jr., *Marriage,* Free Press of Glencoe, Inc., New York, 1962, 515 pp.

Bossard, H. S., and Eleanor S. Boll, *One Marriage, Two Faiths,* The Ronald Press, Company, New York, 1957, 180 pp.

——, *Why Marriages Go Wrong,* The Ronald Press Company, New York, 1958, 224 pp.

——, *The Girl That You Marry,* McCrae Smith Company, Philadelphia, 1960, 172 pp.

Bowman, Henry A., *A Christian Interpretation of Marriage,* Westminister Press, Philadelphia, 1959. (Protestant view)

——, *Marriage for Moderns,* McGraw-Hill Book Company, New York, 1965, 545 pp.

Bracher, Marjory, *Love, Sex, and Life,* Lutheran Church Press, Philadelphia, 1964.

Bradway, John S., *Family Marriage and Parenthood—What Family Members Should Know About Law,* D. C. Heath and Company, Boston, 1955, 595 pp.

Brenner, Ralph, and S. Brenner, *Love, Sex and Marriage,* MacFadden Bartell Corporation, New York, 1964, 254 pp.

Brothers, Joyce, *Woman,* Doubleday and Company, Garden City, New York, 1961, 236 pp.

Brisbane, Holly, *The Developing Child,* Charles Bennett Company, New York, 1962, 189 pp.

Butterfield, Oliver, *Sexual Harmony in Marriage,* Emerson Books, New York, 1960.

————, *Planning for Marriage,* Van Nostrand, New York, 1956, 359 pp.

Calderone, Mary S., *Release From Sexual Tensions: Towards an Understanding of Their Causes and Effects on Marriage,* Random House, New York, 1960.

Caprio, F. S., *The Modern Woman's Guide to Sexual Maturity,* Grove Press, New York, 1959.

Cavan, Ruth S., *The American Family,* Thomas Y. Crowell Company, New York, 1963, 657 pp.

————, *The American Marriage: A Way of Life,* Thomas Y. Crowell Company, New York, 1958, 498 pp.

Chesser Eustace, *Love Without Fear,* New American Library, Inc., New York, 1949, 192 pp.

Christensen, Harold T., *Marriage Analysis,* The Ronald Press, New York, 1950.

Clark, Vincent E., *Unmarried Mothers,* Free Press of Glencoe, Inc., New York, 1961, 308 pp.

————, *Sex and You,* Bobbs-Merrill Company, Indianapolis, 1949.

Consumers Union, *Report on Family Planning,* A Consumers Union Publication, Mt. Vernon, New York, 1966, 168 pp.

Craig, Hazel T., *Threshold to Adult Living,* Charles Bennett Company, New York, 1962.

Crawley, Lawrence Q., James Malfetti, Ernest Stewart, and Nini Vas Dias, *Reproduction, Sex and Preparation for Marriage,* Prentice-Hall, Englewood Cliffs, New Jersey, 1964, 231 pp.

Dale, L. Womble, *Foundations for Marriage and Family Relations,* The Macmillan Company, New York, 1966, 559 pp.

Davis, Maxine, *The Sexual Responsibility of Woman,* Permabooks, New York, 1959.

DeFabrigues, Oliver M., *Christian Marriage,* Hawthorn Publishers, New York, 1959, 192 pp. (Catholic view)

Doyle, Charles H., *Cana Is Forever,* Image Books, Garden City, N. Y., 1958, 133 pp.

Duvall, Evelyn M., *Facts of Life and Love for Teenagers,* Association Press, New York, 1963, 352 pp.

————, *Family Living,* Lippincott Company, Philadelphia, 1967, 256 pp.

————, *Inlaws, Pro and Con,* Association Press, New York, 1954, 189 pp.

————, *Marriage Is What You Make It,* Abington Press, New York, 1963.

————, *Why Wait Till Marriage?* Association Press, New York, 1965, 118 pp.

————, and Sylvanus Duvall, *Sense and Nonsense About Sex,* Association Press, New York, 1962, 124 pp.

————, and Reuben Hill, *Being Married,* Association Press, New York, 1960, 430 pp.

————, and ————, *When You Marry,* Association Press, New York, 1962, 337 pp.

————, and Joy Johnson, *The Art of Dating,* Associated Press, New York, 1967, 246 pp.

Duvall, Sylvanus, *Before You Marry,* Association Press, New York, 1959, 252 pp.

Eastman, Nicholsen J., *Expectant Motherhood,* Little, Brown & Company, Boston, 1957, 198 pp.

Eckert, Robert G., *So You Think It's Love,* Public Affairs, New York, 1950.

Ehrmann, Winston W., *Premarital Dating Behavior,* Henry Holt & Company, New York, 1959, 316 pp.

Eichenlaub, John C., *The Marriage Art,* Dell Publishing Company, New York, 1961, 223 pp.

Eisenstein, Victor W., *Neurotic Instruction in Marriage,* Basic Books, Inc., New York, 1956, 352 pp.

Ellis, Albert, *The Art and Science of Love,* Lyle Stuart, New York, 1960.

————, *The American Sexual Tragedy,* Lyle Stuart, New York, 1962.

Farber, Seymour M., M.D., and Roger H. Wilson, M.D., *Teenage Marriage and Divorce,* Diablo Press, New York, 1967, 154 pp.

Fishbein, Morris, and Ruby Reeves Kennedy, *Modern Marriage and Family Living,* Oxford University Press, New York, 1957, 545 pp.

————, *Birth Defects,* J. B. Lippincott Company, Philadelphia, 1963.

————, and Ernest W. Burgess, *Successful Marriage,* Doubleday, Garden City, New York, 1958.

Flanagan, Geraldine, *Nine Months of Life,* Simon and Schuster, New York, 1962, 95 pp.

Fletcher, Joseph, *The New Morality,* Westminister Press, Philadelphia, 1966.

Flower, Janet, *Marriages Are Not Made in Heaven,* Westminister Press, Philadelphia, 1965, 155 pp.

Fraiberg, Selma, *The Magic Years: Understanding and Handling the Problems of Early Childhood,* Charles Scribner's, New York, 1959, 305 pp.

Freedman, Ronald, Pascal Whelpton, and Arthur Campbell, *Family Planning, Sterility and Population Growth,* McGraw-Hill Book Company, New York, 1959, 515 pp.

Fromm, Erich, *The Art of Loving,* Harper & Row Publishers, New York, 1956, 133 pp.

Fromme, A., *Sex and Marriage,* Barnes & Noble, New York, 1959.

Gebhard, P. H., W. Pomeroy, C. Martin, and C. Christensen, *Sex Offenders,* Harper & Row Inc., New York, 1965.

————, *Pregnancy, Birth and Abortion,* Paul Hoeber, Inc., New York, 1958.

Genne, William H., *Husbands and Pregnancy,* Association Press, New York, 1956, 127 pp.

Gilese, John P., *Common Sense in Courtship,* Franciscan Publishers, New York, 1961, 64 pp.

Goode, William J., *The Family,* Prentice-Hall, Inc., Englewood Cliffs, New Jersey, 1964, 120 pp.

Gray, Madeline, *The Changing Years,* Doubleday & Company, Garden City, New York, 1967, 253 pp.

————, Henry, *Anatomy of the Human Body,* Lea & Febiger, Philadelphia, 1959, 1458 pp.

Greene, George, *Sex and the College Girl,* Diablo Press, New York, 1964.

Grumet, Charles, *Reproduction and Sex in Animal Life,* Abelard-Schuman, New York, 1962, 140 pp.

Guttmacher, Alan F., *Planning Your Family,* Macmillan Publishers, New York, 1965, 277 pp.

————, *Pregnancy and Birth, A Book for Expectant Parents,* The Viking Press, Inc., New York, 1956, 335 pp.

————, *Babies by Choice or by Chance,* Doubleday & Company, New York, 1959, 289 pp.

Himes, Norman E., and Donald L. Taylor, *Your Marriage,* Rinehart Publishers, New York, 1955.

Hoeflin, R. K., *Essenitals of Family Living,* John Wiley & Sons, New York, 1960.

Ingelman-Sundberg, *A Child Is Born, The Drama of Life Before Birth,* Delacorte Press, New York, 1967.

Johnson, Eric W., *Love and Sex in Plain Language,* J. B. Lippincott & Company, Philadelphia, 1965, 205 pp.

Kavinoky, Nadine, "Premarital Medical Examination" in Clark Vincent, *Readings in Marriage Counseling,* Thomas Y. Crowell Company, New York, 1957, pp. 126–33.

Kinsey, Alfred C., Wardell Pomeroy, and Clyde Martin, *Sexual Behavior in the Human Male,* W. B. Saunders Company, Philadelphia, 1948, 804 pp.

————, *Sexual Behavior in the Human Female,* W. B. Saunders Company, Philadelphia, 1953, 842 pp.

Kirkendall, Lester A., *Too Young to Marry,* Public Affairs Committee, New York, 1956, 28 pp.

————, *Marriage and Family Relations,* William C. Brown Company, Dubuque, Iowa, 1968, 177 pp.

————, *Premarital Intercourse and Interpersonal Relations,* Julian Press, New York, 1961.

Klemer, R. H., and M. Klemer, *Sexual Adjustment in Marriage,* Public Affairs, New York, 1966.

Krich, Aron, *Facts of Love and Marriage for Young People,* Dell Publishers, New York, 1962.

————, *Women, the Variety and Meaning of Their Sexual Experience,* Dell Books, New York, 1953, 319 pp.

————, *Men, the Variety and Meaning of Their Sexual Experience,* Dell Books, New York, 1954, 319 pp.

Landis, Judson T., *Personal Adjustment, Marriage and Family Living,* Prentice-Hall, Inc., Englewood Cliffs, New Jersey, 1955, 247 pp.

————, and Mary Landis, *Building a Successful Marriage,* Prentice-Hall, Englewood Cliffs, New Jersey, 1958, 320 pp.

Landis, Paul, *Making the Most of Marriage,* Appleton-Century-Crofts, Inc., New York, 1962, 542 pp.

Lantz, Herman R., and Eloise C. Snyder, *Marriage,* John Wiley & Sons, Inc., New York, 1963, 417 pp.

Laycock, S. R., *Family Living and Sex Education,* Baxter Publishing Company, Toronto, 1967, 144 pp.

Lee, Alfred, and Elizabeth B. Lee, *Marriage and the Family,* College Outline Series, Barnes & Noble, New York, 1966, 268 pp.

LeMasters, E. E., *Modern Courtship and Marriage,* The Macmillan Company, New York, 1957, 619 pp.

Lerrigo, Marion, and Helen Southard, *Approaching Adulthood,* American Medical Association, Chicago, 1963, 47 pp.

———, *Finding Yourself,* American Medical Association, Chicago, 1961, 50 pp.

Levine, Lena, *The Modern Book of Marriage,* Bartholomew Press, New York, 1957.

Levy, John, and Ruth Munroe, *The Happy Family,* Alfred A. Knopf, Inc., New York, 1948, 319 pp.

Lloyd, C. W., *Human Reproduction and Sexual Behavior,* Lea & Febiger, Philadelphia, 1964.

Lorand, Rhoda, *Love, Sex, and the Teenager,* Macmillan Company, New York, 1965.

Mace, David R., *What Is Marriage Counseling?* The Public Affairs Committee, New York, 1957, 28 pp.

———, *Marriage: The Art of Lasting Love,* Doubleday & Company, New York, 1952, 200 pp.

Masters, William H., M.D., and Virginia E. Johnson, *Human Sexual Response,* Little, Brown & Company, Boston, 1966, 366 pp.

Mayer, Michael F., *Divorce and Annulment in the 50 States,* Arco Publishing Company, Inc., New York, 1967, 89 pp.

McGinnis, Thomas, *Your First Year of Marriage,* Van Nostrand Publishers, New Jersey, 1967, 198 pp.

McManus, William, *Marriage Guide for Engaged Catholics,* Paulist Press, New York, 1961, 128 pp.

Merrill, Francis, *Courtship and Marriage,* Holt, Rinehart & Winston, New York, 1959, 383 pp.

Mudd, Emily, and Howard E. Mitchell, *Success in Family Living,* Association Press, New York, 1965, 254 pp.

Newman, Horatio Hackett, *Multiple Human Births,* Doubleday & Company, Inc., New York, 1940, 214 pp.

Nimkoff, Meyer F., *Marriage and the Family,* Houghton-Mifflin Co., New York, 1947, 748 pp.

Novak, Michael, *The Experience of Marriage,* Macmillan Company, New York, 1964, 173 pp.

O'Connor, John J., *Preparation for Marriage and Family Life,* The Paulist Press, New York, 1947, 95 pp.

Orenstein, Irving, *Where Do Babies Come From?* Pyramid Books, New York, 1964.

Ploscowe, Morris, *Sex and the Law,* Ace Books, New York, 1962.

Reiss, Ira, *Premarital Sex Standards in America,* Macmillan Company, New York, 1960.

Sands, Sydney, *Growing Up to Love, Sex and Marriage,* Christopher, New York, 1960.

Strain, Frances, *Love at the Threshold,* Appleton-Century-Crofts, New York, 1952.

Sussman, Marvin, *Sourcebook in Marriage and the Family,* Houghton-Mifflin, New York, 1963.

Womble, Dale, *Foundations for Marriage and Family Relations,* Macmillan Company, New York, 1966.

Young, L., *Out of Wedlock,* McGraw-Hill Book Company, New York, 1954.

B

Sources of Free or Inexpensive Sex Education Materials

Abingdon Press, 201 Eighth Avenue South, Nashville, Tennessee 37202.

Ace Books, 1120 Avenue of the Americas, New York, New York 10036.

American Academy of Pediatrics, 1801 Hinman Avenue, Evanston, Illinois 60201.

American Association for Health, Physical Education, and Recreation, 1201 16th Street, NW, Washington, D.C. 20006.

American Home Economics Association, 1600 20th Street, NW, Washington, D.C. 20009.

American Institute of Family Relations, 5287 Sunset Boulevard, Los Angeles, California 90027.

American Medical Association, 535 N. Dearborn Street, Chicago, Illinois 60610. Posters, exhibits, and pamphlets on sex topics. Catalog available.

American Public Health Association, 1790 Broadway, New York, New York 10017. Reprints and other publications.

American School Health Association, Committee on Health Guidance in Sex Education, 515 East Main Street, Kent, Ohio 44240. "Growth Patterns and Sex Education," *Journal of School Health,* May 1967.

American Social Health Association, 1740 Broadway, New York, New York 10019. Pamphlets on sex education, venereal disease, marriage, and parenthood.

Association for Family Living, 32 W. Randolph Street, Chicago, Illinois 60601. Pamphlets on family life, child guidance, adolescence, sex education, courtship, and marriage.

Association Films, Inc., Broad at Elm, Ridgefield, New Jersey.

Association Press, 291 Broadway, New York, New York 10007.

Audiovisual Center, University of Connecticut, Storrs, Connecticut 06268.

Augsburg Publishing House, 426 South 5th Street, Minneapolis, Minnesota 55415.

Bantam Publishing House, 271 Madison Avenue, New York, New York 10016.

Barron's Educational Services, Inc., 113 Crossways Park Drive, Woodbury, New York, 11797.

Beacon Press, 25 Beacon Street, Boston, Massachusetts 02108.

Bell Telephone Company, Lecture Bureau, 101 Willoughby Street, Brooklyn, New York 11201.

Bobbs-Merrill Company, Indianapolis, Indiana.

Brown, William C., Dubuque, Iowa. Books for teachers.

Bureau of Public Health Association, Connecticut State Department of Health, 165 Capitol Avenue, Hartford, Connecticut.

Calderwood, Derrick, Oregon State University, Portland, Oregon.

Center for Mass Communication, Columbia University Press, 2960 Broadway, New York 10002.

Child Study Association of America, 9 East 89th Street, New York, New York 10028.

Classroom Film Distributors, 5620 Hollywood Blvd., Los Angeles, California.

Cleveland Health Museum, 8911 Euclid Avenue, Cleveland, Ohio 44106. Exhibits and teaching materials for sex education.

Columbia University Press, International Documents Service, 136 South Broadway, New York 10533.

Concordia Publishing House, 3558 South Jefferson Avenue, St. Louis, Missouri 63118.

Connecticut State Department of Mental Health, 165 Capitol Avenue, Hartford, Connecticut.

Coronet Films Inc., 65 East Southwater Street, Chicago, Illinois 60601.

Council for Christian Social Action, United Church of Christ, 289 Park Avenue South, New York, New York 10010.

Creative Playthings Inc., Princeton, New Jersey.

Creative Scope Inc., 509 Fifth Avenue, New York, New York 10017.

Crowell, Thomas Y., 201 Park Avenue South, New York, New York 10017.

Dell Publishing Company, 750 Third Avenue, New York, New York 10017.

Denoyer-Geppert Company, 5235 Ravenswood Avenue, Chicago, Illinois 60640.

Department of New Jersey Education Film Bureau, State House Annex, Trenton, New Jersey.

Dodd-Mead Company, 423 Park Avenue, New York, New York 10016.

Doubleday Company Inc., Garden City, Long Island, New York.

Dutton, E. P., Company, 201 Park Avenue South, New York, New York 10003.

Encyclopedia Britannica Films, 1150 Wilmette Avenue, Wilmette, Illinois 60091.

Equitable Life Assurance Society of the United States, 1285 Avenue of the Americas, New York, New York 10019. Booklets and leaflets.

Eye Gate House, Inc., 146-01 Archer Avenue, Jamaica, New York.

Faith Through Education Corporation, Box 517, Skokie, Illinois 60676. (Catholic.)

Family Life Publications, P.O. Box 6725, College Station, Durham, North Carolina 27706.

Family Service Association of America, 44 East 23rd Street, New York, New York 10023. Films, slides, plays, etc.

Fearon Publishers, 2165 Park Boulevard, Palo Alto, California 94306.

Free Press, 866 Third Avenue, New York, New York 10022.

Golden Press Inc., 850 Third Avenue, New York, New York 10010.

Grosset and Dunlop Inc., 51 Madison Avenue, New York, New York 10010.

Guidance Associates, Pleasantville, New York 10570.

Harcourt, Brace & World, Inc., 757 Third Avenue, New York, New York 10017.

Harper & Row, Publishers, 49 East 33rd Street, New York, New York 10016.

Hawthorn Books, 70 Fifth Avenue, New York, New York 10011.

Health Information Foundation, 5555 Ellis Avenue, Chicago, Illinois 60637. Pamphlets, bulletins, and films.

Heath, D. C., Company, Boston, Massachusetts.

Hilts Publishing Company, 6300 Hamilton Avenue, Cincinnati, Ohio 45224.

Hogg Foundation, University of Texas, Austin, Texas 78712. Pamphlets and materials on children, adolescence, and family living.

Holt, Rinehart & Winston, Inc., 383 Madison Avenue, New York, New York 10017.

Houghton-Mifflin Company, 110 Tremont Avenue, Boston, Massachusetts 02107.

Ideal Pictures, 321 West 42nd Street, New York, New York 10036.

Kansas State Department of Health, Topeka, Kansas.

Kimberly-Clark Corporation, Education Department, Neenah, Wisconsin 54957. Films, pamphlets, and teaching guide on menstruation.

Lea & Febiger, Inc., Philadelphia, Pennsylvania.

Learning Resource Center, Audiovisual Department, West Hartford Board of Education, 7 Whiting Lane, West Hartford, Connecticut.

Lippincott Publishing Company, East Washington Square, Philadelphia, Pennsylvania 19105.

Los Angeles County Medical Association, Foundation for Medicine and Education, Los Angeles, California.

Lyons and Carnahan, Inc., Chicago, Illinois.

Macfadden-Bartell Corporation, 205 East 42nd Street, New York, New York 10017.

McGraw-Hill Book Company, Inc., 330 West 42nd Street, New York, New York 10036.

McKay and Davis Company, 750 Third Avenue, New York, New York 10017.

Macmillan Company, 866 Third Avenue, New York, New York 10022.

Maternity Center Association, 48 East 92nd Street, New York, New York 10028.

Mental Health Material Center, 104 East 25th Street, New York, New York 10010. Materials on family life and human relations.

Metropolitan Effort Toward Regional Opportunity, Area Resource Center, University of Hartford, 107 University Hall, 200 Bloomfield Avenue, West Hartford, Connecticut.

Metropolitan Life Insurance Company, 1 Madison Avenue, New York, New York 10010. Materials on family living and VD.

Minnesota Mining & Manufacturing, Inc., 38 Center Street, Minneapolis, Minnesota 55101. Films and records on sex education.

National Association for Mental Health, 10 Columbus Circle, New York, New York 10019. Materials on sex education and family living.

National Congress of Parents and Teachers, 700 East Rush Street, Chicago, Illinois 60611. Materials on marriage and sex education.

National Council of Churches, 475 Riverside Drive, New York, New York.

National Council on Family Relations, 1219 University Avenue, Minneapolis 14, Minnesota.

New Jersey State Museum Library, Trenton, New Jersey.

Pergamon Press, 44-01 21st Street, Long Island City, New York 11101.

Personal Products Corporation, Education Department, Willows, New Jersey 08850.

Pocket Books Inc., 630 Fifth Avenue, New York, New York 10020.

Prentice-Hall, Inc., Englewood Cliffs, New Jersey 07632.

Public Affairs Committee, Inc., 381 Park Avenue South, New York, New York 10016.

Public Health Education Section, Connecticut State Department of Health, Room 114, 79 Elm Street, Hartford, Connecticut 06268.

Putnam Sons, 200 Madison Avenue, New York, New York 10016.

Pyramid Books, Inc., 444 Madison Avenue, New York, New York 10022.

QED Productions, Inc., Division of Cathedral Films, 2921 W. Alameda Avenue, Burbank, California 91505.

Random House, Inc., 501 Madison Avenue, New York, New York 10022.

Ross Laboratories, 235 Columbus Avenue, Columbus, Ohio.

Russell Capen, Consultant, Audiovisual Education Center, Connecticut State Department of Education, State Office Building, Hartford, Connecticut.

San Juan Unified School District, Department of Adult Education, 81 North Street, San Juan, California 95112.

Saunders Publishing Company, Philadelphia, Pennsylvania.

Scholastic Publications, Inc., Englewood Cliffs, New Jersey.

School Health Education Study, 1507 North Street, NW, Washington, D.C. 20005. Materials on family life and sex education.

Science Kit, Inc., 2299 Military Road, Tonowanda, New York 14150.

Science Research Associates, 259 East Erie Street, Chicago, Illinois 60611.

Scott Foresman Company, 1900 East Lake Avenue, Glenview, Illinois 60025.

Scott Paper Company, Home Service Center, Philadelphia, Pennsylvania 19113.

Scribner's and Sons, 597 Fifth Avenue, New York, New York 10017.

Sex Information Education Council (SIECUS) of the United States, 1855 Broadway, New York, New York 10023.

Sexology Magazine, 154 West 14th Street, New York, New York 10011.

Simon & Schuster, 606 Fifth Avenue, New York, New York 10020.

Society for Visual Education, 1435 Diversey Street, Chicago, Illinois 60614.

Syracuse University, Educational Film Library, University Station, Syracuse, New York 13210.

TAMA, Division of Professional Productions, Inc., Suite 795, North Star Medical Office, 608 Second Avenue, Minneapolis, Minnesota 55402.

Tampex Corporation, Educational Department, 161 East 42nd Street, New York, New York 10017. Kit on menstruation.

United States Department of Agriculture, Research Branch, Washington, D.C. 20025.

United States Department of Health, Education, and Welfare, Children's Bureau, Washington, D.C. 20025. Materials for professionals and parents on maternal and child health, including prenatal care, pregnancy, adoption, etc.

United States Government Printing Office, Division of Public Documents, Washington, D.C. 20025. Materials on family planning and sex education.

United States Naval Medical Film Library, Bethesda, Maryland.

University of California, Elementary School Science Project, 2223 Fulton Street, Berkeley, California 94720.

University of Chicago Press, Chicago, Illinois 60620.

University of Minnesota Press, 2037 University Avenue, SE, Minneapolis, Minnesota 55455.

Van Nostrand, Company, Inc., Princeton, New Jersey.

VD Control Program, 211 East State Street, Trenton, New Jersey.

Wayne State University, Audiovisual Department, 5980 Case Avenue, Detroit, Michigan 48202.

Webster Division of McGraw-Hill, 330 West 42nd Street, New York, New York 10036.

Westminister Press, Witherspoon Building, Philadelphia, Pennsylvania 19107.

Wexler Films Inc., Los Angeles, California.

Wiley, John & Sons, 605 Third Avenue, New York, New York 10016.

Williams and Wilkins Company, Baltimore, Maryland.

Visual Aid Service Center, University of Illinois, Division of University Extension, Champagne, Illinois 60620.

Visual Products, 3M Company, Box 2501 Hudson Road, St. Paul, Minnesota 55119.

Yale University Press, New Haven, Connecticut.

C

Glossary for Students
in Course in Sex Education

Abdomen. That part of the body below the front of the chest and extending down to the region between the hips. It contains, among other organs, the stomach, intestines, liver, and pancreas.

Abortion. Premature expulsion from the uterus of the product of conception—a fertilized ovum, embryo, or nonviable fetus; a premature or unnatural birth caused by external influences.

Abstinence. A refraining from the use of or indulgence in certain foods, stimulants, or sexual intercourse.

Adolescence. The period of life between puberty (appearance of secondary sexual characteristics) and adulthood (cessation of major body growth). Also, the age between the periods when the reproductive organs begin to function and before they reach their full growth and development.

Adultery. Sexual intercourse between a married person and an individual other than his or her legal spouse.

Afterbirth. The placenta and fetal membranes expelled from the uterus following the birth of a child.

Amenorrhea. Absence of the menses (menstruation).

Amniotic sac. A thin membrane forming the closed sac or "bag of waters" that surrounds the unborn child within the uterus and contains amniotic fluid in which the fetus is immersed.

Androgen. The general term applied to sex hormones considered to be essentially predominant in the male. Specifically, a steroid hormone producing masculine sex characteristics and having an influence on body and bone growth and on the sex drive.

Aphrodisiac. Anything, such as a drug or a perfume, that stimulates sexual desire.

Artificial insemination. Introduction of male semen into the vagina or womb of a woman by artificial means.

Autoerotic. Pertaining to self-stimulation or erotic behavior directed toward one's self; frequently equated with masturbation.

Bigamy. The crime of having two husbands or wives at the same time.

Birth control. Birth control or planned parenthood is the act of regulating conception. It is the deliberate limitation of the number of children born through such means as contraceptives, the rhythm method, coitus interruptus, abstinence, and the like.

Birthmarks. Skin blemishes existing on the skin at birth and usually due to abnormal increase in the number of blood vessels or excessive pigmentation. Not caused by fright or shock to the mother during pregnancy.

Bisexual. Literally, having sex organs of both sexes, as in hermaphrodites; having a sexual interest in both sexes.

Bladder. The organ (sac) in which urine received from the kidneys is stored until it is excreted.

Breast. *See* Mammary glands.

Caesarean birth (also caesarean section). Delivery of a baby through a surgical incision in the abdominal and uterine walls when it cannot or should not be born in the usual way.

Castration. Removal of the gonads (or sex glands)—testicles in men, the ovaries in women.

Celibacy. The state of being unmarried and abstaining from sexual activity.

Cervix. The narrow portion (neck) of the uterus or womb that forms its lower end and opens into the vagina.

Chancre (shang′ker). The sore or ulcer that is the first symptom of primary syphilis.

Change of life. *See* Climacteric and menopause.

Chromosomes. Microscopic, rod-shaped bodies, found in the nucleus of all body cells, that carry the genes of the parents; definite segment of adhered chromatin found in the nucleus and containing potential hereditary factors.

Circumcision. Surgical removal of the foreskin, or prepuce, of the male penis.

Climacteric. The physical and psychological changes that occur at the termination of the menstrual function (i.e., reproductive capability) in the woman and reduction in sex hormone production in both sexes; menopause; change of life.

Clitoris (klī ′te•ris) (kleitoris). Small, erectile structure at the front of the vagina that contains sexually sensitive nerves and corresponds to the penis of the male.

Coitus (ko-it-us). Sexual intercourse between male and female, in which the male penis is inserted into the female vagina. Also called the sex act, mating, and cohabitation.

Colostrum. A thin, milky fluid secreted by the female breasts just before and just after childbirth.

Common law. Two persons of opposite sex living together as man and wife but not united by marriage ties recognized by law.

Conception. The beginning of a new life, when an ovum (egg) is penetrated by a sperm, resulting in the development of an embryo; the act of creating a new life as a result of fertilization.

Condom. A contraceptive used by males consisting of a rubber or gut sheath that is drawn over the penis before coitus.

Congenital. Passed by mother to child before birth but not inherited.

Continence. Refraining from sexual relations.

Contraception. The use of devices or drugs to prevent conception in sexual intercourse.

Copulation (cop-u-la-shun). Sexual intercourse; coitus; sexual union; the sex act.

Corpus luteum. A yellow mass in the ovary, formed from a ruptured Graafian follicle, that secretes the hormone progesterone.

Courtship. The more serious stage of mate-seeking in which keeping company is limited to the love mate.

Criminal abortion. Illegal termination of a human pregnancy by any type of medical, surgical, or other means of interference, as distinguished from therapeutic abortion, which is done to protect the health or life of the mother.

Defloration. The rupture of the hymen in a virgin's first experience of coitus, or through virginal examination.

Diaphragm. A rubber contraceptive used by women which is hemispherical in shape and fits like a cap over the neck of the uterus (cervix). It prevents sperm from entering or making contact with the egg.

Divorce. Legal dissolution of the marriage contract.

Douche. A stream of water or other liquid solution directed into the female vagina for sanitary, medical, or contraceptive reasons.

Dysmenorrhea (dys•men′or•rhoe′a). Difficult or painful menstruation.

Ectopic. In an abnormal case, e.g., in an ectopic pregnancy, the unborn child develops outside the uterus, either in the abdominal cavity, in a Fallopian tube, or in an ovary.

Egg cell. The female reproductive cell, the ovum.

Ejaculation. The expulsion of male semen from the male urethra, usually at the climax (orgasm) of the sexual act.

Electra complex. Excessive emotional attachment of a daughter to her father.

Emasculate. To castrate; to deprive of manliness or masculine vigor.

Embryo (em-breeo). The unborn young in its early stages of development; in man, from one week following conception to the end of the second month, following which it is called the fetus.

Emission. Discharge of semen from the male penis especially when involuntary, as during sleep (nocturnal emission or a wet dream).

Endocrine gland. A gland that secretes its product (hormone) directly into the bloodstream.

Engagement. The promising or pledging of two people to wed each other.

Epididymis. A network of tiny tubes leading from the testicle to the sperm duct through which sperm passes.

Erection. The stiffening and enlargement of the penis (or clitoris), usually as a result of sexual excitement.

Erogenous zone. A sexually sensitive area of the body, such as the mouth, lips, breasts, nipples, buttocks, genitals, or anus.

Erotic. Pertaining to sexual love or sensation; sexually stimulating.

Estrogen. General term applied to the female sex hormone; a steroid hormone producing female sex characteristics and affecting the functioning of the menstrual cycle.

Eugenics. The science which deals with all influences that improve the inborn qualities of the human race.

Eunuch. A male devoid of testes or of functional testicular tissues; castrated male.

Exhibitionism. A sexual deviation in which the individual—usually male—suffers from a compulsion to expose his genitals publicly.

Extramarital. Literally, outside of marriage; usually used in reference to adulterous sexual intercourse.

Fallopian tubes. The oviduct or tube that extends from each ovary to the uterus in the female, through which the egg passes and in which the egg is fertilized by the sperm.

Feces (fee-seez). Solid waste matter discharged from the intestines (the bowels) and composed of undigestible food materials and bacteria.

Fertility. The state of being capable of producing young; the opposite of sterility. As applied to human beings, fertility is used interchangeably with birth rate.

Fertilization. The union of egg (ovum) and sperm (spermatozoon) to produce a new being.

Fetishism. A sexual deviation in which sexual gratification is achieved by means of an object, such as an article of clothing, that bears sexual symbolism for the individual.

Fetus (fee-tus). The unborn offspring of a viviparous animal. In humans, the unborn child from the third month after conception until birth.

Follicle. A small sac or socket near the surface of the ovary in the female that contains a developing egg cell, and from which it is discharged at ovulation. Also called the Graafian follicle.

Foreskin. The prepuce; the fold of skin covering the glans of the penis or the clitoris.

Fornication. Sexual intercourse between two unmarried persons (as distinguished from adultery, which involves a person who is married to someone other than his coital partner).

Frigidity. A condition in women in which an emotional block prevents sexual expression or enjoyment.

Genes. The basic carrier of hereditary traits, contained in the chromosomes. (a) A hereditary germinal factor which either alone or in combination with other factors, produces a single character. (b) The individual parts that are thought to make up the chromosomes.

Genitals (or genitalia). The organs of reproduction; the external sex organs.

Germ cell. Gamete (ovum or sperm) which can unite with another to form a zygote or fertilized egg.

Gestation. Pregnancy; the period from conception to birth.

Gland. An organ which extracts materials from the bloodstream and converts them into new substances.

Glans penis. The head or terminal end of the penis.

Gonad. The male and female reproductive organs; sex glands; a testicle (male) or ovary (female); gamete-producing organs.

Gonorrhea (gon'or-rhoe'a). A highly infectious venereal disease transmitted chiefly through coitus, characterized by a discharge of pus from the reproductive organs, also known as "clap," "dose," "gleet," "strain," "drip."

Graafian follicle. *See* Follicle.

Gynecologist. A physician specializing in the treatment of the problems of the female sexual and reproductive organs.

Heredity. The transmission of bodily traits and characteristics or of diseases from parents to offspring.

Hermaphrodite. An individual possessing both male and female sex glands (ovary and testicle) or sex gland tissue of both sexes. (Cf. psuedohermaphrodite)

Heterosexuality. Sexual attraction to, or love toward, or sexual activity with persons of the opposite sex; the opposite of homosexuality.

Homosexuality. Sexual attraction to, or sexual activity with, members of one's own sex; the opposite of heterosexuality.

Hormone. A chemical secretion of an endocrine gland that enters the bloodstream and influences the functioning of a part of the body.

Hybrid. An animal or plant bred from two species. The mule, offspring of the donkey and the mare, is a hybrid.

Hymen (hi'men). The membranous fold that partly covers the external opening of the vagina in most virgin females; the maidenhead.

Hysterectomy (hys-ter-ec-to-my). Surgical removal of the uterus, either through the abdominal wall or through the vagina.

Illegitimacy. Child being born to an unmarried mother.

Implantation. The insertion of the sperm to reach the ovary.

Impotence. Inability of the male to have sexual intercourse, often caused by psychological reasons and sometimes by physical deficiencies.

Impregnation. The act of fertilization or fecundation; making pregnant.

Incest. Sexual relations between close relatives, such as father and daughter, mother and son, or brother and sister.

Infertility. The temporary inability to achieve conception; but since conception is a partnership, it is quite possible that the failure lies with the man.

Intercourse. Coitus, mating, copulation, the sex act; the physical joining of the male and female bodies.

Interstitial cells. Specialized cells in the testicles that produce the male sex hormones.

Invert. A homosexual; one who is sexually attracted to persons of his own sex.

Labia majora (sing. labium majus). The outer and larger pair of lips of the female external genitals (vulva).

Labia minora (sing. labium minus). The inner and smaller pair of lips of the female vulva.

Labor. The term for the uterine contractions that finally expel the fetus from the uterus in childbirth.

Lactation. The manufacture and secretion of milk by the mammary glands in a mother's breasts.

Lesbian (lez'bē-en). A female homosexual.

Libido (li-bē'dō). Sex drive or sexual desire or sexual urge.

Love. Ardent affection or personal attachment usually expressed toward one of the opposite sex.

Maidenhead. The hymen or membrane of the vaginal introitus.

Mammary glands. The glands that secrete milk to feed the babies; the breasts.

Marriage. Usually a religious, social, and legal union of a man and woman, for founding and maintaining a family.

Masochism (mas'e-kiz'em). A sexual deviation in which an individual derives sexual gratification from having pain inflicted on him. This behavior, more frequent in women than in men, is an exaggeration of the passivity and submissiveness which characterize the female sexual response.

Masturbation. Self-stimulation of the genitals through manipulation; to obtain sexual satisfaction autoeroticism.

Menarche. The onset of menstruation in girls, occuring in late puberty and ushering in the period of adolescence.

Menopause (men'e-poz). Period of life (usually between the ages of 45 and 55) when the female permanently stops ovulating (producing eggs) and menstruation, also called "change of life" or "climacteric."

Menstrual cycle. *See* Menstruation.

Menstruation (men'stroo-ā-shen). The end of the monthly ovulation cycle of the female (in women between the ages of puberty and menopause), the lining of the womb is sloughed off accompanied by the discharge of blood from the uterus through the vagina.

Miscarriage. Spontaneous expulsion of a fetus from the onset of the fourth to the end of the sixth month of pregnancy; the birth of a baby who has not developed enough to be able to live.

Mitosis. Indirect cell division. The typical mode of active somatic cells and germ cells.

Monogamy. Marriage between one man and one woman.

Mons veneris (or mons pubis). A triangular mound of fat at the symphysis pubis of a woman, just above the vulval area.

Multiple births. The births of more than one baby, such as twins, triplets, quadruplets, quintuplets.

Mutation. A permanent transmissible change in the characters of an offspring from those of its parents.

Narcissism. Excessive self-love; sexual excitement through admiration of one's own body.

Navel. The scar left on the abdomen where the fetus was attached to the umbilical cord; the umbilicus.

Nocturnal emission. An involuntary, normal male orgasm and discharge of semen during sleep; "a wet dream."

Nymphomania. Excessive sexual desire in woman.

Obscene. Disgusting, repulsive, filthy, shocking—that which is abhorrent according to accepted standards of morality.

Obstetrician. A physician specializing in the care of women during pregnancy, labor, and the period immediately following delivery.

Oedipus complex. Excessive emotional attachment, involving conscious or unconscious incestuous desires, of a son in relation to his mother.

Onanism (ō'nen-iz'em). Withdrawal of the male penis from the female vagina before ejaculation; coitus interruptus.

Orgasm. The peak or climax of sexual excitement in sexual activity.

Ovary (o-va-ree). The female sex gland, in which the egg cells or ova are formed.

Oviduct. The Fallopian or uterine tube through which the egg (ovum) descends from the ovary to the uterus.

Ovulation. The release of mature, unimpregnated ovum from one of the Graafian follicles of an ovary; usually occurs about fourteen days before the onset of the next menstrual period.

Ovum (pl. ova). An egg; the female reproductive cell, corresponding to the male spermatozoon, that after fertilization develops into a new member of the same species.

Paresis. A chronic syphilitic inflammation of the brain and its enveloping membranes, characterized by progressive mental deterioration and a generalized paralysis that is sometimes fatal; form of brain damage in tertiary syphilis.

Parthenogenesis. Reproduction by the development of an egg without its being fertilized by a spermatozoon.

Parturition. Labor; the process or act of giving birth to a child.

Penis (pee-nis). The male organ of urination; the male sex organ by which sperm cells are introduced into the vagina of the female.

Perversion. Sexual deviation from the normal; paraphilia.

Petting. Sexual contact that excludes coitus.

Pituitary. Also known as the master gland and located in the head, it is responsible for the proper functioning of all the other glands, especially the sex glands, the thyroid, and the adrenals.

Placenta. The cake-like organ that connects the fetus to the uterus by means of the umbilical cord, and through which the fetus is fed and waste products are eliminated; it is expelled from the uterus after the birth of the baby—afterbirth.

Polyandry. The form of marriage in which one woman has more than one husband at the same time.

Polygamy. The form of marriage in which a spouse of either sex may possess a plurality of mates at the same time.

Polygyny. The form of marriage in which one man has more than one wife at the same time.

Pornography. The presentation of sexually arousing material in literature, art, motion pictures, or other means of communication and expression; writings or drawings intended to create unhealthy sexual excitement.

Postpartum. Occuring after childbirth, or after delivery.

Potent. Having the male capability to perform sexual intercourse; capable of erection.

Precocious sexuality. Awakening of sexual desire at a prematurely early age.

Pregnancy. The condition of having a developing embryo or fetus in the body; the the period from conception to birth or abortion.

Premarital relations. Taking place before marriage.

Premature birth. Born after the sixth month and before the ninth month of pregnancy.

Prenatal. Existing or occurring before birth.

Prepuce. Foreskin, or the fold of skin covering the glans of the penis or the clitoris.

Progesterone. The female hormone (known as the pregnancy hormone) that is produced in the yellow body or corpus luteum of an ovary, and whose function is to prepare the uterus for the reception and development of a fertilized ovum.

Promiscuous. When referring to sexual conduct, having intercourse with many persons; engaging in casual sexual relations.

Propagation. The production of offspring by organized bodies (same as reproduction in plants).

Prophylactic. A drug or device used for the prevention of disease, often specifically venereal disease.

Prostate. The gland in the male surrounding the urethra and the neck of the bladder, which secretes seminal fluids into the urethra at ejaculation.

Prostitute. A person who engages in sexual relationships for payment.

Prostitution. The age-old worldwide practice of providing sex relations for a price.

Puberty (pew-ber-tee). The period during which boys and girls begin to develop and grow into men and women, usually between the ages of 12 and 14 years. The age at which the reproductive organs become functionally operative, indicated in the male by the change of voice and seminal discharge and in the female by the occurrence of menstruation.

Rape. Forcible sexual intercourse with a person who does not give consent or who offers resistance.

Reproduction. The production of offspring.

Rhythm method. A method of birth control that relies on the so-called "safe period" or infertile days in a woman's menstrual cycle; abstaining from sexual intercourse during the days of the month when ovulation takes place and the egg cell is in the female reproductive tract and can be fertilized.

Sadism. Physical or psychological condition in which an individual gets sexual pleasure from inflicting pain on others.

"Safe period." The interval of the menstrual cycle when the female is presumably not ovulating and so the period when fertilization supposedly cannot occur.

Scrotum. The skin pouch suspended from the groin that contains the male testicles and their accessory organs.

Secondary sex characteristics. The physical characteristics—other than the external sex organs—that distinguish male from female.

Seduction. Luring a female (sometimes a male) into a sexual intercourse without the use of force.

Semen (see'men). A thick whitish fluid that contains hundreds of millions of sperm cells and is discharged from the urethra of the male during sexual intercourse.

Seminiferous tubules. The tiny tubes or canals in each male testicle that produce the sperm.

Sex. Sphere of emotional behavior associated with male-female relations and based upon the physiological and anatomical differences between the male and female.

Sex drive. Desire for sexual expression.

Sex gland. A gonad; the testicle in the male and the ovary in the female.

Sex hormone. A substance secreted by the sex glands directly into the bloodstream, e.g., androgens (male) and estrogens (female).

Sex organ. The genital or reproductive organs, usually the male penis, or the female vulva or vagina.

Sexual inadequacy. Any degree of sexual response that is not sufficient for the isolated demand of the moment or for a protracted period of time; frequent or total inability to experience orgasm.

Sexual intercourse. *See* Coitus.

Sexual outlet. Any of the various ways by which sexual tension is released through orgasm.

Sibling. One of two or more offspring of the same parents.

Sodomy (sod' um-i). Copulation in an unnatural manner, variously defined by law to include sexual intercourse with animals, and mouth-genital or anal contact between humans.

Sperm (spermatozoon). The male reproductive cell; one of the mature germ cells of a male animal.

Spermatogenesis. The process of sperm formation.

Spirochete (spi'ro-ket). The corkscrew-shaped microorganism that causes syphilis; its scientific name is *Treponema pallidum.*

Sterility. The inability to produce offspring.

Sterilization. Any procedure (usually surgical) by which a male or female is made incapable of begetting or bearing children.

Syphilis (sif'i-lis). An infectious chronic venereal disease that enters the body through sexual contact, and spreads through the bloodstream to other parts of the body; also known as "pox," "bad blood," "lues," and "siff."

Tampons. The internal method of sanitary protection.

Testicle. The testis; the male sex gland.

Testis (pl. testes). The male sex gland or gonad, which produces spermatozoa; the two oval shaped glandular organs of the male contained in the scrotum.

Testosterone (tes-tos'te-rōn). The male hormone that induces and maintains the male secondary sex characteristics; produced in the testes.

Transsexualism. A compulsion or obsession to become a member of the opposite sex through surgical changes.

Transvestism. A sexual deviation characterized by a compulsive desire to wear the garments of the opposite sex; cross dressing.

Trichomoniasis. An infection of the female vagina caused by infestation of the microorganism Trichomonas and characterized by inflammation, usually resulting in a vaginal discharge, and itching and burning.

Twins. Two persons born of the same mother at the same time. Similar twins: Two individuals the product of a single fertilized egg, and thus having the same hereditary factors. Fraternal twins: Two entirely different individuals who develop from different ova but are born together.

Umbilical cord. The rope-like structure attached to the placenta of the mother at one end and to the baby's umbilicus at the other, and through which nourishment and oxygen are supplied and waste materials carried away during pregnancy; the navel cord.

Umbilicus (um-bil′e-kes). The scar that is left after the cord that attaches an unborn baby to its mother is severed; the navel.

Urethra (yew-ree-thra). The membranous tube that carries the urine from the bladder to the surface of the body in both the male and female. In the male it also carries the semen, containing the sperm cells.

Urologist. A physician specializing in the treatment of the diseases and the disorders of the urinary tract of both sexes, as well as of the genital tract of the male.

Uterine tube. The Fallopian tube which extends from each ovary to the uterus in the female.

Uterus (yew-ter-rus). The womb; the hollow pear-shaped organ in females in which the fertilized egg implants itself and grows.

Vagina (va-ji-na). The passageway in the female body that connects the cervix to the external sex organs, or vulva; the birth canal; the female organ of sexual intercourse.

Vaginitis. The inflammation of the female vagina; usually as a result of infection.

Vas deferens (or ductus deferens). The sperm duct(s) in males, leading from the epididymis to the seminal vesicles and the urethra.

Vasectomy. A surgical procedure for sterilizing the male involving the removal of the vas deferens, or a portion of it. This does not affect his sexual capacity but makes it impossible for him to become a father.

Venereal disease. Venereal disease or VD is a contagious disease transmitted mainly by sexual intercourse with an infected person; syphilis and gonorrhea.

Virginity. The physical condition of a male or female before first intercourse.

Virgin. A male or female who has not had sexual intercourse.

Voyeurism. A sexual deviation in which a person achieves sexual gratification by observing others in the nude.

Vulva. The external sex organs of the female, including the mons veneris, the labia majora, the labia minora, the clitoris and the vestibule.

Wassermann test. A serological test used in diagnosing syphilis, named after August von Wassermann, who discovered it in 1905. More modern tests have been devised by Kline, Kahn, and Kohlmer.

Wet dreams. *See* Nocturnal emissions.

Womb. The uterus; the organ in which the baby grows and is nourished before birth.

X-chromosome. A sex-determining chromosome present singly in males and as a pair in females; if an X-chromosome from the male unites with the X-chromosome of the egg-cell, a baby girl results.

Y-chromosome. A sex-chromosome found only in males; if a Y-chromosome unites with the X-chromosome of the egg, a baby boy results.

Zygote. The single cell resulting from the union of two germ cells (sperm and egg) at conception; the fertilized egg or ovum.

D

Evaluation Instruments

1. Information Test on Human Reproduction

Copy No.: _____   *Name:* _____
Date: _____   *School, class, or address:*
Number correct: _____   _____

_____

                                                      Rating

_____ **1.** An egg is fertilized when it unites with: **1.** ___

     1. A gene   3. Another egg
     2. A sperm   4. A chromosome

_____ **2.** The organ of the human being in which the eggs are pro-   **2.** ___
     duced is called the:

     1. Testes   3. Ovary
     2. Uterus   4. Umbilicus

_____ **3.** In the human female, the egg first passes from the ovary   **3.** ___
     into the:

     1. Vagina   3. Uterus
     2. Fallopian tube   4. Stomach

_____ **4.** In the human female, if an egg is not fertilized it: **4.** _____
1. Passes out of the body through the vagina.
2. Is absorbed into the blood stream.
3. Is stored in the uterus.
4. Is passed back to the ovary.

_____ **5.** In the human male, a fluid is added to the sperms from the: **5.** _____
1. Bladder 3. Scrotum
2. Seminal vesicles. 4. Adrenals

_____ **6.** In the mother, fertilization of the egg usually takes place **6.** _____
in the:
1. Vagina 3. Fallopian tube
2. Uterus 4. Ovary

_____ **7.** The human embryo gets its food through: **7.** _____
1. The placenta 3. Cell division
2. The Fallopian tube 4. The abdominal cavity

_____ **8.** The umbilical cord connects the: **8.** _____
1. Testes and the seminal vesicles.
2. Placenta and the navel.
3. Uterus and the placenta.
4. Throat and stomach.

_____ **9.** Another name for the term *fertilization* is: **9.** _____
1. Reproduction 3. Conception
2. Implantation 4. Sterilization

_____**10.** The periodic process in which the lining of the uterus **10.** _____
breaks down and is discharged is called:
1. Menstruation 3. Menopause
2. Ovulation 4. Emission

_____**11.** Which is inherited? **11.** _____
1. Syphilis 3. Personality
2. Tuberculosis 4. None of these

_____**12.** The physical changes which usually take place in boys and **12.** _____
girls during the high school age are caused by the internal
secretions into the blood stream from the:
1. Prostate gland and the seminal vesicles.
2. Seminal vesicles and the larynx.
3. Testes or ovaries and the pituitary gland.
4. Heart and blood.

_____**13.** Between the ages of 12 and 15 years, girls are usually: **13.** _____
1. Lighter and shorter than boys of the same age.
2. The same size and weight as boys of the same age.
3. Heavier and taller than boys of the same age.
4. Less mature than boys of the same age.

_____**14.** Menstruation most frequently begins between the ages of: **14.** _____
　　1. 15 and 18 years　　　　3. 9 and 11 years
　　2. 12 and 15 years　　　　4. 8 and 10 years

_____**15.** Menstruation usually occurs about once in: **15.** _____
　　1. 15 days　　　　　　　3. 28 days
　　2. 20 days　　　　　　　4. 35 days

_____**16.** Seminal emissions are: **16.** _____
　　1. A sign that a boy is having improper thoughts.
　　2. Due to lack of self-control.
　　3. A normal occurrence in boys.
　　4. A symptom of a disease.

_____**17.** Identical twins are alike: **17.** _____
　　1. In sex only.
　　2. In sex and other hereditary characteristics.
　　3. In all respects except sex.
　　4. In sex and hereditary characteristics except the blood
　　　 type.

_____**18.** The sex of a child is determined by the: **18.** _____
　　1. Nucleus of the egg
　　2. Dominant genes
　　3. Number of chromosomes in a cell
　　4. The X or Y chromosome of the sperm

_____**19.** Acquired characteristics: **19.** _____
　　1. Cannot be inherited.
　　2. Are transmitted by the genes.
　　3. Alter the chromosomes.
　　4. Make it possible to pass on physical and mental im-
　　　 provements to children through the chromosomes.

_____**20.** The seminal vesicles are situated: **20.** _____
　　1. In the scrotum　　　　 3. Below the ovaries
　　2. Near the bladder　　　　4. Above the pituitary gland

_____**21.** The pituitary gland is situated: **21.** _____
　　1. In the neck.
　　2. Near the kidneys.
　　3. Below the thyroid gland and in front of the heart.
　　4. Beneath the brain.

_____**22.** Approximately once a month in the female an egg cell ripens **22.** _____
　　and leaves the ovary. This process is called:
　　1. Menstruation　　　　　3. Pregnancy
　　2. Emission　　　　　　　4. Ovulation

_____**23.** When it is time for the baby to be born: **23.** _____
　　1. The muscles of the uterus contract to force out the baby.

     2. The navel gradually opens to let the baby out.
     3. The Fallopian tube expands to permit the baby to pass.
     4. The ovary enlarges.

_____**24.** During adolescence the rate of general growth and develop-   **24.** _____
    ment is:
     1. Rapid   3. Very slow
     2. Slow but constant   4. Stationary

_____**25.** Which *one* of the following statements about homosexuality   **25.** _____
    is *incorrect*?
     1. It is essentially a form of arrested development in the
       process of emotional maturity.
     2. It is a trait that is inherited.
     3. It is not based on some inborn lack of hormones.
     4. Treatment is largely a matter of re-education and re-
       conditioning.

_____**26.** Of the four following factors in impotence in the male and   **26.** _____
    frigidity in the female, which one is *most often* the cause?
     1. Emotional factors   3. Disease
     2. Endocrine deficiency   4. Accident

_____**27.** The prostate gland: **27.** _____
     1. Is situated in the brain.
     2. Is of no use in the reproductive process.
     3. Secretes a fluid which enables sperms to move.
     4. Secretes hormones which produce bodily changes.

_____**28.** The following statements are related to the topic of con-   **28.** _____
    genital inheritance. Which one statement is *incorrect*?
     1. The term *congenital environment* would be a more ap-
       propriate term.
     2. No germ disease, such as tuberculosis, can be biolog-
       ically inherited.
     3. The toxins of certain diseases of the mother may ad-
       versely affect the embryo.
     4. There is evidence that prenatally acquired characteristics
       can be inherited.

_____**29.** Of the following causes of sterility in women, which is the   **29.** _____
    most common?
     1. Endocrine disturbance   3. Low basal metabolism
     2. The closing of the   4. Displacement of the
       Fallopian tubes   uterus

_____**30.** How long does a woman normally continue to have men-   **30.** _____
    strual periods?
     1. For about 20 years after they begin.
     2. Until she is about 48 years old.

3. Until she is above 60 years old.
4. As long as she lives.

____31. Painful menstruation is: 31. ____
1. A disease.
2. Not a disease but a symptom that something is wrong.
3. A normal occurrence that should be so regarded.
4. Never successfully treated by physicians.

____32. Which one statement concerning fertility and sterility in   32. ____
the male is *incorrect?*
1. Sexual continence before marriage does not lead to
sterility.
2. About 40 to 50 per cent of all instances of sterile marriages may be attributed to the husband rather than to
the wife.
3. There are many causes of sterility including defective
sperm, poor health, and severe diabetes.
4. The infertile male is usually lacking in virility.

____33. Masturbation is a practice: 33. ____
1. Which may lead to insanity.
2. Engaged in by only a small percentage of young people.
3. Over which a person cannot exercise control.
4. Which is not physically harmful.

Key
Information Test on Human Reproduction

1.	2	**12.**	3	**23.**	1
2.	3	**13.**	3	**24.**	1
3.	2	**14.**	2	**25.**	2
4.	1	**15.**	3	**26.**	1
5.	2	**16.**	3	**27.**	3
6.	3	**17.**	2	**28.**	4
7.	1	**18.**	4	**29.**	4
8.	2	**19.**	1	**30.**	2
9.	3	**20.**	2	**31.**	2
10.	1	**21.**	4	**32.**	4
11.	4	**22.**	4	**33.**	4

2. Family Life—Sex Education Inventory [1]

Directions: In the left-hand column, place the letter that represents the answer
which you think is correct or best. On the right-hand side evaluate how important
you consider the information in the question is to you. If you regard it as very

[1] Prepared by Professor Madeline Hurster, Queens College, Health Education Section,
American College Health Association.

important, you should write in an "A." If you regard it as totally unimportant to you, you should write in an "E." If your response is less extreme than "A" or "E," write in one of the intermediary letters "B," "C," or "D," which represent descending orders of importance.

_____ 1. In American families: **1.** _____
     A. The economic role of the male is increasing.
     B. There is an increase in the freedom of its members.
     C. There is an increase in parental authority.
     D. The economic role of the mother is decreasing.

_____ 2. Children in American families are generally regarded as: **2.** _____
     A. Economic assets.
     B. Objects of love.
     C. Biological necessities.
     D. All of the above.

_____ 3. Statistics indicate that American women, at the present time,   **3.** _____
    are:
     A. Marrying at about the same age as their mothers married.
     B. Older than their mothers were when they married.
     C. Less likely to marry.
     D. Getting married younger.

_____ 4. Which of the following is _least_ important in satisfactory   **4.** _____
    emotional development of family members?
     A. Value each for his own accomplishments.
     B. Consider the child as an "extension" of the parent.
     C. Value each for what he/she is.
     D. Treat each other as separate persons.
     E. Respect the rights of others.

_____ 5. Which of the following is associated with most failures in   **5.** _____
    child rearing?
     A. Deep respect for the dignity of every human being.
     B. Recognition that separateness is the right of each human being.
     C. Faith in integrity of the child.
     D. Imposition of parent's personality on the child.

_____ 6. In terms of social behavior which of the following represents   **6.** _____
    the most acceptable function of the family?
     A. Set the standards of social behavior independent of community.
     B. Teach children to accept community standards without question.
     C. Teach children to ignore community standards which violate family mores.
     D. Remove children from exposure to community influences which violate family mores.

    E. Teach children to exercise discriminating judgment in matters of social behavior.

_____ **7.** The role of the mother in the family is *least* described as: **7.** _____
    A. Serving as a model for her children.
    B. Acting as servant for the family.
    C. Setting the emotional climate.
    D. Guarding the health of the family.
    E. Making the home a "retreat" from the world.

_____ **8.** Which of the following describes the most acceptable attitude   **8.** _____
of parents of the rebellious adolescent?
    A. Demand respect for parental authority.
    B. Allow adolescent a "free rein" in behavior.
    C. Let adolescent do what other adolescents do.
    D. Have strict rules regardless of what other adolescents do.
    E. Have reasonable agreements, with expressed faith in integrity of the adolescent.

_____ **9.** The role of the father in the family is *least* described as: **9.** _____
    A. Serving as a provider.
    B. Serving as a model for his children.
    C. Serving as an authority figure.
    D. Guarding the health of the family.

_____**10.** Most divorces occur within: **10.**_____
    A. First three years of marriage.
    B. Three to five years of marriage.
    C. Five to seven years of marriage.
    D. Seven to ten years of marriage.
    E. Ten to twenty years of marriage.

_____**11.** The pattern of family organization which is known as poly-   **11.**_____
andry refers to:
    A. Marriage between one man and one woman.
    B. Marriage of one man to several wives.
    C. Marriage of one woman to several husbands.
    D. Group marriage in a tribal fashion.
    E. A marriage relationship between two persons of the same sex.

_____**12.** Sexual intercourse of an unmarried male with an unmarried   **12.**_____
female is classified as:
    A. Fornication.
    B. Adultery.
    C. Homosexuality.
    D. Heterosexuality.
    E. Fidelity.

_____**13.** Sexual intercourse of a married person with someone other   **13.**_____
than husband or wife is classed as:
  A. Adultery.
  B. Fidelity.
  C. Homosexuality.
  D. Heterosexuality.
  E. Fornication.

_____**14.** The sex urge is more successfully redirected if a person: **14.**_____
  A. Reads romantic fiction as a substitute for experience.
  B. Engages in active sports.
  C. "Pets" moderately.
  D. Drinks moderately of alcoholic beverages.

_____**15.** Probably the best single qualification for successful parent-   **15.**_____
hood is:
  A. Compatibility.
  B. A good education.
  C. A good job.
  D. Wealthy parents.
  E. Emotional stability.

_____**16.** The *primary* reason that many states require a premarital   **16.**_____
blood examination is:
  A. To determine incompatibility of blood types.
  B. To prevent the transmission of venereal disease to
     one's marriage partner or to offspring.
  C. To discover diseases or disabilities which should be
     treated or corrected before marriage.
  D. To assure the individual that his or her sex organs are
     normal.

_____**17.** The characteristic number of chromosomes for the human   **17.**_____
species is:
  (A) 42   (B) 44   (C) 46   (D) 48

_____**18.** The genes that are most likely to manifest themselves in the   **18.**_____
characteristics of the individual are:
  A. Mixed genes.
  B. Recessive genes.
  C. Dominant genes.
  D. Mutated genes.

_____**19.** The hereditary potentials and limitations of the individual   **19.**_____
are provided and determined by which of the following?
  A. Chromosomes.
  B. Genes.
  C. Sperm.
  D. Ova.

_____20. The major danger in a marriage between first cousins is that: 20._____
    A. It is contrary to the beliefs of most major religions.
    B. Both may carry a recessive gene for the same defect.
    C. It is both immoral and illegal.
    D. Both may carry a dominant gene for the same characteristic.

_____21. Changes in heredity that can be transmitted to succeeding   21._____
generations are known as:
    A. Mutations.
    B. Blendings.
    C. Anomalies.
    D. Dominant characteristics.

_____22. The majority of abnormal inherited conditions are caused   22._____
by:
    A. Poor prenatal environment.
    B. Malnutrition.
    C. Recessive genes.
    D. Dominant genes.

_____23. Those diseases that may be transmitted by the mother to her   23._____
sons, are called:
    A. Maternal characteristics.
    B. Sex-linked characteristics.
    C. Zygote characteristics.
    D. Phenal characteristics.

_____24. Syphilis, a venereal disease: 24._____
    A. Is the most prevalent venereal disease in the world.
    B. May be acquired during delivery from an infected mother.
    C. Is transmitted only by sexual intercourse.
    D. May be treated, rendering the victim noncommunicable but not cured.

_____25. The young man in seeking a marriage partner should: 25._____
    A. Seek a mate who will fulfill his needs.
    B. Put his mate's needs first even at the sacrifice of his own.
    C. Select a socially desirable mate and look for need satisfaction outside of marriage.
    D. Seek a mate with whom there can be a mutual fulfillment of needs.

_____26. How often should young married couples have sexual relations on the average?   26._____
    A. Once a week.
    B. Once a month.

    C. About 3 times per week.
    D. As often as they desire.

____**27.** During which of the following periods would it be advisable   **27.**____
for a woman not to have sexual relations?
    A. Pregnancy.
    B. The last six weeks of pregnancy.
    C. The last four months of pregnancy.
    D. The first three months after delivery.

____**28.** Successful adjustment in marriage requires: **28.**____
    A. Conformity to pattern established by the husband.
    B. Adherence to plans developed by the wife.
    C. The realization that sex is the only vital part of marriage.
    D. That finances be managed by the wife.
    E. Working together toward worthwhile goals.

____**29.** When a wife desires to have sexual relations with her hus-   **29.**____
band, she should:
    A. Inhibit her impulses until he makes the first advance.
    B. Sublimate her impulses by doing housework.
    C. Have a few alcoholic drinks.
    D. Clearly communicate to her husband how she feels.

____**30.** When a wife is consistently unresponsive toward her hus-   **30.**____
band's advances, what should be done?
    A. The husband should find a new partner.
    B. The wife should take sedatives or alcoholic beverages before the act.
    C. The couple should consult a physician or a counselor.
    D. The husband should be sympathetic and abstain.

____**31.** Which *one* of the following statements about homosexuality   **31.**____
is correct?
    A. It is a condition that a person can never grow out of.
    B. It is an inherited trait.
    C. It is due to an inborn hormonal imbalance.
    D. It is a form of arrested emotional development.

____**32.** The size of the male sexual organs: **32.**____
    A. Is related to fertility.
    B. Contributes to marital adjustment.
    C. Is related to degree of sexual satisfactions from sexual act.
    D. Is of no physical or physiological significance.

____**33.** The absence of hymen (maidenhead) is: **33.**____
    A. A definite proof of virginity.
    B. An indication of promiscuity.

    C. Related to menstrual flow.
    D. Of no physical or physiological significance.

_____**34.** Circumcision is the removal of the extra skin, or glans, at   **34.**_____
the tip of penis. It is performed:
    A. To keep secretions of the foreskin from accumulating
       and irritating the skin.
    B. As a ritualistic measure among Jews and Moslems.
    C. As a preventive measure against cancer of the penis.
    D. All of the above.

_____**35.** How much weight should a pregnant mother gain during the   **35.**_____
nine months of pregnancy?
    A. Roughly one-third of her normal weight.
    B. About 20 to 25 pounds.
    C. An average of five pounds per month.
    D. 18 kilograms.

_____**36.** A woman may become pregnant: **36.**_____
    A. When she is fully awake and lucid.
    B. During the 48 hours of the life span of the ovum.
    C. Anytime after and before her menstruation.
    D. Only when she has experienced orgasm.

_____**37.** A man who is unable to take part in a normal sexual rela-   **37.**_____
tionship is referred to as being:
    A. Impotent.
    B. Sterile.
    C. Frigid.
    D. Infertile.

_____**38.** The period in the human life cycle in which growth is most   **38.**_____
rapid is:
    A. Prepubertal period.
    B. Adolescence.
    C. Prenatal period.
    D. Postadolescence.

_____**39.** Sexual self-stimulation is known as: **39.**_____
    A. Nocturnal emission.
    B. Ejaculation.
    C. Masturbation.
    D. Semination.

_____**40.** The organ within the mother in which the baby develops is   **40.**_____
called the:
    A. Vagina.
    B. Uterus.
    C. Ovary.
    D. Clitoris.

_____**41.** The process in which the lining of the uterus breaks down   **41.**_____
and is discharged is called:
  A. Ovulation.
  B. Menopause.
  C. Menstruation.
  D. Emission.

_____**42.** The testes are: **42.**_____
  A. The organs in which sperm are produced.
  B. The organs in which ova are produced.
  C. The tubes leading from the prostate gland to the penis.
  D. The tubes leading from the epididymis.

_____**43.** Ovulation and menstruation usually occur: **43.**_____
  A. Simultaneously.
  B. Approximately twenty-eight days apart.
  C. Within 24 to 45 hours.
  D. Five days apart.
  E. Approximately fourteen days apart.

_____**44.** Gradual decrease in the function of the ovaries is the main   **44.**_____
characteristic of:
  A. Menarche.
  B. Pregnancy.
  C. Menopause.
  D. Menstruation.

_____**45.** The male sex hormone is: **45.**_____
  A. Androgen.
  B. Progesterone.
  C. Estrogen.
  D. Spermatogen.

_____**46.** The gonads are: **46.**_____
  A. Sex glands.
  B. Exocrine glands.
  C. Mammary glands.
  D. Digestive glands.

_____**47.** A medical specialist who treats illness of the female repro-   **47.**_____
ductive organs is called:
  A. Obstetrician.
  B. Gastroenterologist.
  C. Gynecologist.
  D. Pediatrician.

_____**48.** The first stage of labor is marked by: **48.**_____
  A. The dilation of the cervix.
  B. The breaking of the amnion.
  C. Rhythmical contractions of the uterus.
  D. The expulsion of the placenta.

_____**49.** Which of the following does not pass through the placenta?   **49._____**
     A. Spirochete.
     B. Toxins.
     C. Antibodies.
     D. Gonococcus.

_____**50.** When fertilization of an ovum occurs, what prevents the   **50._____**
endometrium from stripping off?
     A. FSH is secreted by the pituitary gland.
     B. Progesterone is secreted by the Corpus luteum.
     C. The fertilized ovum nestles in the endometrium.
     D. The pituitary gland stops secreting LH.
     E. The placenta secretes a hormone which stimulates the
        pituitary gland to secrete FSH.

_____**51.** Which one of the following is *not* a serious complication in   **51._____**
pregnancy?
     A. Ectopic pregnancy.
     B. Morning sickness.
     C. Toxemia.
     D. Sepsis.

_____**52.** A mature sex cell is known as a: **52._____**
     A. Zygote.
     B. Chromosome.
     C. Gamete.
     D. Protoplasm.

_____**53.** Normally, fertilization of the ovum takes place in the: **53._____**
     A. Cervix.
     B. Uterus.
     C. Oviducts or Fallopian tubes.
     D. Ovaries.

_____**54.** The organ developed from the fertilized egg that provides   **54._____**
nutrients for the embryo and the fetus is known as the:
     A. Placenta.
     B. Umbilical cord.
     C. Amniotic sac.
     D. Chorion.

_____**55.** An episiotomy is: **55._____**
     A. A surgical sterilization procedure.
     B. An incision of the vulva.
     C. A procedure associated with the afterbirth.
     D. An incision of a Fallopian tube.

_____**56.** The third stage of labor involves: **56._____**
     A. The actual passage of the baby out of the mother's
        body.

   B. Contraction of abdominal muscles.
   C. Dilation of the cervix.
   D. Expulsion of the placenta.
   E. Breaking of the bag of waters.

_____**57.** In the second month of pregnancy the product of conception   **57.**_____
is called:
   A. A zygote.
   B. An embryo.
   C. An anomaly.
   D. A fetus.

_____**58.** The sex of offspring depends upon: **58.** _____
   A. Which ovary the egg comes from.
   B. The amount of progesterone present in the uterus.
   C. The time of ovulation.
   D. Whether the sperm cell which fertilizes the egg con-
      tains the X or the Y chromosome.

_____**59.** In the case of heavy smoking by expectant mothers, research   **59.**_____
has demonstrated that:
   A. Nicotine does not reach the baby.
   B. These mothers have a shorter period of labor.
   C. There is a greater likelihood that the baby will be born
      a "blue baby."
   D. There is a greater chance that the baby will be pre-
      mature.

_____**60.** The average newborn child weighs about: **60.**_____
   A. 10 pounds.
   B. 4½ to 5 pounds.
   C. 9 pounds.
   D. 7 to 7½ pounds.

_____**61.** A positive sign of pregnancy is: **61.**_____
   A. Nausea in the morning.
   B. Stopping of menstruation.
   C. The shadow of the fetus on an X-ray film.
   D. Enlargement of the abdomen.

_____**62.** A pregnant woman should have dental checkups and care if   **62.**_____
necessary:
   A. During the early months of pregnancy.
   B. Postponed until after the birth of the baby.
   C. Done during the last few months of pregnancy.
   D. Postponed because pregnancy weakens the teeth any-
      way.

_____**63.** A pregnant woman should *not* be unduly concerned about: **63.**_____
   A. Swelling of the hands, face, or ankles.
   B. An insatiable craving for particular foods.

C. Obstinate constipation.
D. Vaginal bleeding.

_____64. Every pregnant woman should have a complete and thor-   64._____
ough examination:
A. At least every other month during pregnancy.
B. After the third menstrual period is missed.
C. Within 2½ months of conception.
D. Monthly during the third trimester.

_____65. The disease which is most likely to have serious conse-   65._____
quences if the mother contracts it during the early months
of pregnancy is:
A. Scarlet fever.
B. Measles.
C. Gonorrhea.
D. German measles.

_____66. During pregnancy a sudden increase in weight and the pres-   66._____
ence of albumin in the urine are strong indications of:
A. Multiple births.
B. Morning nausea.
C. Toxemia.
D. Miscarriage.
E. A need for a blood transfusion.

_____67. The cause of a "blue baby" is: 67._____
A. Blood doesn't flow properly from the heart to the
lungs.
B. Lungs don't have enough oxygen.
C. Lungs give off too much oxygen for the body to
assimilate.
D. Mother is Rh positive and the father Rh negative.

_____68. The Rh factor may have an adverse effect on the fetus if: 68._____
A. The mother is Rh negative and the father is Rh posi-
tive.
B. The mother and the father are Rh negative.
C. The father is Rh negative and the mother is Rh posi-
tive.
D. Both parents are Rh positive.

Key
Family Life—Sex Education Inventory

1. B	5. D	9. D	13. A
2. D	6. E	10. A	14. B
3. D	7. B	11. C	15. E
4. B	8. E	12. A	16. B

17. C	**30.** C	**43.** E	**56.** D
18. C	**31.** D	**44.** C	**57.** B
19. B	**32.** D	**45.** A	**58.** D
20. B	**33.** D	**46.** A	**59.** D
21. A	**34.** D	**47.** C	**60.** D
22. C	**35.** B	**48.** C	**61.** C
23. B	**36.** B	**49.** D	**62.** A
24. C	**37.** A	**50.** B	**63.** B
25. D	**38.** C	**51.** B	**64.** A
26. D	**39.** C	**52.** C	**65.** D
27. B	**40.** B	**53.** C	**66.** C
28. E	**41.** C	**54.** A	**67.** A
29. D	**42.** A	**55.** B	**68.** A

3. Student Opinions on Courtship and Marriage [2]

What are your opinions on the following statements? Your answer is correct if it expresses your true attitude. This is not a test, and you are not to be graded. DO NOT OMIT ANY ITEM. In each case, encircle the one letter that represents your own idea about each statement.

SA—Strongly agree; A—Agree; U—Undecided; D—Disagree; SD—Strongly disagree.

1. There is just one person of the opposite sex with whom   SA   A   U   D   SD
one can be happy in marriage. The problem is to find this one person.
2. There is a tendency for people to marry opposites in   SA   A   U   D   SD
looks and tastes.
3. For the person already married, there is little to be   SA   A   U   D   SD
gained from a course on courtship, mate selection, and marriage adjustment.
4. If a girl on our campus wears a boy's fraternity pin   SA   A   U   D   SD
it means that they are engaged.
5. Children should receive their first sex information   SA   A   U   D   SD
when they are between the ages of six and twelve.
6. Those who are poorly adjusted before marriage often   SA   A   U   D   SD
change by outgrowing their personality weaknesses after they marry.
7. A mother can influence the psychological development   SA   A   U   D   SD
of her unborn child by the way she thinks and the things she does during the period of her pregnancy.
8. The most practical approach to husband-wife differ-   SA   A   U   D   SD
ences is to "have it out" in an open quarrel, as this gives release from emotional tensions.

[2] Judson T. Landis and Mary G. Landis, *Youth and Marriage: A Student Manual* (Prentice-Hall, Englewood Cliffs, N. J.), pp. 7–9.

9. One does not "marry his in-laws"; therefore parental objection to a marriage is of little importance. SA A U D SD

10. If possible, it is better to marry before one is 21 years old, since it is easier for younger people to adjust in marriage. SA A U D SD

11. People who date for two or more years are apt to get too well acquainted before marriage. SA A U D SD

12. The real solution to the divorce problem is to make it almost impossible to obtain a divorce. SA A U D SD

13. One should not analyze his love feelings or the love object (fiance(e)), since that may spoil the romance. SA A U D SD

14. One should not marry until he is willing to hold his mate first in his affections and his parents second. SA A U D SD

15. Since each person is "on his own" when he marries, the type of home one comes from has little to do with his chance for success in marriage. SA A U D SD

16. A happy marriage is a rare thing in our society. SA A U D SD

17. If they are really in love when they marry, a young man and a young woman who are from widely different social backgrounds do not face any more difficulties in adjusting in marriage than if they had the same social background. SA A U D SD

18. The husband should control the spending of the family income. SA A U D SD

19. Divorce is usually the best solution if there is conflict in marriage. SA A U D SD

20. Most of the in-law friction in marriage is caused by trouble-making parents-in-law. SA A U D SD

21. Children should get their first sex information from their parents. SA A U D SD

22. Parents should give children their first sex information when the children are between the ages of twelve and fifteen. SA A U D SD

23. Premarital sex experience between engaged couples would tell the couple whether they were mated sexually. SA A U D SD

24. If one follows his instincts, sex adjustment in marriage comes naturally. SA A U D SD

25. Before marriage one should tell the fiance(e) about any past immoral behavior. SA A U D SD

26. It is doubtful that couples who are having marital difficulties could get help from any third person, such as a marriage counselor. SA A U D SD

27. Public demonstration of affection between dating or engaged couples is offensive. SA A U D SD

28. The first two years of marriage are probably the happiest. SA A U D SD

29. Since two thirds of divorces are granted to childless couples, one should have children soon after marriage in order to solidify the marriage. SA A U D SD

30. Since the family has lost many of its traditional functions, it is less necessary to society than formerly. SA A U D SD

31. Democratic procedures of discussion and decision-making are not suitable for family management because of the differences in age and ability of the members. SA A U D SD

32. Marriage while in college involves too many financial and educational risks to be encouraged. SA A U D SD

33. The basic trends of personality are formed in the family by the time the child starts to school. SA A U D SD

34. Such aspects of personality as confidence or lack of confidence, introversion or extroversion, dominance or submission are largely the result of life in the parental family. SA A U D SD

35. The degree of emotional maturity that a young person exhibits is largely the result of how well the family has emancipated him. SA A U D SD

36. Being in love is the most important factor in choosing a mate. SA A U D SD

37. When one "falls in love at first sight" it is not with a person but with an ideal. SA A U D SD

38. No normal person falls in love with more than one person of the opposite sex. SA A U D SD

39. Although practice and precept vary with regard to intimacy during courtship, a person who conforms to the norms has more real freedom than one who doesn't. SA A U D SD

40. One of the important factors in predicting success in marriage is the happiness of the parents of the couple. SA A U D SD

41. Differences in education or in cultural interests do cause conflict if a man and woman are really in love with each other. SA A U D SD

42. A person with an unhappy childhood is just as likely to be happy in marriage as one with a happy childhood. SA A U D SD

43. Sexual adjustment in marriage depends more upon attitudes than upon correct knowledge and skill. SA A U D SD

44. Personality type often changes markedly after marriage. SA A U D SD

45. The techniques a person used for meeting problems before marriage such as illness, escape, rationalization, and drink will probably be used in marriage also. SA A U D SD

46. The child remembers the manner in which sex education is given to him better than he remembers the facts about sex. SA A U D SD

47. Women are naturally better at caring for and under- SA A U D SD
standing children than are men, so the mother should
take full responsibility for the child's development.

48. Authoritarian techniques for handling family prob- SA A U D SD
lems will be necessary when a crisis, such as loss
of financial security, occurs.

49. Since children are community assets and family liabili- SA A U D SD
ties the government should assume more of the
financial burden of housing, medical care, and education now carried disproportionately by child-rearing
families.

50. I would not marry a person who had been divorced. SA A U D SD

51. I would marry a person who was not willing to have SA A U D SD
children.

52. I would marry a person who was of a different SA A U D SD
religious faith from myself (Catholic, Protestant, Jew).

53. I would not marry a person who had had premarital SA A U D SD
sex relations.

4. Achievement Test on Syphilis and Gonorrhea [3]

In the following statements, pick out the answer which best completes the
sentence:

_____ 1. The signs and symptoms of both syphilis and gonorrhea
    A. Are usually painful.   C. Are often hidden.
    B. Are almost always noticeable.   D. Are almost always hidden.

_____ 2. The signs and symptoms of syphillis
    A. Often look like those of other diseases.
    B. Cannot be mistaken for anything else.
    C. Are usually painful in men.
    D. Are always on the "private parts."

_____ 3. Syphilis is most likely to cause serious damage to the body of the infected person
    A. During the first three months after he is infected.
    B. Between three months and six months after he is infected.
    C. Between six months and two years after he is infected.
    D. More than two years after he is infected.

_____ 4. Syphilis
    A. Can be cured, and any damage it has done to the body can be re-
paired.
    B. Can be cured, but any damage it has done to the body remains.
    C. Can be cured, but only in the early stages of the disease.
    D. Is often incurable.

[3] Adapted from *Teacher's Handbook on Venereal Disease Education* by William F.
Schwarts, The American Association for Health, Physical Education, and Recreation,
1201 16th Street N.W., Washington, D.C. 20036, pp. 39–44.

_____ 5. The symptoms of gonorrhea
   A. Are likely to be noticeable and painful in a man, but hidden and painless in a woman.
   B. Are likely to be noticeable and painful in a woman, but hidden and painless in a man.
   C. Are as likely to be noticeable and painful in women as in men.
   D. Are seldom noticeable or painful in either men or women.

_____ 6. Gonorrhea and syphilis are caused by
   A. A strain.   C. Germs.
   B. An injury.   D. Immoral behavior.

_____ 7. Three months after he becomes infected with syphilis, the method most likely to reveal that a man needs treatment for syphilis is
   A. A physical examination.   C. An x-ray examination.
   B. A blood test.   D. Taking of his temperature.

_____ 8. Soap and water, used by a man just after he was exposed to infection, probably would have
   A. More effect in preventing syphilis than in preventing gonorrhea.
   B. More effect in preventing gonorrhea than in preventing syphilis.
   C. About the same effect in preventing both syphilis and gonorrhea.
   D. No effect in preventing either syphilis or gonorrhea.

_____ 9. If a baby caught syphilis from another member of its family four years after that person was infected, that family member would be
   A. The father.   C. A brother or sister.
   B. The mother.   D. One as likely as the other.

_____10. A venereal disease is most likely to be contracted when
   A. Using a public toilet.
   B. Riding in a crowded bus.
   C. Having skin-to-skin contact with another person.
   D. Drinking from an unwashed glass.

_____11. Once you have had syphilis
   A. You can't catch it again.
   B. You can catch it again.
   C. Your children become immune to it, if you're a woman.
   D. You can catch it easier next time you are exposed to it.

_____12. If you thought you might have syphilis, you would be smarter to
   A. Inspect yourself for signs of the disease each day.
   B. Ask your druggist for the proper medicine to get rid of it before it starts.
   C. Tell your doctor what you suspect.
   D. Avoid embarrassment by simply telling your doctor you haven't been feeling well and you want an examination.

_____13. The combination of diseases which *attacks and kills* the most people each year in the United States is
   A. Typhoid, smallpox, and   C. Typhoid, smallpox, and
      plague.   syphilis.
   B. Plague, gonorrhea, and   D. Smallpox, plague, and
      syphilis.   gonorrhea.

_____14. You can be vaccinated against
     A. Gonorrhea.   C. Both syphilis and gonorrhea.
     B. Syphilis.   D. Neither syphilis nor gonorrhea.

_____15. Venereal disease can be a serious problem
     A. Only to people who are careless.
     B. Only to people who don't behave properly.
     C. Only to teenagers and young adults.
     D. To anybody and everybody.

_____16. Syphilis and gonorrhea
     A. Can infect the same person at the same time.
     B. Cannot infect the same person at the same time.
     C. Are two stages of the same disease.
     D. Can both be spread by food, air, and drinking water.

_____17. When a pregnant woman is treated for syphilis
     A. Her baby is treated at the same time.
     B. Her baby requires different drugs.
     C. Her baby needs to be treated separately later.
     D. The treatment endangers the baby's life.

_____18. If a person with gonorrhea is not treated
     A. It will turn into syphilis.
     B. It will always go away in about a month.
     C. It will never turn into syphilis.
     D. It may turn into syphilis.

_____19. If a syphilitic chancre goes away by itself without treatment, the person
     A. Does not need treatment.
     B. Has recovered, just as he would from the measles.
     C. Still needs treatment for syphilis.
     D. Usually develops gonorrhea a little later.

_____20. A syphilitic chancre
     A. Usually hurts.
     B. May appear almost anywhere on the body.
     C. Keeps getting bigger until the person is treated.
     D. Cannot be mistaken for anything else.

_____21. Syphilis causes
     A. More sterility, but gonorrhea causes more crippling.
     B. More blindness, but gonorrhea causes more deaths.
     C. More insanity, but gonorrhea causes more sterility.
     D. About the same number of deaths as gonorrhea.

_____22. It is correct to say that
     A. A negative blood test always means you don't have syphilis.
     B. A positive blood test always means you do have syphilis.
     C. If you have syphilis, sooner or later your blood test will be positive.
     D. If you have syphillis, your blood test may never be positive.

_____23. If both husband and wife had negative blood tests before marriage
     A. She should have two more blood tests each time she becomes pregnant.
     B. She does not need any more blood tests ever again.

C. Neither of them has syphilis.

D. That makes sure that their baby will be born without syphilis.

_____24. The most effective way to stop the spread of syphilis (if we could do it) would be to treat everybody

A. Whose blood test showed positive.

B. Who had contact with an infectious person.

C. Who developed external signs of syphilis.

D. Who wanted to get married.

_____25. Drops of medicine are put in the eyes of newborn babies to protect them against blindness from

A. Syphilis.

B. Gonorrhea.

C. Either syphilis or gonorrhea.

D. Neither syphilis nor gonorrhea.

Key

Achievement Test on Syphilis and Gonorrhea

1.	C	10.	C	18.	C
2.	A	11.	B	19.	C
3.	D	12.	C	20.	B
4.	B	13.	C	21.	C
5.	A	14.	D	22.	C
6.	C	15.	D	23.	A
7.	B	16.	A	24.	B
8.	A	17.	A	25.	B
9.	B				

5. Sex Attitude Scale [4]

AGREE-DISAGREE SHEET I

Directions: The leaders who plan to use this sheet must be aware that it may produce anxiety on the part of parents. Careful preparation of both parents and youth is considered essential. Experimentation has shown the maximum supports occur when persons fill out the form in groups rather than as isolated individuals. Local planning teams may wish to use items from these samples to formulate their own sheets. Please do not avoid some of the controversial areas.

[4] Taken from *Workbook for Junior High Youth on the Role of Sex in Christian Living,* pp. 40–46, by permission of the Board of Christian Social Concerns and the Board of Education of the United Methodist Church. The Workbook is available at 100 Maryland Avenue N.E., Washington, D.C. 20002, at $2.00 per copy.

Underline any word you do not understand.	*Agree*	*Disagree*	*Want to Discuss*	*Don't Understand*
1. Every person is a combination of both masculine and feminine characteristics.	____	____	____	____
2. One reason teenagers like to date is that it increases their experiences of being at ease with the opposite sex.	____	____	____	____
3. Parents do not understand dating practices today.	____	____	____	____
4. Man was created to be a sexual being.	____	____	____	____
5. Part of the problem of Junior Highs dating is that girls mature earlier than boys.	____	____	____	____
6. Sexual feelings are an expression of weakness.	____	____	____	____
7. The person to turn to in any questions about dating or sex is your parent.	____	____	____	____
8. Most adolescents of both sexes masturbate at some time during adolescence.	____	____	____	____
9. A girl should never ask a boy for a date.	____	____	____	____
10. Junior Highs prefer parents to have strict standards.	____	____	____	____
11. Junior Highs should never date Senior Highs.	____	____	____	____
12. Decisions on hours, use of phone, choice of friends, etc., should be a mutual decision of parents and teenagers.	____	____	____	____
13. Today's movies suggest that physical expression of sex is fair for adults but not for teenagers.	____	____	____	____
14. A person may fall in love more than once in a lifetime.	____	____	____	____
15. Every act of intercourse leads to pregnancy.	____	____	____	____
16. A boy is not responsible for his behavior with a girl.	____	____	____	____
17. The movies and magazines show us what a "real" man and woman would be like.	____	____	____	____

Underline any word you do not understand.	*Agree*	*Disagree*	*Want to Discuss*	*Don't Understand*
18. After an adult is 35 years old his sex drives are much less intense.	___	___	___	___
19. The primary reason for sex is to bring children into the world.	___	___	___	___
20. Most Junior Highs have had physical sex experiences with the opposite sex.	___	___	___	___
21. Caressing below the neck is immoral.	___	___	___	___
22. A person who falls in love gives himself completely to the other person.	___	___	___	___
23. Whether we like it or not, our parents are the primary models for us in what it means to be a man or woman.	___	___	___	___
24. I must be good-looking to be desirable to the opposite sex.	___	___	___	___
25. Petting creates sex tensions that are hard to handle.	___	___	___	___

AGREE-DISAGREE SHEET II

Fill out, putting A for Agree; D for Disagree; and W also if you Want to Discuss. *Underline any word you do not understand.*

1. _____ Girls and boys should not talk about sex together.
2. _____ Boys naturally tell dirty jokes but it is wrong for girls.
3. _____ 12–14 year olds are too young to start thinking about a life mate.
4. _____ Girls mature at an earlier age than boys.
5. _____ Boys should decide where to go and what to do on a date.
6. _____ We cannot have personal communications except as sexual persons.
7. _____ Nice girls do not ever ask a boy for a date.
8. _____ It is not as necessary for boys as for girls to pay attention to nice manners.
9. _____ Teenage boys are naturally clumsy.
10. _____ Girls are always more graceful than boys.
11. _____ Kissing is sexual communication.
12. _____ Girls like a boy to be rough and tough.
13. _____ Boys like girls who pet readily.
14. _____ Since girls can stop anytime they want to, it is o.k. to let a boy make out with her.
15. _____ Since a girl can stop anything if she wants to, it is her fault if anything happens or if she gets pregnant.

16. _____ It is natural to want to engage in petting.

17. _____ Only girls have the responsibility of deciding "how far is too far."

18. _____ Sex play ("necking," "petting," "making out") usually is engaged in as merely something to do as a substitute for normal, satisfactory emotional experiences.

19. _____ The physical expression of sex makes control easier.

20. _____ All sexual excitement should be avoided until after marriage.

21. _____ In true love, the male is protective of the one he loves.

22. _____ When one feels excited around someone of the opposite sex, this is a good sign they are in love.

23. _____ When you meet the right person, "you'll know."

24. _____ Teenagers need experience of sexual communication to be properly prepared emotionally to choose a marriage partner.

25. _____ People who have had premarital intercourse are less likely to be happy in marriage than those who have not had such experiences.

26. _____ It is impossible to insure absolute prevention of conception in intercourse.

27. _____ When two people are really in love, they are ready for marriage.

28. _____ Girls are slightly *sick* during menstruation (monthly period).

29. _____ If a boy has a "wet dream" it means he thinks too much about sex.

30. _____ Masturbation can cause insanity.

31. _____ Most boys and many girls practice masturbation at some time.

32. _____ Repressing sexual desires is unhealthy.

33. _____ Restraining sexual desires is unhealthy.

6. Youth Evaluation Sheet [5]

Will you please help us improve this course for future classes by giving your frank answers to the following questions? We want to know what you really think. There is no need to sign your name unless you wish to do so.

1. These sessions have contributed to a better understanding of:

Myself	*My Parents*
Considerably	Considerably
Moderately	Moderately
Little	Little
None	None

2. My feeling in the group (circle one or more which apply):

Comfortable	Frustrated
Pleased	Embarrassed
Neutral	Angry
Uneasy	

[5] Taken from *Workbook for Junior High Youth on Role of Sex in Christian Living*, pp. 49–50, by permission of the Board of Christian Social Concerns and the Board of Education of the United Methodist Church. The Workbook is available at 100 Maryland Avenue N.E., Washington, D.C. 20002, at $2.00 per copy.

3. My contributions in the discussions were:
  Fully accepted
  Partially accepted
  Ignored
  Rejected
4. My level of participation:
  Fully involved
  Moderately involved
  Not involved
5. How do you feel about this course?
6. Of what value has it been to you?
7. Did this course provide what you expected? what you wanted to know?
8. What was left out which should be included?

7. Parents' Evaluation Sheet

My evaluation of these sessions: (Circle one or more responses.)

1. These sessions have contributed to a better understanding of:

Myself	*My Spouse*	*My Child*
Considerably	Considerably	Considerably
Moderately	Moderately	Moderately
Little	Little	Little
None	None	None

2. My feeling in this group:

Comfortable	Frustrated
Pleased	Embarrassed
Neutral	Angry
Uneasy	

3. My contributions in the discussions were:
  Fully accepted
  Partially accepted
  Ignored
  Rejected
4. My participation:
  Fully involved
  Moderately involved
  Not involved
5. The most meaningful part of this experience has been _____.
6. I would like to see the following changes in the sessions for youth _____.
7. I feel the parents' sessions should _____ should not _____ be required.
8. What else can the church do to help in this general field?
9. I attended on Sunday _____ Tuesday _____ Thursday _____

E

Selected Articles from Periodicals

Transition in Sex Values—Implications for the Education of Adolescents

Isadore Rubin

Educators are called upon to draw the necessary educational implications from the fact that in this transitional period of sex morality, sharply conflicting value systems exist among which no consensus is possible. Six contending value systems are analyzed along a repressive-permissive continuum; these systems must be evaluated and an "open forum" created if teachers are to have the dialogue with youth essential for a meaningful educational process. Since most values in our official sex codes have become competing alternatives, the basic values of sex education must be sought in the core values of a democratic society.

This paper concerns the kind of education which the United States as a pluralistic society can give to adolescents and young adults in its various educational institu-

This paper was originally presented at the annual meeting of the National Council on Family Relations, Miami, October 1964. Reprinted by the permission of the *Journal of Marriage and the Family*.

Isadore Rubin, Ph.D., is Managing Editor, *Sexology Magazine,* 154 West 14th St., New York, N.Y., 10011.

tions. The concern is *not* with our private set of values either as individuals or parents, but rather with a philosophy of sex education for a democratic society.

The Confusion of Transition

Family professionals may not agree on the causes of the change, the extent, or the direction, but they do agree that there has been a great transition in sex values in the 20th century. Evelyn Duvall has characterized this transition as a "basic shift from sex denial to sex affirmation throughout our culture." [1]

This transition from sex denial to sex affirmation has not been an easy or smooth one. American culture historically has been rooted in the ideal of asceticism, and only slowly and with a good deal of rear-guard opposition is this philosophy being relinquished. Most official attitudes today still constitute what a distinguished British jurist called "a legacy of the ascetic ideal, persisting in the modern world after the ideal has deceased." [2] As a result of the conflict and confusion inherent in the transition of sex values, there exists today an interregnum of sex values which are accepted in theory and in practice by the great majority of Americans.

The confusion is especially great among those who are responsible for the guidance of youth. Last year Teachers' College together with the National Association of Women Deans and Counselors decided to hold a two-week "Work Conference on Current Sex Mores." Esther Lloyd-Jones, Head of the Department of Guidance and Student Personnel Administration at Teachers' College explained why:

"The reason that made me determine to hold that conference was the repeated statement by deans and counselors—as well as by parents—that the kids were certainly confused in the area of sex mores, but that they thought they were just as confused as the kids. They just plain felt they did not know. They were clearly in no position to give valuational leadership." [3]

It is unnecessary to state that this conference—like many others held before it —did not reach agreement on what the sex mores should be.

The Impossibility of Consensus

At the present time, there seems no possibility for our pluralistic society as a whole to reach a consensus about many aspects of sex values. We cannot do it today even on so comparatively simple a problem as the moral right of persons who are married to have free access to contraceptive information, or the right of married couples to engage in any kind of sex play that they desire in the privacy of the marriage bedroom, or even the right of individuals to engage in the private

[1] *Sex Ways—In Fact and Faith: Bases for Christian Family Policy,* ed. by E. M. Duvall and S. M. Duvall, Association Press, New York: 1961.

[2] G. Williams, *The Sanctity of Life and the Criminal Law,* Alfred A. Knopf, New York: 1957.

[3] E. Lloyd-Jones, "The New Morality," unpublished paper presented at the New York State Deans and Guidance Counselors Conference, November 3, 1963.

act of masturbation. Certainly we cannot expect to do so on so emotionally laden a problem as premarital sex relations.

Even in NCFR, made up of the most sophisticated students of this problem, no consensus has been reached after more than 25 years of debate and dialogue, although, as Jessie Bernard pointed out to NCFR last year, there has been a change. "There was a time," she said, "when those arguing for premarital virginity could be assured of a comfortable margin of support in the group. This is no longer always true. Especially the younger members no longer accept this code." [4]

This change in NCFR thinking reflects the great debate that is taking place on a national and an international scale. This debate reflects the fact that—whether we like it or not—we do not today possess a code of sex beliefs about which we can agree. Significantly, it is not only those who refuse to look to religion for their answers who seek a new value framework for sex. A growing body of religious leaders recognize that our modern sex morality can no longer consist of laws which give a flat yes-or-no answer to every problem of sex. These leaders concede that there are many moral decisions which persons must make for themselves.[5]

The Major Competing Value Systems

This writer has found it of value to define six major conflicting value systems of sex existing side by side in this transitional period of morality.[6] These value systems extend along a broad continuum ranging from extreme asceticism to a completely permissive anarchy. The major ones are characterized as follows: (1) traditional repressive asceticism; (2) enlightened asceticism; (3) humanistic liberalism; (4) humanistic radicalism; (5) fun morality; and (6) sexual anarchy. To discuss each of these very briefly:

1. Traditional repressive asceticism—which is still embodied in most of our official codes and laws—proscribes any kind of sexual activity outside of the marriage relationship and accepts sex in marriage grudgingly, insisting upon the linkage of sex with procreation.[7] This value system is intolerant of all deviations from restrictive patterns of heterosexual behavior, it places a taboo on public and scientific discussion and study of sex, and it conceives of sex morality solely in absolute terms of "Thou shalt" and "Thou shalt not."

2. Enlightened asceticism—as exemplified in the views of such spokesmen as

---

[4] J. Bernard, "Developmental Tasks of the NCFR, 1963–1988," address delivered at the annual meeting of the National Council on Family Relations, Denver, August 1963, published in *Journal of Marriage and the Family,* 26:1 (February 1964), pp. 29–38.

[5] See, for example, A. T. Robinson, *Christian Morals Today,* Westminister Press, Philadelphia: 1964; and J. M. Krumm, "The Heart and the Mind and the New Morality," unpublished baccalaureate sermon, Columbia University, June 2, 1963.

[6] I. Rubin, *Conflict of Sex Values, in Theory and Research,* unpublished paper, Workshop on Changing Sexual Mores, Teachers' College, August 2, 1963.

[7] See A. C. Kinsey *et al., Sexual Behavior in the Human Male,* W. B. Saunders, Philadelphia: 1948; and A. Ellis, *The American Sexual Tragedy,* Grove Press, New York: 1963.

David Mace [8]—begins with a basic acceptance of the ascetic point of view. Mace sees asceticism as a safeguard against the "softness" to which we so easily fall prey in an age when opportunities for self-indulgence are so abundant. He sees youth as the time when invaluable lessons of self-control and discipline must be learned, with sex as one of the supreme areas in which self-mastery may be demonstrated, and he opposes any slackening of the sexual code. However, he takes neither a negative nor a dogmatic attitude toward sex and has been an ardent exponent of the "open forum" in which issues can be stated and weighed.

3. Humanistic liberalism has been best exemplified by the views of Lester Kirkendall.[9] Kirkendall opposes inflexible absolutes and makes his prime concern the concept of interpersonal relationship. He sees the criterion of morality as not the commission or omission of a particular act, but the consequences of the act upon the interrelationships of people, not only the immediate people concerned but broader relationships.

Kirkendall thus is searching for a value system which will help supply internalized controls for the individual in a period when older social and religious controls are collapsing.

4. Humanistic radicalism—exemplified best by the views of Walter Stokes [10]—accepts the humanistic position of Kirkendall and goes further in proposing that society should make it possible for young people to have relatively complete sex freedom. He makes it clear that society must create certain preconditions before this goal may be achieved. He envisions "a cultural engineering project" which may take generations to achieve.

5. Fun morality has as its most consistent spokesman Albert Ellis.[11] Without compromise, he upholds the viewpoint that sex is fun and that the more sex fun a human being has, the better and psychologically sounder he or she is likely to be. He believes that, despite the risk of pregnancy, premarital intercourse should be freely permitted, and at times encouraged, for well-informed and reasonably well-adjusted persons.

6. Sexual anarchy has as its philosopher the late French jurist René Guyon.[12]

---

[8] D. A. Mace and R. Guyon, "Chastity and Virginity: The Case for and the Case Against," in *The Encyclopedia of Sexual Behavior*, ed. by A. Ellis and A. Abarbanel, Hawthorn Books, 1961, New York: pp. 247–257; D. A. Mace and W. R. Stokes, "Sex Ethics, Sex Acts and Human Needs—A Dialogue," *Pastoral Psychology*, 12 (October–November 1961), pp. 15–22, 34–43; and W. R. Stokes and D. A. Mace, "Premarital Sexual Behavior," *Marriage and Family Living*, 15 (August 1953), pp. 235–249.

[9] L. A. Kirkendall, *Premarital Intercourse and Interpersonal Relations*, Julian Press, New York: 1961; L. A. Kirkendall, "A Suggested Approach to the Teaching of Sexual Morality," *Journal of Family Welfare* (Bombay, India), 5 (June 1959), pp. 26–30; and T. Poffenberger *et al.*, "Premarital Sexual Behavior: A Symposium," *Marriage and Family Living*, August 1962, pp. 254–278.

[10] W. R. Stokes, "Guilt and Conflict in Relation to Sex," *The Encyclopedia of Sexual Behavior, op. cit.*, pp. 466–471; W. R. Stokes, "Sex Education of Children," in *Recent Advances in Sex Research*, ed. by H. G. Beigel, Hoeber-Harper, New York: 1963, pp. 48–60; Mace and Stokes, *op. cit.;* and Stokes and Mace, *op. cit.*

[11] A. Ellis, *If This Be Sexual Heresy*, Lyle Stuart, New York: 1963.

[12] R. Guyon, *The Ethics of Sexual Acts*, Alfred A. Knopf, New York: 1934; and Mace and Guyon, *op. cit.*

Guyon attacks chastity, virginity, and monogamy and calls for the suppression of all anti-sexual taboos and the disappearance of the notions of sexual immorality and shame. The only restriction he would apply is the general social principle that no one may injure or do violence to his fellows.

Can educators resolve these competing philosophies of sex? Judging by present disagreements, it is hardly conceivable that a consensus will be possible for a long time to come, even by our best social theorists. In fact, it would be dangerous—on the basis of the fragmentary information we now have—to come to a conclusion too quickly.

Education versus Indoctrination

What then are the educational implications of the confusion and conflict which exist in this transitional period?

The beginning of wisdom for educators is the recognition of the fact that the old absolutes have gone; that there exists a vacuum of many moral beliefs about sex; and that we cannot ignore the conflicting value systems which are openly contending for the minds not only of adults but particularly of youths.

Our key task—if we are to have a dialogue with youths—is to win and hold their trust. This means that we cannot fob them off with easy, ready-made replies; that we cannot give dishonest answers to their honest questions; that we cannot serve up information tainted with our bias.

If we tell them, for example, that there is only one view concerning the need for sexual chastity, they will quickly learn that there are many views. If we give them false information about any area of sex, they will sooner or later learn that we have lied. If we withhold the available data and merely give them moral preachments, they will nod their heads . . . and seek their answers elsewhere.

Our major educational problem is this: How can we help young people (and ourselves) to find some formula for coping with our dilemmas? How can we help them keep their bearings in a period of rapid and unending change, and help them make intelligent choices among the conflicting value systems?

If we indoctrinate young people with an elaborate set of rigid rules and ready-made formulas, we are only insuring the early obsolescence of these tools. If, on the other hand, we give them the skills and attitudes, the knowledge and understanding that enable them to make their own intelligent choice among competing moral codes, we have given them the only possible equipment to face their future. This type of guidance does not deny that a dilemma exists whenever choices must be made. Each choice commands a price, and the individual must weigh the price to be paid against the advantages to be gained.[13]

There are some adults who would try to hid the obvious from adolescents—that we adults ourselves have no agreement about sex values, that we too are searching. To do this, however, is to forfeit our chance to engage in a dialogue with our youngsters. It is far wiser to admit our own dilemmas and to enlist them frankly in the task of striking a balance in this interim of confusion.

[13] C. Kirkpatrick, *The Family: As Process and Institution,* Ronald Press, New York: 1954.

When it comes to sex education, most parents and educators have overlooked a rather simple lesson. The fact of the matter is that we do have a time-tested set of basic principles of democratic guidance that serve us well in many fields, but which are unfortunately laid aside the moment we enter the taboo-laden area of sex.[14]

In teaching politics and government, we do not feel the need to indoctrinate all students into being members of one or another political party. Rather we try to teach them the skills and attitudes which they require to make intelligent choices as adults when faced with a changing world and an array of alternatives.

In science and industry, we do not equip them with a set of tools that will be outmoded in a rapidly evolving technology, but try to equip them with skills which can adjust to a changing field.

Certainly indoctrination of moral values is an ineffective educational procedure in a democratic and pluralistic society where a bewildering array of alternatives and conflicting choices confront the individual—particularly in a period of transition.[15]

A Democratic Value Framework

At this point, the writer hastens to say that he is not advocating that we jettison all the moral values that we have developed over the centuries. He would be very loath to abandon anything that has been tested by time, particularly those institutions that have been found to be almost universal. But there have been virtually no universals in sex values, with only the prohibition of incest coming close to being one.[16] And as the anthropologist Murdock pointed out, as a society we have been deviant—not typical—in our past attitudes toward sex and premarital chastity.[17]

We do have need for a value framework for sex guidance. Value commitments are necessary for any person who forms part of a social group, and no society can survive without a set of core values which the majority of its members really believe in and act upon.[18] However, it is clear that most of the values represented in the official sex code have left the core of our culture and entered the arena of competing alternatives.

We must then seek our core values for sex education in the core values of a democratic society. These values have been defined as (1) faith in the free play of critical intelligence and respect for truth as a definable moral value; (2) respect for the basic worth, equality, and dignity of each individual; (3) the right of self-determination of each human being; and (4) the recognition of the need for co-operative effort for common good.[19]

The acceptance of a scientific point of view in our thinking about sex ethics would be of inestimable importance in the education of youth. Since a great deal

---

[14] W. H. Kilpatrick, *Philosophy of Education,* Macmillan, New York: 1951.

[15] J. F. Cuber, R. A. Harper, and W. F. Kenkel, *Problems of American Society: Values in Conflict,* Henry Holt, New York: 1956.

[16] M. Edel and A. Edel, *Anthropology and Ethics,* Charles C Thomas, Illinois: 1959.

[17] G. P. Murdock, *Social Structure,* Macmillan, New York: 1949.

[18] A. Kardiner, *Sex and Morality,* Bobbs-Merrill, New York: 1954.

[19] Kilpatrick, *op. cit.;* and E. Nagel, "Liberalism and Intelligence," Fourth John Dewey Memorial Lecture, Bennington, Vt.: Bennington College, 1957.

of thinking about sex has been based either on religious values, prejudice, or irrational fears, the consistent application of this point of view would be of tremendous significance in bringing about a re-evaluation of our thinking about sex.

It would imply, first of all, that the effect of practices which are not sanctioned in our official codes would be described objectively and scientifically rather than in terms of special pleading for the official code. Reiss has shown that treatment by leading marriage and family texts of the consequences of premarital intercourse "neglects or misinterprets much of the available empirical evidence.[20] Studies by Gebhard *et al.*[21] (on abortion), Kirkendall (on premarital intercourse, see footnote 9), Vincent [22] (on unwed mothers), and other investigators, for example, have shown that behavior contrary to the accepted codes cannot be described solely in terms of negative consequences for individuals engaging in it, even in our present culture.

The application of critical intelligence also implies that moral behavior would be viewed not in terms of obedience to fixed laws, but on the basis of insights from various disciplines "that add to the picture of the world in which man lives and acts, that throw light upon the nature of man and his capacities, social relations, and experiences." It would also mean that adolescent sex activities would be limited for the actual protection of their health and well-being rather than for the protection of adult moral prejudice.[23]

There is no doubt that there is an extremely difficult problem for social control when the individual is allowed a choice in moral behavior. Landis asserts: "In moral codes taboo acts must be condemned regardless of advantages gained by certain individuals or groups who violate them. . . . When acts are no longer forbidden to all, when the individual is authorized to decide whether or not violation will be advantageous, the moral code vanishes." [24]

This is indeed a dilemma for society. Unfortunately, at the present time many of the taboos still present in our official codes are no longer accepted either in precept or in practice by the vast majority of our people. We can take as an obvious example the proscription against birth control. A great debate has been opened on many other aspects of our sexual codes. If we do not equip our adolescents to participate intelligently in this debate, we do not ensure the protection of our moral codes. What we do ensure is that youngsters will have no rationale to enable them to make intelligent decisions.

To advocate autonomy is not necessarily to encourage the flouting of conventional mores or to encourage libertarian behavior. In the absence of fixed and rigorously enforced codes, a great deal of adolescent sexual behavior is determined by the mores of the teen-age subculture. The advocacy of self-determination,

[20] I. L. Reiss, "The Treatment of Pre-Marital Coitus in 'Marriage and the Family' Texts," *Social Problems,* 4 (April 1957), pp. 334–338.

[21] P. H. Gebhard *et al., Pregnancy, Birth, and Abortion,* Hoeber-Harper, New York: 1958.

[22] C. E. Vincent, *Unwed Mothers,* Free Press, Glencoe, Ill.: 1961.

[23] R. A. Harper, "Marriage Counseling and Mores: A Critique," *Marriage and Family Living,* 21 (February 1959), pp. 13–19.

[24] P. H. Landis, book review in *Marriage and Family Living,* 24 (February 1962), pp. 96–97.

therefore, may foster resistance to teen-age pressures rather than to conventional norms.[25]

In short, what the educator must do is not provide ready-made formulas and prepackaged values, but provide knowledge, insight, and values on the basis of which the adolescent may choose for himself with some measure of rationality among competing codes of conduct.[26] In a changing world, we must develop "a frame of mind which can bear the burden of skepticism and does not panic when many of the habits are doomed to vanish." [27]

Sex Education and Social Policy

In our thinking about sex education and the adolescent, we almost always think solely in functional terms of helping the adolescent cope with his problems and of preparing him for courtship and marriage. We tend to overlook completely the aspect of social policy—the fact that increasing knowledge of all areas of sex is being required of all individuals as citizens.

Issues dealing with all aspects of sex are more and more entering the arena of national and international debate and decision. On an international scale, problems of birth control, venereal disease, and prostitution have been subject to wide-scale discussion and decision. In legislative and legal arenas, with the concomitant aspects of public discussion, there have been sharp conflicts about public policy concerning censorship, pornography, birth control, abortion, illegitimacy, changes in sex laws, homosexuality, and emergent problems like artificial insemination.

All of these require for their solution an informed citizenry sufficiently open-minded to make required decisions on the basis of rational consideration rather than prejudice and irrationality.

Summary

In summarizing the major tasks of sex guidance of the adolescent, the writer would like to repeat the proposals which he made to the Deans' Workshop on Changing Sexual Mores at Teachers' College last year:

1. Create the "open forum" that Mace has emphasized in the family life field. Do not attempt to hide the obvious from college students—that major value conflicts exist in our society and that no consensus exists among adults. Enlist students to take responsibility for helping resolve the confusion inherent in the transition of

[25] D. Riesman, "Permissiveness and Sex Roles," *Marriage and Family Living,* 21 (August 1959), pp. 211–217.

[26] D. P. Ausubel, "Problems of Adolescent Adjustment, *The Bulletin of the National Association of Secondary-School Principals,* 34 (January 1950), pp. 1–84; and I. Rubin, *A Critical Evaluation of Certain Selected Operational Principles of Sex Education for the Adolescent,* unpublished Ph.D. dissertation, New York University School of Education, 1962.

[27] K. Mannheim, *Diagnosis of Our Time,* Oxford U. Press, New York: 1944.

values. Re-evaluate texts and curricula so that in this field, as in others, the principles of scientific objectivity will hold.

2. Apply the time-tested and traditionally accepted principles of education in a democracy—give guidance by education rather than indoctrination; deal with all the known facts and results of research; teach critical judgment in dealing with ethical controversy.

3. Adopt as the main goal in regulating adolescent conduct measures that will equip students for intelligent self-determination rather than conformity to procedures which will have no educative effect on their real choices of conduct.

4. Help identify and destroy those outmoded aspects of the ascetic ideal which no longer represent the ideals of the vast majority of American ethical leaders or of the American people, and which no longer contribute either to individual happiness and growth or to family and social welfare.

All of this in no way denies that teachers should have strong ethical convictions of their own, or that they should feel it necessary to conceal these convictions from the adolescents with whom they deal. What they should *not* do is play the role of the apologist for the status quo, devising a "new rationale for an established policy when it has become clear that the old arguments in its favor are no longer adequate." [28]

Recommendations from Women Doctors and Gynecologists about Sports Activity for Girls
A Report by the Research Committee of the Division of Girls' and Women's Sports

MARJORIE PHILLIPS, *Indiana University*
KATHARINE FOX, *University of Washington*
OLIVE YOUNG, *University of Illinois*

To supply a firmer foundation for recommendations on the participation of girls and women in physical activity, sports competition, and swimming during the menstrual period, the DGWS undertook a special opinion survey. Results show that the large majority of doctors place no restrictions on physical activity, sports competition, and swimming during any phase of the menstrual period for girls and women who are free from menstrual disturbances.

Reprinted from the *Journal of Health-Physical Education-Recreation,* December 1959. Copyright, 1959, by The American Association for Health, Physical Education, and Recreation, National Education Association, 1201—16th Street, N.W., Washington 6, D. C.

[28] D. Callahan, "Authority and the Theologian," *The Commonweal,* 80 (June 5, 1964), pp. 319–323.

TABLE 1. RECOMMENDED ACTIVITY FOR GIRLS AND WOMEN WHO EXPERIENCE NO PREMENSTRUAL DISCOMFORT OR DYSMENORRHEA

TYPE OF ACTIVITY	GYNECOLO-GISTS N = 8	WOMEN PHYSICIANS N = 9	TOTAL N = 17
Premenstrual Period			
Customary participation in vigorous physical activity	8	8	16
Participation in moderately vigorous physical activity	0	1	1
Customary participation in intensive sports competition	8	8	16
Limited participation in intensive sports competition	0	1	1
Customary participation in swimming	8	9	17
No swimming	0	0	0
No undue physical activity of any kind	0	0	0
First Half of the Menstrual Period			
Customary participation in vigorous physical activity	7	8	15
Participation in moderately vigorous physical activity	1	1	2
Customary participation in intensive sports competition	6	6	12
Limited participation in intensive sports competition	2	3	5
Customary participation in swimming	7	7	14
No swimming	1	2	3
No undue physical activity of any kind	0	0	0
Second Half of the Menstrual Period			
Customary participation in vigorous physical activity	8	9	17
Participation in moderately vigorous physical activity	0	0	0
Customary participation in intensive sports competition	8	9	17
Limited participation in intensive sports competition	0	0	0
Customary participation in swimming	8	9	17
No swimming	0	0	0
No undue physical activity of any kind	0	0	0

The Division for Girls and Women's Sports of the AAHPER has as one of its important functions the development of sports standards for girls and women, including the health and safety of the players. A study, conducted by the Research Committee of DGWS, was undertaken to provide information which would supply a firmer foundation for recommendations relative to the participation of girls and women in sports activity during the menstrual period.

It seemed evident that the answers to this problem could best be secured from medical doctors, since extended experimental research was unfeasible. The Research Committee agreed that the selection of a few specially qualified doctors would produce a more satisfactory result than a survey in which larger numbers of doctors were randomly selected. Two kinds of doctors were contacted: gynecologists, because of their specialized training, and women physicians, because it was felt that, in addition to their medical training, their sex might provide them with further insights into the problem. Eight gynecologists and nine women physicians cooperated in the study and each completed a check list.

The questions on the check list were designed to elicit information relative to the participation of girls and women in vigorous physical exercise, intensive sports competition, and swimming during the menstrual period. The period was divided into three phases: the premenstrual period, described as the three or four days preliminary to the actual onset of the menses; the first half of the menstrual period; and the second half of the menstrual period.

The questions were posed for three types of girls and women in terms of the nature of their menstrual period: (1) girls and women who experience no premenstrual disturbances or dysmenorrhea, (2) girls and women who experience some premenstrual disturbance, such as slight headache, nervous irritability above normal, some pelvic discomfort, and/or dysmenorrhea, but not sufficient to cause loss of time from daily responsibilities and (3) girls and women who experience considerable premenstrual disturbance and/or severe dysmenorrhea which is sufficient to cause loss of time from daily responsibilities.

Definitions for the Study

The doctors were directed to give consideration in their responses only to normally healthy girls and women, who would under ordinary circumstances participate without restriction in strenuous physical activity and intensive sports competition.

Strenuous or vigorous physical activity was defined as "any large muscle activity which may demand a maximum physical exertion, but such exertion is not beyond the ordinary capacity of the individual." Situation examples given were the exertion that would be required to play three sets of tennis, engage full time (32 minutes) in a basketball game, or run the 100-yard dash.

Intensive sports competition was defined as "those situations in which there may be demand for maximum physical exertion, but in addition there may be attendant emotional stresses frequently associated with keen competition, but neither the exertion nor the stresses are beyond the ordinary capacity of the individual." The situation example provided was the emotional stress such as might occur during a hotly contested basketball game.

A directive was given relative to the questions on swimming. It was explained that in answering these questions it should be assumed that the water and air are reasonably temperate and that the duration of the immersion is reasonable, so that

TABLE 2. RECOMMENDED ACTIVITY FOR GIRLS AND WOMEN WHO EXPERIENCE MODERATE PREMENSTRUAL DISCOMFORT AND/OR DYSMENORRHEA

TYPE OF ACTIVITY	GYNECOLO-GISTS N = 8	WOMEN PHYSICIANS N = 9	TOTAL N = 17
Premenstrual Period			
Customary participation in vigorous physical activity	6	5	11
Participation in moderately vigorous physical activity	1	4	5
a Customary participation in intensive sports competition	6	5	11
Limited participation in intensive sports competition	1	3	4
Customary participation in swimming	8	9	17
No swimming	0	0	0
No undue physical activity of any kind	1	0	1
First Half of the Menstrual Period			
Customary participation in vigorous physical activity	5	5	10
Participation in moderately vigorous physical activity	2	2	4
a Customary participation in intensive sports competition	4	4	8
Limited participation in intensive sports competition	3	2	5
Customary participation in swimming	7	7	14
No swimming	1	2	3
No undue physical activity of any kind	1	2	3
Second Half of the Menstrual Period			
Customary participation in vigorous physical activity	7	8	15
Participation in moderately vigorous physical activity	1	1	2
a Customary participation in intensive sports competition	7	8	15
Limited participation in intensive sports competition	1	0	1
Customary participation in swimming	8	9	17
No swimming	0	0	0
No undue physical activity of any kind	0	0	0

a One woman doctor failed to answer the question on competition.

no body chilling occurs and no undue fatigue results. It was further directed that all swimming questions should be answered from the health standpoint only without reference to possible sanitary considerations.

Summary of Recommendations for Participation

Table 1 presents a summary of the physical activity recommendations of eight gynecologists and nine women physicians for girls and women who experience no premenstrual discomfort or dysmenorrhea. There is almost complete agreement between the gynecologists and the women physicians, the only discrepancies being such as could be attributed to the unlike numbers of the two kinds of doctors.

The large majority of doctors place no restriction at all on participation in vigorous physical activity, intensive sports competition, and swimming during all phases of the menstrual period. Among the few doctors advising moderation, the largest number (5) makes the recommendation for limited participation in intensive sports competition during the first half of the menstrual period. There is perfect agreement that customary participation in all activities should be permitted during the second half of the menstrual period, that swimming should be allowed during the premenstrual period, and during no part of the menstrual period should there be complete abstinence from physical activity.

Table 2 presents the physical activity recommendations for girls and women who experience moderate premenstrual discomfort and/or dysmenorrhea. Again there is a close agreement between the gynecologists and women physicians, the one exception being a somewhat more conservative attitude of the women physicians toward physical activity and competition during the premenstrual period.

A majority of the doctors recommend customary participation in vigorous physical activity throughout all phases of the menstrual period. However, the emphasis on moderation is more pronounced than for girls who are free from menstrual disturbances. The strongest recommendation for moderation in physical activity is for the first half of the menstrual period, with a small minority of the doctors advising no undue physical activity of any kind.

A majority of the doctors recommend customary participation in intensive sports competition during the premenstrual period and the second half of the menstrual period. They are, however, divided on their recommendations for the first half of the menstrual period with half approving customary participation and the other half advising either limited or no participation.

There is perfect agreement that swimming should be permitted during the premenstrual period and the second half of the menstrual period, and a large majority would permit it during the first half of the menstrual period.

Table 3 presents the physical activity recommendations for girls and women who experience considerable premenstrual disturbance and/or dysmenorrhea. There is somewhat less agreement here between gynecologists and women physicians than prevailed in the recommendations given in Tables 1 and 2. Agreement is still reasonably high, however. In all cases where there is some disparity, the figures suggest that the women physicians are more conservative in their attitudes than the gynecologists.

Although there is considerable disagreement among the doctors as a group, the majority of them recommend participation in at least moderately vigorous exercise and limited participation in intensive sports competition during the premenstrual period and first half of the menstrual period. All of the doctors approve such activity during the second half of the menstrual period. Abstinence from physical

TABLE 3. RECOMMENDED ACTIVITY FOR GIRLS AND WOMEN WHO EXPERIENCE CONSIDERABLE PREMENSTRUAL DISCOMFORT AND/OR DYSMENORRHEA

Type of Activity	Gynecolo-gists N = 8	Women Physicians N = 9	Total N = 17
Premenstrual Period			
Customary participation in vigorous physical activity	5	3	8
Participation in moderately vigorous physical activity	2	3	5
a Customary participation in intensive sports competition	4	3	7
Limited participation in intensive sports competition	3	2	5
Customary participation in swimming	8	7	15
No swimming	0	2	2
No undue physical activity of any kind	1	3	4
First Half of the Menstrual Period			
Customary participation in vigorous physical activity	4	2	6
Participation in moderately vigorous physical activity	2	4	6
a Customary participation in intensive sports competition	3	1	4
Limited participation in intensive sports competition	3	4	7
Customary participation in swimming	6	3	9
No swimming	2	6	8
No undue physical activity of any kind	2	3	5
Second Half of the Menstrual Period			
Customary participation in vigorous physical activity	5	5	10
Participation in moderately vigorous physical activity	3	4	7
a Customary participation in intensive sports competition	5	4	9
Limited participation in intensive sports competition	3	4	7
Customary participation in swimming	8	8	16
No swimming	0	1	1
No undue physical activity of any kind	0	0	0

a One woman doctor failed to answer the question on competition.

activity during the first two phases of the menstrual period is more often advised for girls and women with severe menstrual difficulties than for those who experience little or no difficulty.

A large majority of the doctors permit swimming during the premenstrual period and the second half of the menstrual period, but they are approximately evenly divided between approving and prohibiting swimming during the first half of the menstrual period.

Doctors' Comments

Provision was made in the check list for the doctors to express their opinions or to make qualifying statements if they so desired. Five of the gynecologists and seven of the women doctors availed themselves of this opportunity.

The comments of the gynecologists were primarily concerned with emphasizing the desirability of exercise and the possible psychological aspects of menstrual discomfort. One typical statement reads: "Menstruation is a normal natural phenomenon and all pain and stress are caused by the individual's psychogenic reaction. Pelvic endometriosis, inflammatory disease, or congenital abnormalities are the only exceptions. . . . I believe it is very desirable for women to pay as little attention as possible to the normal physiological activities of menstruation, not only for the physiological benefits that are received, but also for the psychogenic." Other similar statements include such comments as "make no mental or emotional concessions," "no undue consequences of physical activity have been observed, usually it is beneficial," "should restrict only in the case of excessive bleeding," "many women have found exercise helpful," and "activity *may* very well be therapeutic in that attention and thoughts are directed to an outside activity." One gynecologist recommends that participation of all women in their customary activity be permissive but not necessarily compulsory since "a woman is entitled to take it easy if she wishes."

The statements of the women doctors were quite similar to those of the gynecologists, with a little more emphasis on permissive but not compulsory exercise. They stated that girls should be urged to participate as usual but not necessarily expected to do so. One specific comment was made by two women doctors suggesting the possible undesirability of hard running and jumping during the early stages of the menstrual period, although neither prohibited it.

Summary of Findings

There is very little difference in the recommendations of the eight gynecologists and the nine women physicians on desirable activity for girls and women during the menstrual period. Where some disparity in recommendations occurs, the women physicians are consistently more conservative in their views.

The seventeen doctors as a group agree quite closely in their recommendations for girls and women who experience no premenstrual discomfort or dysmenorrhea. As the severity of the menstrual disturbance increases the agreement among the doctors decreases.

Relative to the three phases of the menstrual period, as defined in this study, doctor's recommendations for the second half of the menstrual period show the highest agreement, for the premenstrual period the next highest agreement, and for the first half of the menstrual period the least agreement.

There was a very much higher agreement among the doctors in their recommendations for swimming than there was in their recommendations for participation in vigorous physical activity and intensive sports competition.

Restrictions were leveled against participation in intensive sports competition more frequently than against participation in either vigorous physical activity or swimming.

For all types of girls the strongest recommendation for moderation in all forms of activity is during the first half of the menstrual period, followed by the premenstrual period, and finally the last half of the menstrual period.

The large majority of doctors place no restrictions on physical activity, sports competition, and swimming during any phase of the menstrual period for girls and women who are free from menstrual disturbances. For girls and women who experience premenstrual discomfort, the restrictions increase as the severity of the discomfort increases.

The Identity of Men and of Women in Contemporary Culture

DAVID R. MACE

One of the troublesome characteristics of modern life is our great confusion about our identity. With this goes a corresponding confusion about motivation. If I'm not sure who I am, how can I be sure what I ought to be doing, and whether it's worth going on doing what I *am* doing?

Why do we have this crisis in our contemporary world? Because of deep and farreaching changes that are taking place in the nature of human society.

As far as I have been able to find out, all the great human civilizations have been authoritarian and hierarchical. This has been the keynote of our human tradition. You have to fit into your destined place, and do what you are told. Your identity is quite clear. It is settled for you, usually before you are born. You are the son of your father; therefore you take his nationality, his politics, his religion; you probably also take over the farm or estate he has run, or the craft or labor in which he has been engaged. If this happens to be uncongenial to you, that makes no difference at all. You have to do your duty, and to accept your appointed lot. That is the true meaning of human life.

All the great cultures have accepted, and enforced, this view. And all the great religions have supported it, except in a few special circumstances. The destiny of man is to accept his predetermined identity, and to undertake with unquestioning obedience the task appointed for him.

Today, in our Western culture, this concept has largely disappeared. What we

Speech delivered at Luncheon Meeting of Council for Lay Life and Work at United Church of Christ Assembly at French Lick. Reprinted by permission from the United Church of Christ Council for Lay Life and Work.

call democracy insists on the right of the individual to find his own identity, to live his own life, to shape his own destiny. He doesn't have to accept his parents' way of life or their views about life—at least, not once he is out of his childhood. At the public school he meets other children, with other and often very different parental backgrounds. The teenage culture brings adolescents together, for the first time in human history, with the right to determine their own values and standards, sometimes in defiance of the authority figures in their lives. At college our young people live in an open society, where the emphasis is on finding yourself and being yourself. We have structured our society so that a man can change his job, change his home, change his religion, and even change his wife, and meet with little or no disapproval. In his quest for his true identity, he can make any number of experiments. If these get him into trouble, he can hire a psychotherapist to help him tidy up the situations; or to support him while he makes more experiments.

So we are all busily involved in a great search for identity. And this is not only an individual quest. We are searching also for group identity. We want to know exactly what an executive should be like. What kind of house should he live in, what kind of car should he drive, what kind of wife should he have? We want to know what a Presbyterian should be like, and what an American should be like. Last, but not least, we want to know what a man should be like, what a woman should be like.

When we speak of group identity, we are thinking of what we call roles. We don't mean, what should men and women be like in their physical structure or function. We all know what a man looks like organically. He has a penis and a woman hasn't. We all know how a woman functions physiologically—she has babies and a man can't. These things are predetermined and they can't be changed—at least, not yet! But what are the particular *roles* of men and women that derive from these unalterable differences of physical structure and function that differentiate them?

Here we encounter differences of opinion. Let's look at two opposite viewpoints. One is well represented by some Jungian writers, who emphasize the deep psychic differences between men and women, and their complementary roles. They speak of *animus* and *anima,* as though men and women were essentially different kinds of beings. At the other extreme there are those who minimize the differences. Perhaps Margaret Mead illustrates this school of thought. The idea is that what we consider to be typical masculine and feminine behavior is not rooted in personality differences, but is simply a matter of cultural conditioning. By producing appropriately controlled environmental conditions, a man could be brought up to feel and behave like a woman, a woman to feel and behave like a man. Perhaps this is illustrated by some homosexuals, who have the physical apparatus of one sex but the feelings and desires of the other.

I don't, however, intend to be drawn into this controversy. What I'm concerned about is not theories, but what has actually happened. Let me say something briefly about the history of masculine and feminine identity, and then focus on the situation existing in our culture today.

In most of the great cultures, the differences between man and woman have not only been clearly recognized, but have also been interpreted in terms of superiority and inferiority. It may be worth taking a look to see how this has come about.

It is obvious that a man has normally greater *physical strength* than a woman. In a fist fight, a man would in most cases win. So, it is argued, the man assumed the role of the hunter, and therefore of provider. This sounds plausible enough. However, I had always considered the male lion to be a great hunter, until I went into the African bush and discovered that it's the female that does most of the hunting! As I already knew, many female hawks are larger and more powerful than their male consorts. We have plenty of evidence today that the woman certainly has more endurance than the man, so it's doubtful that we can really say that man is physically superior. Indeed, a compatriot of mine in the United States, Ashley Montagu, has actually written a book entitled "The Natural Superiority of Woman"!

Another view often taken is that man is *intellectually superior* to woman. In India, the Brahmins used to say—"Educate a woman, and you put a knife into the hands of a monkey!" My friend, Geoffrey Parrinder, when he was a professor at the Nigerian University in Ibadan, told me that he once said, to a class of male African students, that women were capable of just as much intellectual achievement as men. To his consternation, the class greeted this statement with tumultuous roars of laughter. They thought the professor was making a joke, and they also thought that it was a very good joke! We know today that this concept of the intellectual weakness of woman is not true. Even Africans are getting to know it now. What has often happened is that men have proclaimed women to be inferior, proceeded to deprive them of opportunities of education, and so kept them ignorant; and then declared triumphantly "There you are! I always told you they had no sense!"

A third view, prominent in Marxist literature, is that man has achieved superiority by *exploiting women economically*. But of course that doesn't answer the question "Why?" It simply suggests that he has been more aggressive, and she has been more pliable and accommodating. And this, of course, is moving into the area of functional difference. What Marx (or more properly speaking, Engels) says is that the man took advantage of his male role, to impose slavery on his sex partner. This was not difficult, because the male role gives the man the advantage at two points. First, in the sex relationship he assumes the function of dominance. He acts, she is acted upon. He pursues, she runs away—"just fast enough to be caught," as one psychologist explains it! Secondly, the woman during pregnancy, and when she is involved in the care of children, is preoccupied and diverted from other tasks. So her child-bearing and child-rearing functions make her vulnerable, and result in her being dependent upon and, therefore subservient to, the man.

Another factor which I consider to be very important, but which is ignored in all discussions of the subject I have ever seen, is an interesting fact I came across when I was preparing material for my book on Hebrew marriage. Before the invention of the microscope, it was impossible to know about the existence of the sperm and ovum, and consequently the ancient concept of gestation was quite different from ours of today. In the whole of the ancient world, it was believed that the child developed from the coagulation of the seminal fluid of the man, when this was deposited in the womb of the woman. This means that the only function the woman served was that of an incubator. In one of the poems of Aeschylus, Apollo says—"The mother of what is called her child is not its parent, but only the nurse of the newly implanted germ. The begetter is the parent, whereas she, as a stranger for a stranger, doth but preserve the sprout." I could match that quotation with similar views from most of the ancient human cultures. The idea, you see, is that the women contributes nothing of her essential self to the making of her child. She is just the soil, nourishing the seed. This makes her inevitably an inferior partner in the drama of reproduction, and the passing on of life from generation to generation. This, I believe, rather than any of the more frequently quoted ideas I have already mentioned, is the real root of the whole patriarchal concept, which has produced the hierarchical distinction between men and women, and the concept of male superiority. Interestingly enough, it is not among primitive peoples, but in the great civilizations, that male dominance has been most vigorously asserted. And these great civilizations have all had in common the patriarchal family system.

So there has come down to us, through the ages, a deep-rooted belief in male superiority and female inferiority. But there is more to it than that. There is another factor, which has been largely transmitted through our Christian culture.

Not only have we inherited a concept of female inferiority; but also a concept of female uncleanness and sinfulness. Woman has been regarded not only as weak and dumb. She is also full of guile. After all, did she not have dealings with the serpent, and so become the instrument of man's downfall?

This idea has two roots in human culture. First, the concept of uncleanness is related to the female functions of menstruation and childbirth. There is a vast literature on this. I remember, in the mountains of Northern Thailand, there was a Buddhist temple that I liked to visit, because it was a building of great beauty. At the entrance to the inner courtyard there was a sign, prominently displayed, which forbade any woman to venture beyond that point. The reason, as the priest explained, was that a woman by her very presence would contaminate the holy place.

The other root is the fact that woman, as a sexually seductive being, is always enticing man away from the higher things to which he should be giving his attention. She diverts him from his quest of spiritual goals. She even sets men in conflict against each other—a fact well dramatized in the story of Helen and the Trojan War.

This concept has unfortunately deeply influenced Christian teaching. I don't believe it is to be found in the sayings of Jesus, but it is obvious in some passages written by St. Paul. And by the time we get to the book of the Revelation, we find that dramatic passage about how the best seats in heaven are reserved for those who "have not defiled themselves with women." However, it was in the early and medieval Church that this concept really came to flower. It runs like a dark thread through almost all of Christian history. Frank Harris has summed it up in a statement—"The Christian Church has sullied desire and degraded woman, and has rendered abject and infamous the deepest and best of our instincts." Whether we like it or not (and we obviously don't) there is a great deal of truth in this statement. And one of the results is that, in the contemporary world, the Christian Church has been described as "the last stronghold of the concept of male dominance."

Our Western Christian culture, as Freud has pointed out, has been in a great dilemma about woman. Somehow it couldn't get her into focus. It could only see her in two extreme forms—the nonsexual woman, as virgin, enshrined as the Queen of Heaven; and the sexual woman, the temptress, as the Gate of Hell.

Well, that brings us to our contemporary world. In our time, we have seen a widespread revolt against the concept of male superiority and female inferiority. The first dramatic manifestation of this was in 1893, when New Zealand was the first country in the world to give women the vote. This set off a chain reaction among the nations, and I believe there are only eight of them in the world today where women may not vote. Political freedom, however, was not the only factor, and perhaps not the main factor. Professor Richard Titmuss, the British demographer, in an essay on the Welfare State, suggests that birth control has done more than the vote to emancipate women.

Be that as it may, women *are* now emancipated. The progress has come at differing rates, with a variety of institutions, both helping and hindering. It is perhaps a melancholy fact that Communism seems to have done the most to help, and the Christian Church the most to hinder.

But now we must ask, what has the emancipation of women done to us? It has obviously thrown us into great confusion about the identity, and the roles, of men and women. And one of the major tasks confronting us today is to try to straighten it all out. What does this involve?

We must begin by facing a question that has been at the root of most of the confusion—the fact that men and women, in relation to each other, have two quite different kinds of roles to play.

I believe the true way to describe the identity of a man is to say that he is first a person, and then a male. Similarly a woman is first a person, and then a female. So a man and woman can interact as two persons—communicating, cooperating, agreeing or disagreeing, just as two men or two women may do. But they can also interact as male and female—the male aggressive, the female receptive; the male dominant, the female submissive. In a good marriage, both partners must learn to play both roles—husband and wife must learn to be good partners, and good lovers.

Throughout human history, these two roles have been constantly confused. What the patriarchal societies did was to make the sexual roles of dominance and submission, and make them models for the identities of man and woman as persons in society. So men were viewed as superior persons, women as inferior persons. Today, we are tending to swing to the opposite extreme. We have taken the personal roles of equal partnership, and made them models for the interaction of man and woman in marriage. So in the past the equality of men and women was suppressed in favor of their complementarity. Today we are suppressing their complementarity in favor of their equality.

This confusion is running us into a lot of trouble. I think these are unavoidable consequences of the enormous readjustments we are having to make. But the result is that, in American society, women are going through a major crisis of identity. Men, too, are having their troubles. But the focus is on the woman, because she is having to make much greater adjustments. A great many articles, books, discussions, and forums have focused on the American woman, and these indicate the anxiety our culture is suffering around this question. By way of illustration, let me refer to four aspects of it—

1) The Virginity Crisis. *We are talking these days about a "sexual revolution," and in my opinion this term is fully justified. Great changes are taking place in our concepts of sex behavior. Notice, however, that the changes largely focus on the sex behavior of* women. *Our studies suggest that men are behaving before marriage pretty much as they have always done, but with the advantage that premarital sex partners are today much more accessible and on the whole less expensive. It's the women who are changing—especially the middle-class educated women, among whom now premarital virginity is rapidly becoming the exception rather than the rule. We are not yet clear what this is doing to us, although reports like "Sex and the College Girl" give us some useful clues. About one thing there is no doubt whatever—that this is a subject of vigorous controversy amongst our young women. Some think they have won their final liberation, and are starryeyed about it. Others are beginning to wonder whether they have not been tricked into a new and more subtle form of male dominance. Time alone will tell.*

2) The Orgasm Crisis. *We are told that the days in which we are living are the "sexy Sixties," and certainly the subject of sex is not being overlooked in our time. The great emphasis on sex in marriage has, among other things, led to the discovery of female orgasm by the masses. I have been a marriage counselor for more than thirty years, and I have seen three definite phases in the way married people view their sex life. First, the wives used to come to complain that their husbands were unreasonably and excessively demanding in the area of sex. Then the husbands began to come and complain that their wives were not responding as the marriage manuals said they should. The third phase, and the one we are in now, is marked by the wives coming to complain that their husbands' technique is so bad that they are unable to give the wives the orgasms to which they are entitled!*

Tied up with this orgasm crisis is a great deal of what we call "role reversal" in the marriages of today. We are hearing about "demasculinizing females" and "castrating females," whose assumption of near-masculine roles has robbed their husbands of their power to function as normal males.

3) The Femininity Crisis. *American women seem to be deeply troubled about their femininity, or lack of femininity. This is partly because American men are constantly nagging them about it. Traveling abroad, our men have sometimes found qualities in women of other cultures that their own American women seem to lack. Of course, this may have been in part that the foreign women had the traditional attitude of submissiveness, but that is not an adequate explanation. Many American women are themselves troubled, deep down, on this question. Betty Friedan has written a very perceptive and a very provocative book about his whole question. Before her, Marya Farnham had written on American women as "The Lost Sex."*

This perplexity about their femininity can be clearly seen in women's fashions today. Our whole culture is involved in a serious confusion between femininity and sexuality. American men, feeling that there is a lack of femininity in their women, are demanding that they dress and behave in a more sexually provocative way. But this is really an adolescent misconception of what femininity is. The erotically aggressive woman is often the very opposite of feminine, because what she is doing is to try to compensate for her inward lack of femininity by putting on a big show on the outside. True femininity, of the kind that attracts a mature man, is marked by a shy, modest sweetness, rather than sexual aggressiveness.

However, American women are clutching desperately at straws, and they have gotten the message from their men. So now, with the help of fashion designers and cosmetics manufacturers, they are going all out to parade their erotic qualities. Lips, busts, and legs are prominently displayed, in a pathetic attempt to regain outwardly what they have somehow lost inwardly. These modern American women are in fact doing just the opposite of what the Suffragettes did in their struggle for the franchise. The Suffragette was saying to men—"Look, we all know I'm a woman. But can't you see I'm also a person?" The modern American woman is saying to men—"Look, we all know I'm a person. But can't you see I'm also a woman?"

4) The Mother-Role Crisis. It could be said that women today have greater opportunities to be persons than ever before in human history. But women as wives are having a lot of troubles. And women as mothers are having the most trouble of all.

The reasons for this are quite complex. Women are being asked to do a great many rather contradictory things. They are being urged to function as persons, to get out to work, to pull their weight in community affairs, in the professions, in politics. They are being pestered to play sexy roles. All this is not emphasizing their maternal functions, which were traditionally regarded as their greatest achievement and their true glory. The modern woman isn't being given much leisure to concentrate serenely on what Evelyn Underhill calls "The high emprize of motherhood." In her busy, active life, small children seem sometimes like fetters, chaining the mother to the kitchen sink. Older children, in our highly permissive culture, present problems more complex than any generation of mothers have ever had to cope with. And because patriarchalism is in ruins, and more people are living in vast urban complexes, modern fathers are absent most of the time, and don't exercise much authority even when they do come home. Some of them, indeed, stop coming home altogether. So the modern woman often has to take over the functions of both mother and father; and when she has done her best, the psychology books point accusing fingers at her and lay all her children's misdemeanors at her door.

These are some of the crises that are the outward manifestations of our confusion about identity and roles of men and women in our contemporary culture. Seen from one angle, it can look like a pretty sorry mess. Yet fundamentally it represents something we've never had before—a real opportunity to find out what are the true roles of men and women in human society. And this I consider to be a great gain.

I have been reading a history of the world by Rene Sedillot, the French economist. This is an attempt to compress into one volume the whole story of the human race. It is well done. But it has produced in me the same feeling of depression that I had when I first read a similar history of the world by H. G. Wells, perhaps a quarter of a century ago. The story of mankind, whether we like it or not, is largely the story of war and destruction—one virile people falling upon another and destroying it, only to be destroyed in turn by yet another barbaric horde. Of course, this is typical masculine behavior. And for most of human history, it has been a man's world.

I believe we could manage much better if women, as women, and not as cheap copies of men, could begin to take their full share of the task of running the world. I would even settle for some demasculinizing of our males if this led to their being a little less aggressive and competitive. And there are whole areas of human culture where women have many advantages, and where I think they could do a better job than men. Medicine, as the Soviet Union has discovered, is really a woman's sphere. I think law is a field where women have a great contribution to make; and I would venture to say that religion is yet another. So I believe that what is happening today is that we are painfully, by trial and error, trying at last to shape a world where men and women can both find their true identity—a world where we shall not subjugate their equality to their complementarity to their equality; but where the whole rich potential of their working together, in the family and in society, will be further developed than has ever before been possible. I personally believe that such a world would be a wonderful place to live in.

A Distinguished Doctor Talks to Vassar College Freshmen About Love and Sex

MARY STEICHEN CALDERONE, M.D.

(In September, 1963, Dr. Calderone spoke to the freshmen class at Vassar in connection with the college's program of sex education. Dr. Calderone, herself a graduate of Vassar, is an associate member of the American Association of Marriage Counselors, author of "Release from Sexual Tensions" and then the Medical Director of Planned Parenthood—World Population. This is the text of her talk.)

"Now, girls, keep your affections wrapped in cotton wool until Mr. Right comes along." In 1921, these were the red-letter words of the last lecture of the required freshmen hygiene course. Rumor had it that girls had been known to faint at that annual notorious "sex" lecture, when the facts of life and reproduction were supposedly explained in a 40-minute talk by the college physician. That was the extent of sex education offered at Vassar in those days—and I may say that parents did no better, for many of my contemporaries can testify that on their wedding night they knew nothing at all about the sex act.

The need for panel discussions on sex and lectures such as this one was not then apparent. Problems such as those faced by young people today existed, of course, but they were not as general or as obvious. With little or no access to cars, very limited weekends, and no parties without chaperones, a college girl almost automatically led a very protected life, and indeed had to exercise considerable ingenuity to get into a situation which could lead to pregnancy. O tempora! O mores!

My oldest daughter graduated from Vassar in 1948, and I also have a 20-year-old and a 17-year-old daughter, but as a mother and physician I am deeply impressed by the fact that the customs and behavior patterns of young people have changed far more in the 15 years since my oldest daughter's graduation than they did in the 25 years between my graduation and hers.

In the panel discussions on sex you will be presented with a full complement of sound, factual information in response to your own questions—questions that a generation ago young women would not have dared to ask even had they known enough to frame them. I have listened to tape recordings of these discussions and I know that the facts will be placed at every student's disposal. But the meaningfulness of knowledge depends on the use one can make of it, so I would like to explore with you how you as individuals may feel about the facts and knowledge that will be offered to you. For not only have you come to college to acquire facts, but also, I hope you realize, you are here to initiate, if you have not already, that life-long process by which past experience and knowledge are continually and creatively integrated with new knowledge and new experiences. Jacob Bronowski, in his essay "Science and Human Values," sensitized us to an awareness of the similarity between the creative processes in art and in science. Today I would like to sensitize you to an understanding that the building of a human relationship is just as creative a process. For most of us, no achievements of the mind, whether in art or in science, can be fully meaningful if we have not also succeeded in the creation of meaningful human relationships.

There is a developmental scale in these human relationships beginning with child to parent, and progressing to friend to friend, lover to lover, man to woman, and finally full cycle, parent to child. Note that I distinguished between the lover-to-lover and the man-to-woman relationships. The lover-to-lover relationship is by its very nature transitory, though it may be, and often is, transmuted into the permanent man-woman relationship that should transcend all others.

As an integral part of creative experience you are seeking something special in these years, and your presence here today proves this. Stretch out your visible hands and you will touch the hands of other seekers. Stretch out your invisible hands—across land and sea and mountain, backward in time and forward in time—and the invisible hands of myriads of others touch yours, also in seeking. You are not alone. The meaning and significance particularly of the man-woman relationship has been, is and always will be sought by each human soul. This meaning is like quicksilver—we think we have it, then it may elude us for a time, then we may come upon a flash of its deepest significance at a moment unaware. The search can and does continue as long as we live, for this most fundamental of human relationships is never static and can never be considered a finished product, but should be kept dynamic and growing as long as we live—unless, of course, we give up, abdicate, throw up our hands, as some do, deciding that nothing has any meaning, especially the man-woman relationship. Then we are indeed lost, for our fundamental polarity has disappeared.

What do I mean by polarity? I remember in my junior high school in biology we sprouted some beans and meted the polarity of the roots. Nothing could change that natural gravity—tropism—for those roots found their way down toward the earth around any obstacle. But when we mounted the sprouted beans on the minute hand of a clock so that they traveled full circle once every hour, what happened then? The polarity was disturbed and the roots no longer "knew" which way to go to reach the earth, so they went every which way in disturbed and distorted confusion. The man or woman who has lost his or her polarity becomes confused and chaotic and finds it hard to establish straight, firm roots in life. The fundamental polarity of human beings is the one having to do with our constant seeking toward the basic relationship.

In recent times, the process of the search for the basic relationship has been profoundly modified by a sort of chronological superimposition on it of still another process that used to precede it. That process by which the adolescent girl develops into the adult woman and that process by which she searches for a mate tend to proceed simultaneously nowadays, rather than sequentially.

Formerly a young girl would literally take years to become an adult. Between 12 and 18 she had time to learn, to feel, to experience, to observe, to meditate, to experiment in the meaning of being an adult; and the college years from 17 to 21 were then used by her to consolidate the process of growing up by assuming some of the responsibilities of adult life. She had time to test not only her ability to carry on adult responsibilities, but also her ability to form friendships with both men and women. There were some girls who superimposed the search for the relationship on the last two years of college, but most, at least, did not reach a final decision on marriage until after graduation. In both of the processes there was time—for reflection, deliberation, rectification.

Now both processes have been tremendously accelerated. "Growing up" starts earlier and is considered by the girls themselves to have been completed by 16 or 17 at the very latest. This in itself constitutes a trap, for it simply is not possible, no matter how you rush it, for a person of 17 to be able to develop the judgment and maturity that a slower pace would have ensued by 21. Indeed, the very speeding up of the process may produce such dislocations that what the person might have become at 21 may now be impossible to achieve. A quite accurate similarity can be drawn with the very homely process of making Jello, the setting time of which depends upon such physical factors as temperature at mixing and surrounding temperature while setting. You can shorten the setting time by lowering the surrounding temperature and this is what one does by putting the Jello into the refrigerator. Any of you who has been faced with forgetting to make the dinner dessert until late and tried further to shorten the setting time by putting the Jello into the freezing compartment will remember that ice crystals usually form, and the smooth, homogeneous consistency of the Jello is disturbed. This is what I mean when I say that speeding up of the maturation process in the human being beyond a certain rate may—and I think does—result in disturbances of the human personality that, unlike the frozen Jello, which can be retrieved by melting and starting over again, are not easily subject to rectification except possibly by later psychotherapy. Another simile is what social scientists now consider to be the orderly sequential development of muscular control in the baby. If the child is kept confined in a crib or playpen until he is well into his standing and walking phase, and thereby forced to skip entirely his crawling phase, psychologists feel, not only does he not develop his back erector muscles as they should be developed, but also his muscular coordination and indeed his mental coordination may suffer, and speech itself may be delayed for some time. The feeling is that the human animal should normally go through a sequence of developmental phases, and short-circuiting any of these phases will tend to interfere with his complete development. We know little about the normal variations in rates of emotional development in human beings, so that at this time it is not possible to measure the effects of speedup in maturation. No one knows what effect sex, precociously experienced, will have on the immature psyche.

As I indicated, the process of searching for the man-woman relationship has also been speeded up, and is now going on simultaneously with the maturation process. What the result of this superimposition is on each of the processes, again, no one knows, nor do we have any measuring rods for finding out. We do know, from certain studies of marriages, that those that were the result of a relationship beginning in childhood or adolescent friendship and enduring for measurable periods of time before turning into the love relationship—those marriages tend to be enduring and stable. Note that I do not use the word "happy," because this is probably the least definable of all terms and the one that depends upon the greatest number of ever-changing variables.

Lester Kirkendall, author of a most valuable study, Premarital Intercourse and Interpersonal Relationships, pointed out that any relationship between two people is bound to be dynamic; for a short or a long period of time it grows, matures, changes, becomes transmuted into another kind of relationship, perhaps more positive, perhaps negative—in other words, no relationship is ever static. Nor can its conclusion ever be foreseen even in its earliest days, and this should lead one to question the concept of "love at first sight"—that is, enduring love. Kirkendall points out some of the elements that are essential to any long-time relationship. Confidentiality, for instance. Surely a person with whom you are going to live over a period of time, whether it be a roommate or a husband, must be one in whom you have confidence and to whom you can give confidence. When a girl you hardly know rushes up to you and tells you all of the intimate facts of her family and love life, do you not instinctively recoil from this overconfidentiality? Confidentiality by its very nature must be a step-wise, time-wise process.

Another major element of a relationship is empathy—the ability to feel with another person. How can you feel with that other person until you have learned how that other person feels—and he likewise about you? So that the empathy must be a two-way process, and the infinite variety of cues and clues about each other's feelings and convictions is impossible to learn except over a period of time.

The most delicate and the most critical element of a deep relationship is trust, and there is absolutely no way of arriving at trust overnight, for it can be tested only by common experience, and—once more—time. Thus it is obvious that there are no short cuts to any true relationship. This leads to the conclusion, by those thoughtful adults in our culture who have been forced to watch sadly and helplessly while young people try these short cuts, that sex experience before confidentiality, empathy and trust have been established can hinder, and may actually destroy, the possibility of a solid, permanent relationship.

We should now question why it is that an increasing number of young people are having early sex experiences. Is it that we adults have not realized the importance of getting over to young people what sex is for? Many of us did teach our children the facts of life, thinking, with our limited understanding, that we had done a complete job when we talked about the reproductive role of sex. Apparently it never occurred to most of us that this is just a small part of sex education, and that the major part has to do with understanding and interpreting the relationship role of sex. This failure left the field wide-open to the forces in our society that exploit sex for commercial advantages, with the result that people both in and out of marriage use sex for all sorts of reasons that have little to do with its true, fundamental purposes. Curiosity, sensual pleasure, bribe, reward, threat, punishment, emotional blackmail—these are some of the exploitive ways in which human beings use the gift of sex—against each other. If there is one thing, however, that I wish I could possibly get over to you, it would be some glimmering of awareness of how the gift of sex can be used for each other by two people in the primary relationship, when the communicative role played by sex is its highest function. In one way sex is a sixth sense, for when it is used nonexploitively it serves to give each participant full knowledge of the other.

You will notice that there are a number of words that I have not used and do not intend to use, such words as ideals, morals, sacred, and so on. But this brings us right up to the all-pervading question of premarital sex. Answers to it, as given by many people, are counted in terms of the more than 250,000 babies born every year out of wedlock in this country, and the studies that show one out of every six brides as pregnant on her wedding day. Let me first suggest to you that meaningful sex between a man and a woman probably does not remain meaningful for any appreciable length of time outside of the marriage relationship; and in using the term "marriage relationship" I am not talking only of the legal ceremony itself but of the intent behind it. It is the presence of this intent that provides continuity to the sexual relationship, gives it meaning and validity, turns it into something to develop, to deepen, to protect and to sacrifice for. In the repeated sexual act within marriage, a man and woman are saying to each other, "I chose you once above all others, and I now choose you again. I'll choose you tomorrow and next year and the year after that and when we're forty or fifty or sixty and neither of us is any longer so attractive." Outside of marriage the sex act may mean this for a while, but it cannot continue to mean indefinitely. Thus a time limit is implicit in the sex act if the man and the woman do not look upon it as on the way to marriage.

For herein lies the key: marriage is not something imposed by society and religion—far from it. Marriage is a state freely and consciously and joyfully sought by men and women. It is an elective state. Why is it sought successfully by some, vainly by others? What is the secret of the highly constant polarity of most human beings toward this relationship? The answer is that only within the self-sought marriage bond can two people create for themselves the security of peace and solitude and time—lifetime—by which they can accomplish that which is pivotal and central to all else—namely, total communion. The report of the Committee on the Family of the Lambeth Conference of the Anglican (Episcopal) Church of 1958 put it this way: "The need of man and woman for each other, to complement and fulfill each other, and to provide a durable partnership against the loneliness and rigor of life. . . ." Time—to laugh, to cry, to fight, to work, to hope, to fear, to know each other in the Biblical sense, to procreate—for all these shared experiences the state of marriage is essential not only as symbol but as protector.

Sex before marriage has always existed. There is no question that first sexual love can have an intrinsic and breathtaking sweetness that belongs to it and to no other. But first love can be first love only once, and attempts to repeat it or to prolong it simply turn it into hollow fakery, like the woman who tries to stay 17 when she is 30. Deliberately to try to maintain the man-woman relationship at a superficial "we enjoy sex so let's just have that" level thwarts the polarity toward a deepening permanent relationship. Some of you may not now agree that there is a natural drive toward permanency that inevitably seeks the marriage relationship. But I believe that you will discover this is true, and that deeply underlying the wish to please or to be popular or to have fun now lie deep yearnings for a permanent relationship.

So we come to the two really big questions that up to 15 years ago were asked openly by few individuals but that nowadays are asked openly by what seems to be the majority of them. First, "What do I do about sex until marriage?" and second, "Whose business is it anyway but mine?" It is particularly the second that raises issues in institutions such as colleges.

As you sit here before me, you all are in different stages. Some of you have had sexual relations already, some of you expect to very shortly, some of you have never had sex experience or even thought of doing so, some of you wonder if you ever will. You have come from all your varied backgrounds to a new experience where people of other persuasions and backgrounds than yours will be pointing out different ways of feeling and doing. As freshmen you can expect that many crucial situations involving sex will confront you in the next four years as you move into adult life. How will you react to these highly personal decisions? On the spur of the moment? Curiosity? Thrill-seeking? Persuading yourself that it's the "real thing"? As a "right"? As evidence of your emancipation? In fear or withdrawal? In rebellion or to "show" someone? Or persuading yourself to do something that is looked upon as a status symbol?

Answers to these questions depend on still other questions: What value do you set on yourself? What value do you set on the other person? Whether he is someone you know now or someone not yet known to you, you can be fairly sure that at this very moment he is probably struggling with these very same questions. How able are you to sacrifice a possible pleasurable moment now for a later, greater sureness in saying yes or no? Has the moment come to merge yourself, as a unique and whole person, with another unique and whole person?

For make no mistake, there is absolutely no possibility of having a sexual relationship without irrevocably meshing a portion of your two nonphysical selves. Sex is each time such a definitive experience that a part of each of you remains forever a part of the other. So let me expand my last question. How many times, and how casually are you willing to invest a portion of your total self, and to be the custodian of a like investment from the other person, without the sureness of knowing that these investments are being made for keeps?

I am, therefore, not so concerned about chastity per se as concerned about the total interpersonal relationship that is marriage, and I have a passionate desire that young people, who are today so free, not only should understand and respect, but also should aspire to and achieve, the permanent man-woman relationship. William Genne substitutes for the word "chastity" the phrase "premarital fidelity"—fidelity to the marriage that you will someday have.

In the end, the answer to this question of premarital sexual relationships lies, of course, within each one of you, for no one's words of wisdom can carry as much weight with you as your own. However, colleges can and should make rules just as parents can and should, for what else can young people realistically expect from parents or from representatives of responsible educational or social institutions? Can we adults do otherwise if we truly believe that experimental or casual sexual intercourse may interfere with the later establishment of a permanent relationship? Can we say, "Go ahead" and still be honest? No. If you do decide to go ahead it must be without the connivance of the responsible adults around you. You cannot realistically expect us to be accessories before the fact, and when we make available to you every bit of safeguarding information that we have at our disposal, this should not be taken by you to mean that we go along with you.

At the present time the best we adults can do is to set some rules and expect you to obey them; give you as much factual information as we possibly can; and last but not least, place on the record our conviction that sex should never be casual or accidental, but should be the result of the conscious decision of two people mutually arrived at after they have taken time to consider their total relationship, its past, its present and its future.

The whole structure of society is changing, and changing fast; and you will need all the facts we can give you, and whatever wisdom we can pass on to you, and strength to make intelligent decisions, in order to cope with the pressures and problems that will confront you and your brothers and sisters and your children to come. Right now there is a revolt against the "no" that society has always said about premarital sex, and the revolt against "no" has resulted in pressure for "yes." You will find this "yes" pressure not only from the boys you meet but also from older girls, and this especially may unsettle you. But note this. The girl who, subtly or not, pressures you toward a "yes" decision must be a girl who is questioning the wisdom of her own "yes" decision, and her pressure on you can only be an attempt to justify her own actions to herself. Would she feel the need for this justification if she were entirely comfortable in her "yes" decision and convinced of its rightness? Will you? Twenty-five years from now, when the daughters of some of you may be sitting right here, I wonder who will be talking to them about sex, but I wonder even more what you will want to have said to them.

I'll wind up by suggesting to you that if you put the question to older people who have had a stable marriage, most of them will answer that it was all worth it—waiting lonely years for it, investing a total life in it, the angers, the difficulties, the self-disciplining—all made worth it by the golden moments of true communication, both sexual and nonsexual. "A durable partnership against the loneliness and rigor of life." Only time can assure this—plenty of time, first, to grow up into the woman you were meant to be; then time to seek, to identify and to get to know the person you want to relate to; and at long last, time to commune with that person within the permanence of a marriage relationship that was entered into by yourself consciously and as a whole person, not as one who has been nibbled at by bits and pieces given away prematurely.

So I have come full circle to the very meaning of the words I used at the beginning in quoting that college physician so long ago. The words are dated and quaint, but their meaning is of even greater significance now than then. I sincerely wish the time and the patience and the discipline that will discover for each one of you the fullest and deepest meaning of those words.

How Young Men Influence the Girls Who Love Them

MARY STEICHEN CALDERONE, M.D.

(In the following article, based on a talk originally given at the University of Notre Dame, a distinguished doctor warns young men, "If you are not concerned about a girl as a human being, consider what it will do to your sense of yourself to use her for temporary gratification.")

Rare is the young man who is fully aware of the important part he inevitably plays in the life of every girl with whom he has a close personal relationship. He is indeed the exception if he has any real understanding of his role in the evolution by which a girl becomes a woman. For no woman is truly a woman until a man has participated in and completed the process that makes her one.

But because it is a *process,* the subtle, complex evolution of a young girl into a woman occurs over a substantial period of time and cannot be explained by any single act or any single relationship. The French word for it, *épanouissement,* which has no exact English translation, conveys the idea of "becoming," and includes such nuances as growth, development, unfolding, flowering and, most particularly, fulfillment. Often the completion of a girl's coming of age will occur as a consequence of her relationship with the one young man who proves to be *the* man in her life. But in maturing into womanhood, she will be influenced by her involvements with all the men to whom she becomes emotionally attached, including friends, teachers, relatives, brothers and especially her father.

A girl's development is also influenced by her associations with other women, and profoundly so by her relationship with her mother. And a boy's evolution into manhood is similarly influenced by the girls and the women he chooses to like or love. But I am concentrating here on the impact of men on the life of every young girl with whom they share an emotional bond. In my experience, men are generally unaware of the extent of this impact—or unconcerned about it. As a result, their behavior is all too often irresponsible. My hope is that in sharpening their awareness of how a girl grows up, I may increase both their concern and their sense of responsibility.

In the early years of her development, a girl must strive to accomplish what one psychiatrist has called the four tasks of adolescence. She must separate herself from her parents—that is, become emotionally free of them without rejecting them. She must establish a value system for herself, deciding on the moral principles and value judgments by which she will live. She must choose her life goal, which will eventually enable her to be independent of her parents' financial support. And finally, she must determine and accept her sexual role, which means discovering what it means to be a mature woman and accepting not only the joys but the responsibilities of her sexual nature.

Similar tasks must be accomplished by the adolescent boy. But our society has not made equal demands of boys and girls, especially in terms of their acceptance of the joys of sex as contrasted with the responsibilities. Boys have always been encouraged to develop their healthy drives toward sexual manhood, but little has been demanded of them in exercising responsibility. The opposite has been true for girls. Even in this day of the emancipated female, girls are hardly encouraged to express their sexual nature, but they are still expected to bear the burden of responsibility for all heterosexual relationships. In a changing society, however, as women increasingly share with men a healthy enjoyment of sex, so men should increasingly share the burden of its responsibilities.

There are two sides to responsibility, and they are equally important. One is responsibility to ourselves, and this includes the need to know what is right and healthy and nurturing *for us;* and then there is responsibility for the other, the need to try to understand, to the limits of our ability, what may be best *for the other person.* In the latter sense, a young man can hardly be counted on to assume responsibility for the well-being of girls he dates if he lacks any real understanding of what happens to a girl as she slowly matures into womanhood. There is much that he needs to know.

He need to know, for example, that she has in her unconscious an image of the ideal male that has been built up through her relationships with the men in her family and the men she has come to know up to this point in her life. She has also been influenced by our culture with its constant emphasis on sex—in newspapers, magazines, comic books, novels, television, plays, movies and, perhaps worst of all, the commercial advertising that exploits sex for profit.

From this vast flow of experience the girl distills her image of the ideal male. No matter what the character may be of a boy she meets, she tends to see her ideal image reflected in him because of her eagerness to find in the flesh the one male she seeks. Thus a first-love relationship is full of possibilities for misunderstanding, as when a girl who has been reared in a family dominated by a harsh father turns to a boy because he appears sensitive and thoughtful. If he is what he seems to be, he will reinforce her image of the ideal male. But if in reality he is a passive, selfish boy, sooner or later this will become apparent and disillusionment may force the girl to reject that image and accept harshness as the mark of the man.

We certainly cannot expect a young man, who may himself be relatively inexperienced in life, to comprehend fully the nature of a young girl's unconscious image of her ideal male. But it is not uncommon for a boy to sense the girl is looking for certain traits—firmness, perhaps, or sensitivity, or tenderness—and for him to assume these characteristics as a short cut to sexual conquest. If he succeeds in his strategy and then abandons the girl afterward, as often happens, it is because he is unaware of—or unconcerned about—the extent of his irresponsibility. Apart from having consciously deceived the girl, thereby diminishing her trust in all men, he no doubt will have permanently altered for the worse her image of the ideal male.

A young man must therefore be prepared to face the fact that whether he likes it or not, and whether it is for better or for worse, a responsibility rests on his shoulders when he initiates a sexual relationship with a young and inexperienced girl. Often, however, he is in a poor position to assume such a heavy responsibility, since he, no less than the girl, is floundering in a sea of uncertainties and is himself not entirely sure of the ways in which love is related to sex.

Both the boy and the girl are seeking love and sex, but their needs are somewhat different. For the sake of clarifying the point, we can say the girl plays at sex, for which she is not ready, because fundamentally what she wants is love; and the boy plays at love, for which he is not ready, because what he wants is sex. We must understand that in reality both the boy and girl seek love *and* sex, tenderness *and* passion, but that in the early years their drives are rarely synchronized. A girl usually has a greater need for a feeling of legitimacy about the relationship before she can give herself to a boy, a legitimacy rooted in her belief that the boy loves her and that she loves him, for it is this belief that frees her to express the sexual side of her nature. Boys rarely require such a belief to free themselves sexually, but they willingly play at love if this is necessary.

In truth, the girl as well as the boy "plays" at love. For real love in any form is composed of many elements, one of the most important of which is primacy of concern for the beloved one. And few are the girls or boys who have achieved sufficient emotional maturity to be able to identify the best interests of another person and put them ahead of their own.

There is, however, a crucial difference in how the boy and girl play at love. The boy can do so consciously; the girl cannot. In this sense, the boy can play at love as he would at any game, using strategy to win. The girl plays at love in a more profound and vulnerable way, since the person she must mislead—if she is to obtain what she wants—is herself. She has a need to *believe* in love, a need that the boy, in most cases, does not have.

If a young man does use love in this way, as a lure or a weapon, it is usually without his realizing the dangers in doing so, for this gives him the power to arouse the young girl's sexual nature. Whether he has the moral right to do so is, of course, the critical question. I am one of those who believe we need to develop much new knowledge on which to base new moralities adequate to the changing needs of contemporary society. We do not know all the consequences of introducing a psychologically and emotionally immature girl to sexual stimulation. But we do know that in a large proportion of girls, sexual response does not appear spontaneously, as it apparently does in the male, but is learned at one time or another during her development into womanhood. And in this learning, the male plays the obvious lead.

We have always known this. Yet we do not shine in our ability to say to our sons: "Before you make love to a girl, you have an obligation to come to a deliberate decision in full awareness that you will be setting in motion powerful forces in that girl. If you are concerned about her as a human being, you must decide whether or not it is appropriate at her age and stage of development to learn sexual response. And you must decide whether she is ready for this. If you think she is, then you should acknowledge that it will certainly affect her life to some degree, and perhaps more profoundly than you can imagine. If you are *not* concerned about her as a human being, then consider what it will do to you—to your sense of yourself as a responsible human being, to your own character and development—to use her sexually for your temporary gratification. These decisions are your responsibility to make."

In my experience, few young men hear words of this kind. The plain fact is that we have lost the ability—or, more alarmingly, the willingness—to bring up sons with the strength and self-confidence to assume major responsibility for setting standards and developing the moral values by which human beings must live. What lawyers term the "burden of proof" in establishing the rightness or wrongness of a sexual relationship has for too long been placed entirely on the girl's shoulders.

Two years ago, for example, I attended a conference on the sexual behavior of college students, to find that those who had accepted invitations were for the most part deans and counselors at women's colleges. Why shouldn't there have been similar concern on the part of those who are occupied with the sexual behavior of college men? Doesn't it seem almost self-evident that in a society which proclaims the equality of the sexes, men as well as women must come to grips with the question of sexual morality, and that men must at least share the leadership in seeking its resolution?

Man cannot have his cake and eat it too. He cannot expect his eventual marriage to be the most enduring of all possible relationships if, prior to marriage, his relationships with women have been almost exclusively physical and transient. He cannot expect his wife to fulfill him in all ways if, before marrying her, he made little effort to learn about a woman's nature and needs.

Many young men (and women too, unfortunately) appear convinced that pleasurable sexual attraction is the most important single basis for entering marriage. This belief, like all pleasure principles, does not hold up in practice. In his autobiographical book, the writer Nelson Algren says: "I don't think of sex as just something that happens now and then. . . . Sex is a diffused feeling. It diffuses everything and only once in a while would it be called Sex. Sex is diffused with love and affection, and I don't think you can make things like that happen. . . . It's got to be the big thing first."

I believe that every young man needs to know and to accept the fact that because he plays a crucial role in furthering a young woman's emotional maturity, he must also accept the responsibility that goes with it. He must understand that the sexual act for a woman tends to be the ultimate expression of what she feels about life and her belief in it, expressed through her love for and belief in the man with whom she chooses to live the rest of her life. If she engages in sexual experience before she is mature enough, sex may become an end in itself—or the ability to enjoy sexual experience may be crippled forever—and her capacities for a deeper relationship may be arrested.

Young men must face these realities. We know that many young people today place their sexual lives beyond the reach of adult authority. But if they also place them beyond the reach of a better understanding of the place of sex in the life of man, they serve themselves and society poorly. We are changing and so is society. If we do nothing to direct the flow of change, negative and destructive forces will determine its course.

Of most profound importance to man and his well-being is his own sexuality and the use he makes of it. It underlies his most important relationship, and indeed pervades all his relationships in one way or another. The Reverend Kenneth Greet, of the Methodist Church in Great Britain, puts it this way: "The beginning of understanding is the recognition that sex is not primarily something we do, but something we are. We have been made male and female in order that we can come together in a unique kind of relationship. Marriage is the most vital form of it. The same act which secures, promotes and deepens that relationship can also produce a child. But there ought not to be any child until the relationship is there as the only fitting environment for it. This approach provides us with the right perspective for a fuller recognition of the immense importance and significance of sex. When we begin to accept it, it inevitably means death to the old double standard of morality. . . . It is also the means of quickening those elements of respect and responsibility which are a vital part of love, if it is to be worthy of the name."

In my sixties, as mother, grandmother and physician, and from the security of a long and fulfilling marriage, I would like to challenge the young men of this generation to ponder and answer for themselves the profound question: *What is the purpose of sex?*

The kinds of answers being given to this question have created the distorted images and concepts of sexuality for which my generation must accept full responsibility. But unfortunately we are not the ones who can resolve the situations. You are. We can't tell you what to do—only that there is something of first importance to be done. Whether or not your generation does it is your choice. How you do it is your business. The standards of morality that must be set for the society in which you will rear your children are yours to define.

The truth about human sexuality as a great creative and re-creative force is yet to be acknowledged. The truth about the relationship of man to woman in the world of today as it turns into the world of tomorrow is yet to be discovered. Only from these two truths can be derived the moralities that we must have if society is to survive as a community in which men and women can find fulfillment in enduring love.

Index

This comprehensive new text has been designed for the undergraduate and graduate courses on methods of teaching sex education. It will prove eminently useful not only to the elementary and secondary school instructor and administrator responsible for integrating sex education into the curriculum, but to parents, religious organizations, and community agencies, as well.

Aimed at helping the teacher to organize and conduct meaningful learning experiences in family life and sex education, this up-to-date text demonstrates the broad and varied content of sex education, presents ways for its incorporation into the curriculum from kindergarten through the twelfth grade, and suggests appropriate teaching methods, materials, and evaluation procedures.

Special emphasis is placed throughout not only on the acquisition of knowledge, but also on the development of wholesome attitudes and resultant improvement in behavior.

Part 1 deals with the teaching of sex and sexuality in the schools. Chapters 1 and 2 introduce the sex education program and discuss its goals. Sequential curriculum planning for kindergarten through the twelfth grade is taken up in Chapters 3-6. Methods, materials, vocabulary, evaluation of the program, teaching units, and lesson plans are discussed in Chapters 7-10. Such special aspects of sex education as venereal disease and pornography, as well as the special role of the home and family, are dealt with in the last chapters. Part 2 takes up the scientific content of sex and sexuality, considering biological, sociological, and psychological aspects: reproduction, the endocrine system, fertility, prenatal development; puberty and adolescence; such physiological functions as menstruation and menopause; contraception and abortion; health aspects in planning for children, medical examinations, impotence and frigidity; such special topics as sex-linked traits, blood types, artificial insemination, masturbation, and homosexuality; veneral disease and prostitution; and, finally, myths and fallacies about sex.

The teacher will find examples of lesson plans, lists of attitudes by grades, activities at the end of each chapter, and scientific illustrations most helpful. The Appendix contains an extensive bibliography for children and young people, as well

(continued on back flap)

(continued from front flap)
as teachers and other adults, audio-visual aids, a graded glossary, and examples of objective tests with instructions for preparing them.

The author believes that the goal of sex education should be to help the youngster integrate meaningful sexual knowledge into his future and present life, providing him with some basic understanding of virtually every aspect of sex by the time he reaches full maturity. He should be helped to recognize the existence of differential sex patterns so that he can interact harmoniously with those whose sex norms differ from his own, and encouraged to bring critical judgment to bear when dealing with ethical controversy. Professor Kilander treats sex education as a means of demonstrating the immense possibilities for human fulfillment that sexuality offers, rather than merely as a means of controlling or suppressnig sexual expression.

About the author

H. Frederick Kilander is Professor of Education and Special Assistant to the President at Wagner College, where he has also held the position of Dean of the Graduate School. He had previously served as Coordinator of Health Education at New York University, Specialist in School Health to the U.S. Office of Education, and Assistant Director of First Aid to the American Red Cross. Professor Kilander is the author of **School Health Education, Health for Modern Living, Nutrition for Health, Youth Grows Into Adulthood,** the **Kilander Health Knowledge Test,** and the **Information Test on Biological Aspects of Human Reproduction.** His international activities include research in health education in Scandinavia, for which he was awarded honorary fellowship by the American-Scandinavian Foundation, and representation of the United States at UNESCO Conferences on School Health Education. He was presented an Honor Award at the Eighty-Third Anniversary Convention (1968) of the American Association for Health, Physical Education, and Recreation in St. Louis. In 1960 Professor Kilander received the Howe Award of the American School Health Association, an organization which he has served as president.